Science and Education
in Developing States

PRAEGER SPECIAL STUDIES IN
INTERNATIONAL ECONOMICS AND DEVELOPMENT

Science and Education in Developing States

**PROCEEDINGS OF THE
FIFTH REHOVOT CONFERENCE**

Edited by
Philip and Hadassah Gillon

Foreword by
Abba Eban

Published in cooperation with the
Continuation Committee of the Rehovot Conference

PRAEGER PUBLISHERS
New York • Washington • London

The purpose of Praeger Special Studies is to make specialized research in U.S. and international economics and politics available to the academic, business, and government communities. For further information, write to the Special Projects Division, Praeger Publishers, Inc., 111 Fourth Avenue, New York, N.Y. 10003.

PRAEGER PUBLISHERS
111 Fourth Avenue, New York, N.Y. 10003, U.S.A.
5, Cromwell Place, London S.W.7, England

Published in the United States of America in 1971
by Praeger Publishers, Inc.

Library of Congress Catalog Card Number: 74-139881

Printed in the United States of America

Rebovot Conferences, sponsored by the Hebrew University of Jerusalem and the Weizmann Institute of Science, bring together the world's leading scientists and experts in a particular sphere of human activity, and the statesmen and administrators of the developing countries engaged in the day-to-day practical work in the field.

The Fifth Rehovot Conference, on Science and Education in Developing Countries, took place in Jerusalem and Rehovot in August, 1969. There were 115 participants, coming from 54 countries in Africa, Asia, Central and South America, Europe, and North America, and from 6 international organizations. Among the delegates were 20 cabinet ministers and 2 deputy cabinet ministers, 45 administrators in the field of education, and 48 scientists.

The Continuation Committee of the Rehovot Conference wishes to express its profound regret at the illness and untimely death, at the time of the Conference, of Professor Amos de Shalit, Chairman of the Scientific Preparatory Committee and contributor of a paper that appears in this volume.

FOREWORD

By Abba Eban

Minister of Foreign Affairs of Israel
Chairman of the Rehovot Conference

Two transformations dominate the life of our century—the swift rise of Asian and African peoples to independence, and the headlong progress of science and technology. The aim of the Rehovot Conferences is to create a point of contact between those who represent these two decisive movements of our time—scientific progress and national liberation.

As the United Nations Development Decade comes to an end, it becomes evident that none of its goals has been achieved. In the world of abundance, there are one billion people living below a sound level of nutrition. In the age of intellectual and scientific triumph, 700 million adults—constituting one-third of mankind—are plunged in illiteracy. In the era of medical progress, hundreds of millions suffer from preventable diseases.

It is no wonder that the pride which new nations feel in their institutional freedom is sharply reduced by a real lack of adequate progress towards economic, social, and technical equality. National independence is an opportunity. It is not in itself a guarantee of fulfillment. A man can be free in every institutional sense and yet lose the essence of his freedom amidst starvation, squalor, and disease.

This book is a record of the Fifth Rehovot Conference. In 1960 we met to consider generally the role of science in developing states. Then we got down to specifics. At the next conference, two years later, we discussed the problem of rural development and agricultural planning. In the third meeting, we brought together ministers of finance, their administrators, and the world's leading economists to probe the mysteries of fiscal and monetary policies in developing states. In 1967, ministers of health, their aides, and medical scientists reviewed problems of health in developing countries. The Fifth Conference faced perhaps the most acute of all development issues, science and education in the new states.

Many of the developing countries are not poor in natural resources. But, whereas nature has endowed them with much bounty, colonialism and other afflictions have left them with a vast inadequacy of trained human resources. The disparities in achievements and prospects between the advanced and the developing world do not arise because of any inherent inequalities between people. Nothing has been achieved in Europe and America of which Asia and Africa are not intrinsically capable, but one part of humanity has been cut off from the processes of thought and action which have endowed another part of humanity with all the elements of power.

Once men fought for political rights—the right to vote. Then they fought for equality of economic rights—the right to work and earn. Those struggles have not yet ended, but they have yielded many victories. Today the quest for equality is mainly focused on educational rights—the equal right to learn and know.

Fundamentally, science should be taught, not for the advantage that it brings to society, but for the general enrichment that it brings to the human personality. When governments support scientific research for the sake of technological and economic benefits, or for the sake of increasing their physical security, they are usually doing the right thing for the wrong reason. The intellectual discipline, the constructive rationality, the unlimited persistence that mark the scientific method are not only an aid to material development, but are also among the glories of a liberal mind.

The intellectual climate of our generation is marked by revolt, primarily against traditional values. But if we follow the most recent expressions of that revolt in art, in drama, in literature, in social relationships, we find that the area has been widened. The revolt is not only against classical forms; it is against rationality itself. Reason is in retreat and the rational criterion is no longer accepted as a directing principle of human and social enterprise.

Surely the time has come to reestablish the sovereignty of the mind that draws conclusions from evidence, that is sceptical about assumptions that cannot be proved. The unifying, humanizing, and universal influences of science are as necessary in the human predicament as they are in the specific role of development. Reason is not enough, but the point is to find the balance between reason and passion. The point of equilibrium between them defines the predicament and the challenge of the educator.

CONTENTS

xi

Science and Education in Developing States

INTRODUCTION

By René Maheu

*Director-General, The United Nations
Educational, Scientific and Cultural
Organization (Paris)*

The extraordinary journey of the men who set foot on the moon, thereby crowning gigantic efforts put forth by a powerful scientific and technical community, has brought home to us most forcibly the immense, the intolerable disparities which still exist among the peoples. For this exploit, opening up new horizons for the human race, has been achieved in a world still largely given over to poverty and ignorance. It must, alas, be acknowledged that the gulf which separates the advanced nations from the rest, far from narrowing, is becoming wider and deeper every day.

The industrialized countries have at their disposal 90 percent of the world's scientific personnel. The developing countries have a percentage of scientists and engineers in the population twenty times less than that of the industrialized countries; among the scientists, the proportion engaged in research and therefore contributing to scientific and technical innovation is four times smaller in the developing countries than in those that are already developed. The nonindustrialized countries have been said to be a desert as far as research is concerned; three-quarters of the world's population live in that desert.

Moreover, thanks to techniques in the van of progress, such as electronics and data processing, we are seeing the most advanced countries reach a new stage of industrial development—the scientific age of production. In the present circumstances, this is quite out of the question for the rest of the world, so that the result is an aggravation of existing inequalities and an additional handicap for the countries that have lagged behind.

In this connection, it is interesting to compare the subject of the first Rehovoth Conference, "Science and Technology in the Developing States," with that of today's conference. Today we are no longer discussing simply science and its applications, but science and education. It has, of course, never occurred to anyone to separate the two completely. But it is nonetheless true that, more particularly in international circles, a long and still unfinished battle has had to be waged to gain acceptance for the idea that there can be no economic and social development without a scientific infrastructure, which itself presupposes an adequate system of education.

3

Science cannot be limited to simply using borrowed knowledge and processes to make good, after a fashion, particular deficiencies in economic activities. The essence of science, and the secret of its impact, is a creative, inquiring spirit, deeply rooted in the fabric of society and animated by a vitality of its own while at the same time giving life to all around it. The first prerequisite for the existence of such a spirit is the spread of the scientific attitude of mind, and its thorough assimilation by broad strata of society, through education. It is only by such a spreading and assimilation of the scientific spirit that the developing countries can be enabled to turn to lasting and fruitful account their material and human resources, in the first place by the implantation and then by the endogenous development of science on their own territory.

We must not tire of repeating that, if science is to be the common property of the whole of society, it must be founded on education. Conversely, one of the prime aims of modern education must be to prepare people's minds, everywhere, to think scientifically. For many, this training will be confined to developing their ability to reason and understand; in the case of some, it will bring out their ability to use inventively and originally the theoretical knowledge or the techniques furnished by the labors of scholars the world over.

Scientific activities, increasingly specialized as they become, are the concern of comparatively small groups of people: research workers, engineers, technicians. Nothing could be more mistaken, however, or more dangerous, than to believe that they do not require the active interest of society as a whole. Experience shows that, if it is to be able to take advantage of the opportunities for progress afforded to it by science, society in general must be psychologically ready to accept scientific and technological innovations. Only on this condition can the community at large assimilate the results of science. And assimilation, incidentally, is not everything. Each society must be able to contribute actively to the advancement of science and technology, since no community can live indefinitely off others and must therefore be in a position to train its own scientists and technicians to undertake creative work.

It is not enough, however, merely to consider the social environment. The cultural atmosphere, too, must be taken into account. In fact, there is no society where scientific thinking is completely unknown, since any man of intelligence observes, experiments, sifts. But there are societies in whose culture the old values occupy so strong a position that there is no place in it for science as a value.

We should not think that this is solely due to inertia and that science as a value is bound to assert itself everywhere, sooner or later, automatically as it were, by reason of the truth and power it brings to mankind. Things are not so simple. Truth is by no means the only, or even the principal, ideal cherished by mankind, as is abundantly proved by history. The power that derives from science by no means always gives us cause for unqualified satisfaction, for there are occasions when it so far exceeds man's ability to control its use—or even simply to perceive the effects its use may have on natural balances—that it terrifies more than it attracts. For instance, even in the most advanced societies—I would say, above all in the most advanced societies—we find men today inquiring with increasing anxiety into the value of the civilization that modern technology is preparing for them. Among young people in particular, it is a fact, of which we must take heed, that the challenging of this civilization is in some countries taking a turn which is fairly definitely hostile to science, and especially to the natural sciences.

That is why the role of education and communication should not be restricted to familiarizing people's minds with science from the dual standpoint of knowledge and method. This is necessary, but it is not enough. People must also be brought to understand, and I would almost say to feel, that science is a value, that is to say, a reason for living and a style of living: the category and the style of the human universal. Science will really have taken root only when the humanism that it represents has found its place in people's minds beside other forms of humanism—more particularist, often of much longer standing—and in constructive association with them.

However, social and cultural factors can only predispose people in favor of the advent of the scientific spirit. To enable science to be an effective social activity, specific intellectual and technical measures must be taken to organize it, give it a direction, and provide it with the necessary means, so as to meet not only the immediate but also the longer-term needs of development. Hence the importance of a national science policy—its vital importance, to which UNESCO has for several years past been continually drawing everyone's attention, and especially that of the less advanced countries.

This policy constitutes the indispensable system of data and targets, which, established in the light of material and human resources on the one hand, and of social and economic needs on the other, makes it possible both to form the required potential, by planning the training of scientific and technical personnel, and to schedule the work, by assigning priorities to the different sectors of research. The greater the range of responsibility and knowledge of those involved in a country's scientific activities, the more necessary it is to establish such a framework. But it is also necessary in situations marked by scarcities. It is known that among the developing countries there are some where certain specialists are underemployed, or even without employment, whereas other kinds of specialists are not available. It is also known that, in the developing countries, the number of scientists that are trained is generally too large in comparison with the number of technicians: too large both from the point of view of the advancement of science and from that of development.

These considerations lead to a linking of science policy with educational planning. The latter has to take account of the staffing requirements for scientific work, especially in its relation with development, and to organize appropriately varied scientific teaching accordingly. Without calling in question the underlying unity of the scientific spirit, or the general balance of education, this variety will mark both the subjects to be taught and the mental attitudes to be developed.

Lastly, let us not hesitate to say that the acquisition of knowledge and of the scientific and technical spirit should be an essential ingredient in the training of the leaders of a country in the various sectors of public life and economic life. In a modern society, no one can properly exercise functions of responsibility unless he has some inner understanding, as I would call it, of the relations between science and society and of the application of scientific thinking to nature and to history. The age of the craftsman and the magician is past!

The range of objectives that education has to set itself so as to contribute to the implantation of science and technology in society is therefore very wide. All social groups and all age groups must be affected. General scientific education, as opposed to specialized science teaching, must form an integral part of any education—of school education first and foremost, but also of out-of-school education, whether designed for adults already at work or for young people. Each individual must have a minimum of scientific knowledge, adequate for the needs of his professional, civic or personal life. The rules of rationality, which are the essence of the scientific attitude of mind, must form part of his mental structure. Lastly, he must be as intuitively convinced of the value of these rules as he is of the traditional elements of his culture.

We cannot but recognize that scientific education is a comparatively new notion. In the nineteenth century, even well after the first successes of the industrial revolution, science teaching had only a very modest place in school education. Not so very long ago, it was constantly held up against an arts education, which usually enjoyed much greater prestige. The generation to which the world's present leaders belong has generally experienced this cleavage and has had to choose between the two cultures, to use Lord Snow's famous expression. In the developing countries, however, the cleavage is even sharper, the choice clearer cut, than in the industrialized countries. Whence the painful indecision on the part of individuals, the tensions and antagonisms between groups, and more especially the clashes between generations, that are in these countries the concomitants of development—which, in the final analysis, is none other than science become culture.

No one could nowadays deny that the consequences or the requirements of scientific progress are among the most important factors necessitating decisive changes in education.

One of these factors, which is particularly spectacular in its effects, is the speed with which knowledge becomes obsolete, as a result of the ever more rapid advances made in research. This swift obsolescence of knowledge means that curriculums must be continually revised, both from the point of view of their theoretical content, so that pupils may be enabled to understand the latest achievements of science and the new paths on which it is embarking, and from that of their practical content, so that vocational training may keep abreast of technological progress.

Textbook revision and refresher courses for teachers provide a means of remedying the most obvious deficiencies of established practice. But more is needed. The whole conception of science teaching, in its content, its methods, and its techniques, must be thought out afresh. Above all, science teaching must rid itself of any dogmatic approach and rely instead on the actual experience of both teacher and pupil so that it may be intimately related to that experience and, as a result, revitalize it. As regards methods, science teaching should provide the most appropriate setting for the use of active methods and teamwork. Instead of handing out cut-and-dried facts, the teacher should be a source of inspiration to his pupils, essentially concerned with helping their intelligence to develop by participating in the process of instruction. As regards techniques, it is already established that the use of audio-visual aids and programmed instruction can be admirable factors in science teaching. UNESCO, for its part, has been endeavoring to promote these new techniques in a series of pilot projects for the modernization of physics, chemistry, and biology teaching.

The school is not, however, the only educational institution that has to be considered. Despite—or rather because of—the slight account still taken of them, even in the developed countries, I feel that I should mention here how important, from the point of view of awakening the scientific spirit, museums, planetariums, and science exhibitions can be; they are particularly fitted for introducing children and young people, by means of films and increasingly sophisticated equipment, to the achievements of modern technology and to the laws of physics, chemistry, and biology. But here, too, the active participation of the pupil in the process of education remains the ideal method for the assimilation of ideas and knowledge, and in this connection I should like to emphasize the formative value of junior science clubs, where initative and the team spirit have an opportunity to develop side by side.

There is one more aspect of the changes to be made in science education, which, it seems to me, deserves particular attention in connection with this conference. Although science is universal so far as its concepts are concerned, the various circles to which it is directed are by no means equally well prepared to receive it. So we have the problem of adaptation.

Students in the advanced countries complain—often bitterly—that the teaching they receive is not in keeping with their situation, their interests, or their needs. What, then, can be said of the validity of curriculums and methods transplanted bodily, as it were, to countries where the prevailing culture, and even the conditions of daily life, are profoundly different? Considerable progress has already been made—in regard to biology, for example—to ensure that, in teaching at all levels, account is taken of the ecology, in the widest sense, of the society in which those for whom that teaching is intended are living. The greater part of the work, however, has still to be done. There must be an all-out, comprehensive effort to make science truly at home wherever it may find itself. And there could be no place more suitable than this for drawing attention to the vital importance of enabling certain national languages to become vehicles of modern scientific and technological thought.

After this rapid survey of the main *problems* which must be solved if the scientific spirit is to spring up and flourish in the developing countries, I should now like to consider the *measures* that need to be contemplated for the reform, with that same purpose in mind, of the science teaching currently provided at the primary, secondary and higher levels of education.

First of all, a study should be undertaken of the inner mechanism of the system of science education, with a view to determining the optimum reciprocal relationship between content, methods, physical equipment and the role of the science teacher. In other words, a sort of model should be evolved, for each situation, which would enable educational establishments to make the best use of the resources available to them.

Up to now, the policy followed both by the developing countries and by those already developed, in their endeavors to improve their science teaching, has been an empirical one, dictated by the urgency of the needs to be met. Thus, at different times and places, we have seen priority accorded, for example, to quantity rather than quality, to secondary rather than primary or higher education, to textbooks rather than teaching methods. This approach carries with it an obvious risk of serious disproportion. It is hardly an exaggeration to say that, in one and the same country, we may find a system of university education still carrying on dogmatic practices inherited from the Middle Ages, side by side with a system of secondary education based on active methods, without anything being done to bring the two systems into harmony with one another. In the same way, very serious discrepancies may be found in the relative importance of the educational roles assigned to the different disciplines.

Curriculum reform is, of course, an extremely delicate affair, but one is sometimes obliged to choose the lesser of two evils; and nothing could be more dangerous than to subject science teaching to a series of piecemeal adjustments using, as circumstances might permit, the results of the most advanced educational research. The time has come for a determined attempt *to forge a new, coherent system of education*, taking into account both the practical and intellectual objectives to be attained and the already very considerable body of data which has been made available by educational research.

The second direction in which, it seems to me, consideration should be given to the improvement of science education is that of *integrated instruction*. The tendency toward differentiation which is at the root of modern science, with its ever-increasing specialization, has always been accompanied by an opposite tendency towards the integration of the different disciplines and the expression of the fundamental unity of science in the form of common principles and basic hypotheses capable of explaining the greatest possible number of phenomena. Integration is thus seen to be essential to science teaching because of the very nature of scientific thought. It is also necessary for educational reasons, since it enables time to be saved by avoidance of useless repetition, attention to be drawn to the analogies that exist between one subject and another, and above all the methods of general education to be given the essential place that is their due. Depending on the level of education, there can be either integration proper, which means combining several different subjects in a single course, or coordination, which implies harmonization or, rather, carefully planned cooperation in the parallel teaching of a number of different disciplines.

The age of the pupils will determine the limits of the integrated sector, since complete integration is easier in junior classes. During the first stage of secondary education, where the emphasis is on observable phenomena and on general education, there should be an integrated course in the natural sciences—physics, chemistry, biology, geology, and astonomy. This would provide an opportunity, through the choice of such topics as air, water, nutrition, and energy, to arouse the pupil's interest in some of the major problems of our time. It would also enable the experience and knowledge inherited from a local culture to be used as a basis for the teaching of sciences. At a higher level, coordination and integration must reinforce each other, since those pupils who are to continue their science studies at the university need to be prepared to enter upon the multidisciplinary sectors which are developing on the confines of several sciences and which often provide opportunities for particularly fruitful research.

I should also like to mention another factor in the reform of science teaching, namely the integration and coordination of the teaching of the natural sciences with the teaching of the social and human sciences. As the latter are still in the process of being organized and consolidated, they are only rarely taught at primary and secondary level, with the result that science teaching concentrates almost exclusively on man's physical environment at the expense of his human environment, although the latter is infinitely more meaningful to him.

The formative value of the social and human sciences, in particular the so-called "nomothetic" disciplines such as psychology, anthropology, demography, economics, and sociology, cannot be overemphasized. Because of the nature of the human phenomena which they study, an extra effort is required towards objectivity in the gathering and analysis of complex data, and toward painstaking accuracy in their interpretation. The knowledge to be gained from these sciences is vital to an understanding of the historical stages through which we humans have passed. Useful as this knowledge is to everyone, it is perhaps still more useful to scientists, whose profession puts them in a position to influence the destinies of their fellow men and who, for this reason, often have, whether they wish it or not and whether they realize it or not, very heavy moral responsibilities. It is obvious that the social and human sciences and the natural sciences have complementary parts to play in education. The reservations that some people express in regard to the former seem to me very ill-advised, for it is absolutely impossible to enable people to have a practical and at the same time deep understanding of the relations between science and society without recourse to the social and human sciences.

In the course of this address I have several times referred to the idea of integration. I shall now return to this idea for the last time, to say that science teaching can fulfill its function in the education system as a whole only if it is completely integrated in that system. For this reason, I firmly believe that the stage in which the scientist and the educator made separate contributions to the progress of science teaching must give place to a stage in which both cooperate closely in devising *jointly* and developing *through their combined efforts* systems of education imbued with the scientific spirit.

One final word. Scientific education offers the most direct access to an understanding of the human universal. Not only, therefore, is it a vehicle of truth and a source of power, but it leads naturally, logically I should say, to a vision of humanity which transcends particularist contradictions and antagonisms and repudiates the injustices and the passions from which conflicts spring.

It is not a misuse of words to say that this vision has an ethical significance. Justice and solidarity, and hence peace, cannot be established other than by recourse, above and beyond the chaos of history, to a universal human order, the germ of which is carried in every human mind and of which the most striking translation into intellectual and practical reality is science in action. Nowhere is it more important, at this time, to recall these basic truths than on this tragically disputed territory. May the world, and above all this most sorely troubled region, see in this conference, devoted to opening up to the developing countries, by means of education and science, the way of genuine progress, an act of faith in the power of reason as the principle of justice, understanding, and peace, yes, *peace*!

PART |

THE AIMS OF SCIENCE AND EDUCATION

1

AIMS, CONTENTS, AND METHODOLOGY OF SCIENCE TEACHING

By Albert V. Baez

Consultant, Office of Science and Technology, United Nations (New York)

The Search for New Guidelines in Science Education

The modern curriculum reform movement in science education began in the late fifties in the advanced countries with a series of pioneering projects in the basic sciences. A second wave of projects began in the early sixties, some of them in the developing countries. We are now on the threshold of a concerted action to improve science education around the world. A new round of projects—the third-generation projects—is about to get under way, many of them in the developing countries. It seems opportune, therefore, to rethink the aims, contents, and methodology of science education.

The newly developing countries are eager for science and technology. They have seen that they bring to its possessors power over nature, life, death, sickness, and people. Only religion, it seems, has affected the lives of men as profoundly as has technology.

These countries now realize that although they could buy the fruits of technology if they had the money they cannot have the long-range benefits of science unless they educate a new indigenous generation to cope with accelerated change—the most characteristic feature of a technological society.

But science and technology have been a mixed blessing to the advanced countries. Along with wealth and material comforts that come with industrialization they have also brought with them the perils of noise, pollution of air and water, and weapons of mass destruction. Are the developing countries headed down the same path? Some of them are, unfortunately, and they include the countries most eager to advance their systems of science education.

Can the introduction of new objectives for science education redirect their efforts to avoid what seems like unavoidable disaster? Can the newest members of the developing countries learn their science and technology in a way that will enable them to acquire more of their benefits and fewer of their evils? We shall review the course of science curriculum reform to date in search of new guidelines for science education.

The aims of science education are related to important questions like "*why* teach science?," ". . . to whom?," and ". . . at what age?" Contents deal with "*what* should you teach?" and methodology deals with "*how* do you teach it?" It seems logical that aims should be considered first. Surely it should help to have a clear idea of why one is teaching science before one decides what to teach or how to teach it. Aims, in other words, ought to animate contents and contents should animate methodology, but that is not the way it has usually happened, as we shall see when we consider the origins of the reform movements.

In most of the developing countries, and in many advanced countries as well, education is highly centralized and controlled at the ministerial level. The decision to strengthen science education is, in other words, at least in part a political decision. It involves allocation of huge sums of public money. Hence aims are often chosen by lawmakers and politicians who have only a very vague idea of what is involved. They are seldom scientists by training and when they get advice from scientists they weigh it against opinions coming from many other sources.

The decision-makers may have been influenced by opinions about science and technology such as the following:

1. Science can root out ignorance, superstition, fear, and poverty.
2. Without indigenous science and technology the natural and human resources of the nation cannot be organized for industrial expansion or national defense.
3. Economic and social development require a climate of popular understanding and acceptance of science.

But the decisions they make about science education depend, of course, on their own personal motives as well as on those of the nation-state whom they serve. Some leaders may actually thrive personally if ignorance, superstition and fear persist among the masses! The motivation for science teaching reform may be the fear, based upon military and political considerations, that another nation may get ahead in the technological race.

The explicit objectives for science teaching reform that emerge as national policy are, in other words, based on the aims and motives of the people in power. These people bear responsibility for answering such philosophical questions as: "What are the real needs of society?" or "What do we want the young people of tomorrow—the products of our schools—to be able to *do* as a result of science teaching that their present counterparts cannot do?" It is at this point that the decision-makers need assistance, since they should have a clear understanding of what science is all about. Where should they turn for help?

In the realm of contents there are experts. They are the scientists themselves who, working at the cutting edge of new knowledge, can give advice on what to delete from the old curriculums and what to add to the new. In the realm of methodology there are experts in education and in the psychology of learning and practicing teachers to whom one can go for advice. But there are no "experts" in the realm of aims and objectives. Yet those who make decisions in this realm can influence the course of science education negatively through error or positively through understanding. The guidance that politicians need from experts in the realm of science education is comparable in importance with the guidance they need from scientists concerning nuclear energy, natural resources, and science policy.

Scientists and educators in the past were willing to accept guidelines on matters of policy from political leaders. They often treated these guidelines as if they were mathematical boundary conditions over which they had no control. It is now obvious, however, that scientists and educators must make a greater effort to educate the politicians on the scope, power, and limitations of science so that they, in turn, can make realistic decisions towards a science education policy which reflects worthy and achievable objectives.

Pioneering Science-Teaching Projects in the United States

By choosing the pioneering efforts in the United States we do not mean to discount reform activities in other countries. We have chosen these projects because we know more about them than about others and because they were sizable and eventually had a stimulating effect on projects elsewhere.

We will indicate first the shortcomings which existed at the time and which prompted the reform. We will then identify, in general terms, who the leaders were and something about their aims, objectives, and motivations. We will examine the sources of support they enlisted, the target populations they chose to work with (they didn't call them that—the term has become popular more recently), the role of contents, methods, and approaches in the projects, and the nature of the outputs. Since all of these facts are well known to this audience, what follows will be in the nature of a rapid summary for the purpose of understanding the subsequent stages of the movement.

The initiative was taken by university scientists. They discovered that the content of children's science books had not changed appreciably since the turn of the century, so they broke with their traditional non-involvement in secondary education and became vigorously active in reform. They also discovered that science was still being taught in authoritarian fashion and dispensed as a set of stable facts, to be memorized in rote fashion by the students and handed back on the examinations. They found that the excitement of discovery so characteristic of science was missing and that teachers were poorly prepared.

It is understandable that the scientists tackled content first. Science had grown explosively in the first half of the century, so they had to invent criteria for choosing what should be discarded, what should be kept, and what new topics should be added to the new textbooks and syllabi. They usually began by writing textbooks first. This created the new body of content on the basis of which other teaching materials for the field, the classroom, the laboratory, the library, and the home were produced.

Broadly speaking, the aim of the projects was to upgrade science teaching by rectifying the errors and relieving the shortcomings of science teaching as they saw them. Their objectives were to give the teachers and the students new and improved tools for learning.

The motives that drove the scientists varied, but by and large they were idealistic, in the sense that they wanted the younger generation to derive excitement, pleasure, and profit from participating in activities which characterize the scientific endeavor and which, it was felt, should begin while the students were young. There was a sense of urgency in the early days due, in part, to the cold war. The launching of the first Sputnik did not launch the science-teaching reform movement, but it certainly helped to loosen the government and private purse strings for financial support on a scale previously unmatched.

The movement was strongly nationalistic and motivated in part by the desire to remain ahead in the technological race. It was strongly linked with efforts to strengthen the economic and defense position. Most of the projects started by producing approaches and materials for the upper secondary-school level. The arguments in favor of this are well known and defensible. It was also recognized that the artificial boundaries between the basic sciences should be torn down. In fact, the Physical Science Study Committee, as its name implies, originally set out to produce a course in which the basic concepts of both physics and chemistry were presented in an integrated way. But they ended up producing a physics course instead, possibly because the pressure to produce was upon them as soon as they had received their first grants from federal and foundation sources and it was easier to remain within one known field than to enter into a collaborative venture with experts from other fields. So the germ of the idea of integration was already there. We wonder now what different paths reform might have taken if aims and objectives had been given higher priority than contents in the early projects.

Materials were produced to stimulate inquiry and discovery on the part of teachers and students. In physics, especially, the importance of personal experimentation by the student motivated the invention of inexpensive but stimulating materials for student use.

The output of the projects included, besides the textbooks, teacher's guides, laboratory guides for both teachers and students, supplementary reading materials, and films. Over 90 projects exist now, too many to be listed here; but the names of such early pioneers as PSSC, CHEM Study, CBA, BSCS, and SMSG are now well known round the world.

The Second Wave of Science-Teaching Reform Projects

Just as the pioneering reform projects began when concerned people uncovered deficiencies in the existing patterns of science education, so a new wave of projects began in the early sixties to try to rectify the shortcomings of the earlier projects.

By the first half of the decade the idea of reform had taken firm root in many countries of the world—in Brazil, the United Kingdom, Sweden, and Australia, to name only a few. In the United States, the so-called "second-generation projects" began to appear. They usually paid homage to the inspiration and the stimulus provided by the pioneering projects, but they asserted their individuality by criticizing some of their deficiencies all the way from aims, objectives, approaches, methods, and outputs down to the fact that they had never been adequately evaluated. Evaluation had not been built into the early projects, possibly because it had taken so much effort to launch the programs and produce materials, and possibly because it was, and still is, a very difficult thing to do.

The critics also observed, for example, that in spite of the enormous sums that had been spent in certain sciences the high school enrollment in these fields was declining. They criticized the fact that, in some cases, massive effort had gone into one huge project with its basic approach when there might have been several projects experimenting with different approaches. It was also true that world events were affecting trends in education as a whole so drastically that it was difficult to measure whether the existence or nonexistence of the science curriculum reform projects had had any influence whatsoever.

Let us now look briefly at the same factors in the new projects which we considered earlier in discussing the pioneer projects. The leadership still included the scientists, but not so exclusively. Closer collaboration began among educators, teachers, and the scientists. Although the earlier projects had been forced to recognize the importance of retraining teachers, since the program could not run without them, the importance of having the enthusiastic support and approval of science supervisors, teacher trainers, and practicing teachers forced the new projects to work more closely than ever before with scholars and administrators in education. Psychologists began to make more of a contribution, especially those in the fields of learning theory and behavioral technology.

As was to be expected in a second round, more thought and reappraisal were given to aims, objectives, and motivation. These cannot be discussed without considering the target populations involved. It should, therefore, be pointed out that the original projects, although they had professed an intention of catering to the student in general education as well as to the future specialist in science, had in fact satisfied very well the needs of the elite who would go on to specialize in science but had left inadequately served many students of average capabilities and the great majority of students who had no interest at all in science. Hence there was a tendency to broaden the target population, first by including those at the secondary-school level who had no intention of specializing in one of the subject areas—including some very gifted people in the arts and humanities—and subsequently by moving both down to the elementary grades and up to the university where the need for improvement was being felt, partly because some of the high-school students enrolling were coming in better prepared than they had been in the past.

Words like "social commitment in science" and "humanistic education" began to appear more often in the description of the objectives of the new projects. The adjective "behavioral" began to appear as a modifier to the term "objective." Soon those who had at first objected to the introduction of the jargon of behavioral technology, which included terms like "specification of terminal behavior" and "specification of target population," were appeased when they learned it simply meant that in preparing teaching materials one should state clearly and possibly in quantitative terms the qualifications of those whom you intended to teach and should state in advance what you wanted them to be able to *do* ("behavioral objective") at the end of the course which they were not able to do before taking it.

All of this had a healthy effect in stressing that learning was the ultimate objective of teaching. That being the case, since it could be demonstrated that students were able to learn certain kinds of facts and some behavior patterns with proper self-instructional aids, even without a teacher, it opened up the possibility that the teacher shortage might be relieved with the proper kinds of aids for auto-instruction.

Greater emphasis began to be placed on the notion that science has a liberating and liberalizing influence and should properly take its place among the humanities. The target population soon covered the academic range from elementary school to the university and it began to reach out to the underprivileged groups within the advanced nations and to the pupils of other countries through programs of bilateral assistance. The increasingly effective international programs of United Nations Agencies such as UNESCO served as catalyzers of new projects in less developed countries and as internationalizers of the projects from other countries.

One of the important trends in content was the increased variety of resource materials put at the disposal of the teacher so that he could fashion from them a course which he could more readily feel was his own. The variety also extended to the choice given to the students. This catering to individuality and individual differences was, in effect, an expression of the idea that the broad human needs of the teachers and students had to be met.

One heard less about inquiry and discovery and more about "process" since, it was claimed, science is both a "product" and a "process" and we benefit from both in our daily lives.

The new projects and the whole movement began to be characterized by a broadening of interest. The need for experimental courses of an integrated nature was acknowledged; science courses were considered in relation to the overall curriculum; and it was recognized that curriculum reform is not a "one-shot deal" but has to be implemented on a continuing basis. Science teaching centers began appearing whose function was, among others, to carry on the kind of research and development work that had been done in one subject at a time in the old projects but now would be done with all the basic sciences and mathematics undergoing continuous reform, possibly integrated and sometimes under one roof. The term "rolling reform" was coined for this process of continuous upgrading of contents, approaches, methods, teachers, and materials. All of these trends required a closer collaboration among scientists, educators, and specialists in psychology and communication.

Guidelines for Third-Generation Projects

We now find ourselves in the late sixties, and even before we consider the "state of the art" in science education, we must take notice of what has been happening in the world at large because it has serious implications for education.

We find great turmoil among university and other students, especially in the advanced countries. They are dissatisfied with facilities, courses, examinations, and the limited range of opportunities. They find much of what the traditional university offers irrelevant to the modern scene—all the more reason for concern because we have seen in the past that events which occur in the advanced countries have a way of recurring at a later time in the developing countries.

Whether or not it can be proven that the reform movement in science education played a part, it is a fact that science and technology have progressed by leaps and bounds in the advanced countries in the last few years. Age-old dreams of space exploration are coming true and even more spectacular achievements are expected in the fields of biology and medicine as a result of the power that new knowledge at the molecular level has given us. Yet these achievements are almost crowded off the front page by news of riots on the campuses, new wars flaring up and old ones refusing to die out. Events seem to have their own momentum and the guidance we expected from education eludes us even if it is there. Many young people dismiss existing education as irrelevant and they become activists. Either they are out to destroy the establishment or they succumb to the soothing escape of drugs.

At this very moment, however, the developing countries are on the threshold of an upsurge in science education reform. They are appealing for help from bilateral, regional and international agencies. One of the purposes of reviewing the curriculum reform projects of the past was to see what light they can shed on the problems of today and tomorrow. Violence, fear, and hatred are abroad in the land and we ask, does science education have anything to offer with regard to these highly relevant concerns?

The times cry out for a new emphasis in education in general and science education in particular. If it is true, as it has been said, that science is the most powerful force for social change in the world, it should be utilized for constructive ends. We must seek out those values of science that have given it its power and see whether or not they can be made to infuse all aspects of education.

A study produced by a distinguished group of scholars has listed the following as the values of science:

1. Longing to know and understand
2. Questioning of all things
3. Searching for data [and for relations that give them meaning]
4. Demand for objective verification
5. Respect for logic
6. Consideration of premises
7. Consideration of consequences[1]

---

[1] Educational Policies Commission, National Education Association, "Education and the Spirit of Science" (Washington, D.C.: National Education Association, 1966).

"Consideration of consequences" implies, among other things, a sense of social responsibility. To the guidelines "spirit of inquiry," "spirit of discovery," "the process approach," and "the preservation and exploitation of individual differences," we now propose adding "social responsibility" as an important guideline for all future science teaching projects. It is a natural extension of the humanistic ideas that were already cropping out in the second-generation reform projects.

More generally, we propose that one of the most important aims for science education should be the development of "the spirit of science" not only in those who will become scientists, but among the populace as a whole. In a restricted sense, the spirit of science refers to the spirit of rational inquiry which motivates scientists in their endeavors. More generally, we interpret it to mean the spirit embodied in the list of values given above.

Guided by these values, men of science have scored a constant progression of phenomenal successes which have brought them great power and prestige, but these patterns of behavior need not be limited to scientists. Certainly "longing to know and understand" is the spark which distinguishes human beings from other animals. It is apparent in children and when it is not suppressed by improper education—which is sadly prevalent—it can survive to produce a scientist, a philosopher, or a poet, and it can also brighten the daily lives of people in many other walks of life.

What better guideline in politics or ethics than "questioning of all things?" In countries that have only recently achieved nominal independence, what better guarantee that real independence—economic, social, and cultural—will be achieved than to have a population that has literally learned to question all things? Could a scrutiny of national histories stand up to this? What are the implications in areas where authority is now respected blindly?

It is characteristic of scientists to observe, measure, and record data which in some cases lead to a generalization called a theory or a law. But, to a lesser degree and in other forms "searching for data and for relations that give them meaning" is a characteristic of the inquiring mind in all realms of thought and action, including art, literature, religion, and music.

The "demand for objective verification" is a value which is sorely needed not only in primitive societies and less developed countries, but even in the most advanced countries of the world (witness the astrology columns still prevalent in some important newspapers). It is perhaps in science that the most precise meaning is given to "objective verification," but the need for it is apparent in all walks of life.

How about "respect for logic" in the realms of politics or statesmanship or in the strategies for survival? Would "respect for logic" help us in assessing the relative merits of the nonviolent point of view and that of the modern militarist who has created the extraordinary doctrine that a nation must have the capability of *completely* destroying an enemy who is, to a certain extent, a creation of his own imagination?

How about "consideration of premises" in helping to decide whether to deploy an antiballistic missile whose cost might rise to the tens or hundreds of billions of dollars, and how about "consideration of consequences" when advocating a ban on dissemination of information on birth control or for that matter in advocating curriculum reform in science education itself?

It seems clear that these values which we have associated with science have here been stated in such a form that they can infuse many forms of activity, including religious, esthetic, humanistic, and literary, besides science itself.

Suppose we grant, then, that one of the important new aims of science education is to diffuse the spirit of science and to propagate the spirit of inquiry. How will that determine the other two factors which we set about to discuss, namely, contents and methodology? We said earlier that we thought it more logical to begin with aims and later to proceed with contents and methodology in the hope that they would inform one another in that order.

Obviously a great deal of effort by many different investigators will be needed to study the implications of the aims of science stated in the above form. How do you infuse the spirit of inquiry into the whole educational structure? How do you generate a sense of social responsibility which seems to be implicit in "consideration of consequences"? Will it actually help us in determining the content of any specific course, say nuclear physics or organic chemistry or molecular biology? We do not have simple and ready-made answers to these difficult questions. We can only say that just as we had to do a great deal of research and development to create the materials that came out of our first- and second-generation reform projects, we now need to put in a massive effort to scrutinize the set of values that we have listed and to perform experiments with the intention of determining how they can help us in guiding the future content and methodology of science teaching. We believe that they can reinforce some of the trends toward a humanistic education which we already see arising in existing science curriculum reform projects.

At the personal level, our ultimate aim should be the development of informed, sensitive, responsible, and useful human beings. We believe that the values of science can go a long way toward achieving this goal. Many people will have to expend a lot of effort before we see clearly how to implement programs that will bring us a step closer to this ideal. We have not yet expressed the new objectives in operational terms. We have not specified what we expect the students of the future to be able to do. That should be the aim of some initial pilot projects in this new field.

With regard to methodology, if we adopt the point of view expressed above, it can have a very definite effect on the kinds of new methods that we emphasize in the future. It should cause us to think twice before we promote schemes for automated or computer-assisted instruction that may separate the individual from society or allow him to lose touch with the human aspects of science. An awareness of "consideration of consequences" should make educators of the future more sensitive to the effects that concerted efforts in science education may have if they are started too soon or if they do not take the natural inclinations and capabilities of youngsters into account.

The spirit of science may create a trend toward international cooperation in science and education. It is clear that scientists and educators will have to lead politicians and statesmen to a better understanding of what may be the gains for all mankind of a proper diffusion of the spirit of science.

The developing countries should be reminded that science-teaching reform is difficult and costly. It would pay them to study carefully the successes and failures of the different curriculum reform movements in the advanced countries and, above all, not only to benefit from the actual materials that have been produced abroad but to examine carefully their own aims, objectives, and motives as regards science education. In this way, they need not repeat the errors of the past. They may instead point the way by pioneering in new directions that will promote social responsibility and international cooperation.

DISCUSSION

Senator A. B. Gamede (Swaziland) emphasized the need to reconcile religious leaders to the new and revolutionary concepts involved in science teaching. In many developing lands, he pointed out, religion plays a great role in determining the philosophy of a country, and, since what they are trying to evolve is fundamentally no less than a modern philosophy of education, it is essential to have the support, and not the opposition, of religious leaders.

Science educators should also work closely with sociologists and anthropologists, urged *Dr. Elkanah Gali* (Israel). It is important that the aims, content, and methodology of science education should blend together with the culture of each society. Concepts of space, time, and force are not the same everywhere.

Mr. Frixos Vrahas (Cyprus) wondered how science education and general education are to be fused. Cyprus is planning an International Year of Education, during which free education will be made compulsory up to the age of 15 instead of only until the age of 12. The question is how to define education and how to treat, for instance, science and history: are they to be taught as strictly independent branches of education, or are they to be integrated in some way?

Another difficulty was raised by the *Hon. Onofre D. Corpuz* (Philippines). He thought that there is considerable danger in the use of the phrase "developing countries," since this conjures up an image of homogeneous societies. In fact, not only are the countries concerned different from each other but there are also differences inside the countries themselves, pockets of modernization contrasting with the old and unchanged. "In the midst of a panorama of barren rural culture, there may be some gleaming factories," he said. "There are some cities where there are laboratories and offices and commercial buildings, that are indeed very modern. So our task is now to generate that capacity to create these pockets, or, where there are pockets already, to expand and to extend them."

2

THE SCIENTIFIC METHOD

By Amos de Shalit

Weizmann Institute of Science,
Israel

This conference poses two main questions:
1.   In trying to achieve better living conditions in developing states, what is it that *science teaching* can provide and how best can it be done?
2.   In trying to improve and expand *general education* in developing states, what benefit can one derive from recent scientific and technological developments? Are we approaching a scientification of education?

The Aims and Methods of Science Teaching

The teaching of the scientific method as such has great relevance to the first question—that of the merits of science teaching. But rather than elaborate on this point, I shall try to apply this method itself to analyze to some extent these two questions. Let us take the science-teaching question first. Since we are not concerned with science teaching for its own sake (which, incidentally, is quite a noble goal all by itself), we want first to make sure that science teaching does have something to do with achieving better living conditions. It is, of course, clear that better health, improved agriculture, efficient food preservation, faster means of communication, a more thorough exploitation of energy resources, better-quality clothing and dependable housing all involve the use of scientific and technological progress. In many cases it is even rather recent and sophisticated developments which are called for.

Yet it may be argued that large societies, maybe even whole nations, can benefit from all those developments without necessarily being partners in making them possible, and without being fully aware of what there is behind them. After all, even in the most progressive societies the fraction of people who have even the slightest notion of what goes on inside a TV set is rather small. So perhaps developing states should not give a high priority to the difficult, and somewhat costly, adventure of improved science curriculums in their schools, and be satisfied, for the time being, with ready-made knowledge and products. Do we really know that a higher level of science education in a community is relevant to the improvement of its living conditions? Do we know that improved science teaching is not the *result*, rather than the *cause*, of a higher standard of living?

It is, I believe, important to clear this point rather thoroughly, for in its clarification one may find the seeds for the appropriate way to teach science. There is no use running faster if you don't know which direction you are heading for. So let us take one question after another and see what we know about these various points.

Can We Rely on Buying, or Otherwise Getting, All the Good Things That Science and Technology Produce?

The answer to this question obviously depends on the size of the community one is talking about. A single family can rely on buying everything. There are probably many millions of families in developed countries, none of whose members have the slightest notion of science, who nevertheless enjoy the benefits of science just as much as their learned neighbors. It is equally obvious that humanity as a whole could not rely on buying anything because there would be no one to buy from. So there is a certain size for a community, somewhere between the size of a family and that of the whole of humanity, where self-involvement in the production of new knowledge becomes advisable or even necessary.

One can think of various factors that determine this critical size of community. It may, for instance, be big enough to have indigenous problems that are not common to other, developed, communities; tackling such problems very often requires the strong incentive of being a member of that community and being rewarded by it. Financial incentives may sometimes help bring foreign experts to do such work, but successes using this line are the exception rather than the rule.

A community may also be big enough not to want to rely on purchased knowledge and technology in periods of emergency. The availability of people in a community who have enough knowledge and experience in science and technology and at the same time have a developed sense of loyalty to that community has proved to be of paramount importance in many cases, even very recently.

Then there is the question of numbers, which is always a good exercise to go through (this, incidentally, is another thing the scientific method teaches us!). In an address at Indiana University Dr. G. T. Seaborg, Chairman of the U.S. AEC had the following things to say:

> . . . A student . . . should be aware that a certain amount of technological sophistication will personally benefit him in almost any walk of life. Virtually every line of work, from business to poetry, is feeling the effects of scientific advancements, and ill-prepared workers are finding it increasingly difficult to cope. I recently read that some 35 percent of the top management in this country [U.S.A.] has a technical background, and this figure is certain to increase. School administrators are involved with systems analysis, writers must work with mass communications and electronics, and

virtually every branch of the government is dealing with sophisticated technology.

It would seem, therefore, that the mere *running* of a modern community utilizing the developments of science and technology, let alone the maintenance and production of such developments, requires a fairly large number of people who have some technological and scientific background. To give just one example: Computer programming can probably be taught to everyone, but its efficient use for any purpose requires the development of a habit of translating your problems into a set of successive precise operations; this training is a common element in all the sciences. Thus the number of people with general scientific background required for that and similar purposes makes it very impractical for sizable societies to rely on the purchase of foreign know-how.

There is another important aspect of having local people trained broadly in the sciences and technologies. When we buy know-how and products from other communities we tend to buy things which exist, are well tested, and usually represent great achievements of 30 or 40 years ago. When a community plans new developments locally there is very often the urge to do something new, daring, with a view to the future. Although this does result sometimes in embarking on ill-conceived projects which are doomed to failure, I personally believe it is a worthwhile price to pay for having forward-looking development rather than imitations of past achievements. Looking, for instance, at the problems that have already been created by the accessive urbanization in the developed world, I wonder whether the developing countries do not want to design their new urban developments in a way which will foresee possible solutions to the problems the developed world faces now.

Can We and Should We Teach Everything in School?

Faced with the immense development of science and technology, one is often led to the wrong conclusion that many more hours should be devoted to the teaching of science in schools, often at the cost of teaching other things. To my mind there are two reasons why one should not overdo the teaching of science and technology in the school system, one of them being an inherent feature of science itself, the other being connected with education in general.

The acquisition of scientific knowledge is probably one of the purest manifestations of the fundamental difference between human beings and animals. It has been known for some time that animals, like human beings, can "teach" their offspring all sorts of things. To be more precise, parents can transfer to their offspring knowledge and experience accumulated during their lifetime, which may be of special beneficial value to the preservation of the species. Unlike human beings, however, animals cannot abstract the information which they transfer to their offspring and are therefore able to transfer only a very limited amount of information during their lifetime. The result is that in the animal world each generation must learn essentially everything from the beginning and there is no progress except that provided by biological mutations. The great advantage of the human being over animals lies in man's ability to abstract and to transfer in a very concise, yet meaningful, form information and experience gathered over long periods of time. Thus, a new generation can acquire the accumulated experience of the past generations in a fraction of its lifetime and devote the rest of its lifetime to the accumulation of new knowledge and the increase of its own experience. The laws of nature that science tries to uncover are extreme examples of such compression of long and tedious experiences into very concise form. It is therefore contrary to the spirit of science to expand in the teaching of details, and this should be avoided in schools.

From the educational point of view it is also very important not to overdo the teaching of one subject at the cost of another. Although there are many applications in the teaching of science to other areas of our life, neglect of the humanities, arts, social sciences, etc. for the purpose of the promotion of science and technology will not pay in the long run. The art of today is the environment of yesterday, and by the same token the science of today is the environment of tomorrow. Both have to be taught to children in order to provide for the continuity of the human race and to develop a respect for its place on earth.

There is also a practical problem involved in regulating the teaching of science and technology. Despite all our progress and achievements babies are still born, to the best of our knowledge, with zero information about the world which surrounds them. We thus have to start our training and education of the young always from the same point, no matter how much material we want to transfer to them. To teach science and technology today in the same detail that was useful and applicable a hundred years ago would only mean that we should have to devote to it probably ten times as much time and effort. This we cannot afford to do, nor do we want to do it.

What Do We Want to Achieve Through Science Teaching in Schools?

There are probably many answers to this question and different people with different tastes will legitimately emphasize one aspect or the other. For example, mathematics as a language is becoming now more and more useful in many branches of our activities. Most of us who studied mathematics in the conventional form have not really developed a sense for mathematics as a language. We can carry out our simple computations more or less reliably, but whereas we can translate problems from their expression in the English language into their expression in the French or in any other language, few of us can translate them into a mathematical language. Questions like the relative merits of different communication patterns or those of the social behavior of large groups of people can be formulated in mathematical language just as well as in any of the other languages, if not better. The difficulties that many of us encounter in translating statements pertaining to such situations from spoken languages to mathematical languages are due, I believe, to the improper teaching of mathematics many of us have experienced. It is possible that now, with the rapid introduction of computers, it will be easier to teach mathematics as a language, since the computer language, which still retains the precision and clarity of the more concise language of mathematical symbols, is closer in its structure to the spoken languages. I therefore believe that the teaching of mathematics as a language, which is undoubtedly an important element in the education of the future generations, is feasible and should become an important aim in the teaching of science as a whole. Many branches of science lend themselves most easily to be translated into mathematical language and can therefore serve the purpose of teaching this language in a most suitable way.

Another important element in the teaching of science in schools is that of going through the experiences of abstracting or, equivalently, those of developing an insight on the basis of a finite amount of information and knowledge. Out ability to abstract and analyze stems from the fact that in many cases it is possible to guess the complete pattern of a certain situation from the availability of partial information only. This is true of the exact sciences as well as of the social sciences and the arts. The great merit of the sciences, however, is that they provide easy methods for repeated tests of the validity of our guesses. The proper teaching of science is therefore an exercise not only in abstractions and generalization, but also testing the validity of these conclusion. Scientists are trained to look for abstraction and generalizations which lend themselves to objective testing, and very often they think about these generalizations in terms of the possible tests to which they will be put.

There is still another important purpose for the teaching of sciences in school, which is actually shared by that of the teaching of all other subjects. In our teaching of science we want to acquaint the children with the work of the scientist and the engineer in order for them to be able to assess for themselves whether or not they want to make their career in one of these areas. Since it seems that the demands of society on technologically and scientifically trained people are going to increase considerably in the foreseeable future, it is very important that more children are properly directed into these areas with a full understanding of what is expected of them.

The teaching of science also has important educational values. A member of present-day society, whether he is a scientist or not, ought to be in a position to appreciate orders of magnitude of various phenomena. He may be called upon very often to make decisions, or to help in making decisions, about questions the details of which he is not familiar with. He will have to listen to the opinions of experts and to be guided by them. But in so doing he will want to be guided by his own feelings at least as to the order of magnitude of the things he is talking about.

There is also the educational value of learning to know man's proper place in the universe through the better knowledge that we have acquired of our universe. There is the development of the sense of responsibility of modern man in modern society because of the tremendous power that new developments in science and technology put in the hands of the individual. There is the appreciation of the beauty and harmony in nature and the unified underlying principles of all known phenomena around us. There is education for humility and willingness to admit a mistake in the face of indisputable new experimental results.

The Content of Science Teaching

What Should We Include in the Teaching of Science?

In view of these aims in the teaching of science, I think that it becomes quite obvious that it is not at all necessary to give a complete course in the sciences in the framework of our educational program in the elementary and secondary schools. Apart from the fact that there is no hope of doing so during the time put at our disposal, it is completely superfluous, unnecessary, and a waste of time for the majority of the pupils. Rather, one can pick on specific topics from the various fields of science that may be most appropriate either to the community in question or to the period in human development or to the availability of equipment and personnel and try to extract from these special topics as much as one can. One should not be frightened by the possibility that our children will learn nothing of the classical fields that we were taught in school. The fact that we have been exposed very thoroughly to the law of Archimedes, for instance, does not mean that our children have to go through this experience as well. Not that the law has been found to be wrong since then, or that it has lost any of its importance, but it may just turn out that one can achieve the important goals that we have set ourselves through the teaching of electricity rather than mechanics, or through the teaching of something that cannot be broken into the classical disciplines of electricity, mechanics, heat, light, etc. We all have a tendency to think that whatever we have been taught is naturally important and relevant, and we would hate to see our children grow up without an acquaintance with all the detailed facts that we have been taught in school. Yet we have to realize many important facts were never brought to our attention in school, and our teachers' preference for one set of facts over another should not dictate the program of our children as well. Our personal and emotional involvement in the teaching program is something we should learn to overcome. We should teach ourselves to look objectively at these problems and ask in all honesty what is it really that the child is going to get out of our program and what best should we do for him.

How Can We Test Whether We Have Achieved Our Aims?

This is perhaps one of the most difficult problems in the teaching of science and in education in general. The real effects of education are seen only a long time after the child has been through school and are the product of so many different factors both in school and outside of school that it is really very hard to associate directly the behavior of any given community with the education it has been given in schools. Yet, if we are to make changes and to look for new ways and new possibilities of teaching sciences in our schools, we ought to be able to develop at least some methods to test whether we are really achieving the goals and aims that we set before ourselves. I do not really know a good answer to this question. Maybe there is no simple answer altogether. But perhaps some of the following tests could be used at different stages of a child's education in order to see whether we have or have not achieved our aims:

The analogy between mathematics and the spoken languages suggests that we may test the extent to which a child has really grasped mathematics as a language by requesting him to read and learn an entirely new text in some field of mathematics and then work out some exercises connected with this particular text. We shall then be testing not his ability to memorize things which he has learned at school, or to work out mechanically answers to different problems, but rather the extent to which he is able to read new texts and understand their meaning. This is exactly what we do when we test whether a child has learned English well enough by placing before him a text which he has never seen before and asking him to comment on the contents of this text.

I would expect a child who has been properly trained in the sciences and in technology to be able to answer questions like: What does a bridge engineer do? Whom would you consult if you see cracks in the walls of your building?

I would also expect a child with a proper training to reject the feasibility of systems which obviously violate the conservation of energy. If faced with a situation of a simple perpetuum mobile his reaction should be not that of testing whether it would work or not, but rather that of looking for the place in which it went wrong.

I would expect the proper teaching of science in schools to enhance the frequency with which children borrow popular science books from the school's library. This, as a matter of fact, may be a very easy test for the success of any given course, although it obviously represents a combination of both the value of the course material and the ability of the teacher to transfer this material.

Looking at the general technological progress of our society, one cannot but wonder why is it that education and the methods of teaching have undergone so little change in the last 2,000 years. The increased quest for knowledge is becoming a characteristic feature of our own generation, and that of our children's and grandchildren's. If the quest for equipartition of rights can characterize the period of the French Revolution, and if that of the equipartition of property can characterize the social revolutions at the beginning of this century in both the socialist and the capitalist countries, it is the quest for the equipartition of knowledge among all people that is going to characterize the end of this century and the beginning of the next one, since the possession of knowledge is a prerequisite for power in its best sense. The demands which this quest for knowledge is going to put on the general educational systems of our communities will force us to introduce new methodologies, new techniques, and new technologies into this field. It is estimated that toward the end of this century the developed countries will have more than 50 percent of their manpower involved in the processing of data, its condensation in one form or another, and its transfer to others. Such a tremendous effort cannot be conceived unless one realizes that a revolution will have to take place in the classical tools employed in the transfer of knowledge. Those of us who are in the fortunate position of planning our educational systems essentially from scratch may want to consider very seriously the introduction of new technologies in an early stage in their development rather than go through the whole procedure of first developing a classical educational system and then going through the pains of changing into a more modern one.

TOMORROW'S SCIENCE IS TODAY'S EDUCATION

By Michael Feldman
Weizmann Institute of Science,
Israel

[A Supplementary Address]

We are all aware that science progresses very rapidly today. We also realize that the progress of science is based on the contributions of individual scientists or of very small teams, and these contributions accumulate very rapidly, because, in fact, scientific methods are such that new information is being published at great speed and constitutes the new world of know-how. On the other hand, we need big teams, committees, ministries, approvals and so on, if we want to formulate a new curriculum. So the time that it takes to reformulate and reshape a new curriculum is far longer than the time needed to make new scientific contributions. Thus the gap between tomorrow's science and today's education will increase, if we do not find some new solutions enabling us to bridge it somehow, to narrow down the difference in the rate of activity of the respective groups and units.

I do not offer any solution to this problem, but I would like to raise a model of a technical dilemma which faces us. We realize that science develops very rapidly. The world of science today differs significantly from the world of science which existed 20 years ago. So we can make a safe assumption that the world of science in 20 years will differ significantly from the world we face today. We teach today people who will have to function within 10 or 20 years. We have somehow to ensure that they will be capable of coping with problems which today do not exist at all, of using methodologies which are rapidly being developed, of answering questions which we do not know will be asked. How then can we teach somebody who will have to function in a different world?

In order to train people to function in a world which of necessity they cannot study, I think we must ensure that two conditions will be fulfilled. All people, in order to be able to cope with the world in 20 years' time, will have to learn about new things that will develop within that period; in order to learn them, they must be made to desire new knowledge. How then can we teach the desire to acquire new know-how? This, I think, is one of the most crucial problems in science education today.

There is one simple way to kill this desire. That is to teach in such a way that the students are bored. Thus you will ensure that they will not want to acquire any new know-how. If we don't want this, the problem is how are we to keep out of education the kind of boring teacher to whom so many of us were exposed in the past?

I know that there are no simple formulas to solve this problem. All of us realize that if in teaching we somehow stimulate, or trigger, or elicit an emotional experience, a real feeling of joy, of satisfaction, an intellectual experience, then, of course, we trigger the desire to acquire new know-how, simply because the student will believe that by this acquisition he can extend his enjoyment further. But how do we get this desired result?

We must analyze the various methods of teaching of science to find those which may create the desire to acquire new know-how. In many places the old system of teaching scientific facts still prevails. There is nothing more boring than learning scientific facts. As a biologist I can tell you that the fact that the nucleus within a cell controls the genetic property of an organism is nothing but a boring fact, although it is a very important fact. It is completely boring, whereas the sequence in logical deduction based on the experimental approach which has led to the appreciation of that fact is very stimulating.

The interest and excitement generated by this sequence in logical deduction should not be less than that generated by a detective story. The question therefore is: how can we transform our teaching system? How can we apply methodologies that will ensure that the students will not be bored, but will instead undergo emotional and intellectual experiences that will generate their interest? Obviously there is another very great problem here. It is not enough to desire to acquire knowledge. One should do something in order to ensure that the desire can be satisfied so that the student will understand the development of science in the future.

Many people may be thinking that perhaps I am overemphasizing these points, that they may seem more important in the so-called developed countries but the developing countries can be satisfied with lower aims. I think that this is a very great mistake. I think that we must make sure that within the developing countries there is a continuous interest in the scientific world of tomorrow, or otherwise we will perpetuate the gap, or in fact increase the gap, between the developed and the developing countries.

Obviously the question of how to ensure that we will understand tomorrow's world has very many aspects. Can we base our curriculum on some predictions regarding future developments in the sciences? Can we base it on problems which we think will be the crucial, burning problems of tomorrow? Should we lead the students to the appreciation of the borderline between what we know and what we do not know, to sense the frontiers of science during their education?

I think we should consider very seriously the possibility of including within the science curriculums of developing countries problems that seem to be local but that can both serve as models for the teaching of any general principles and also lead the students to a real appreciation of endemic problems, which ought to be approached in the future.

There is the question of how to make the students capable of choosing problems for solution in the future. One can ask: to which kind of people are you referring? I think that they can be classified into three main categories: those who will produce new know-how; those who will implement and make use of the new know-how to be produced; and those who will make decisions about policies involving the application of the new know-how—you can call them, if you wish, politicians.

If we aim at training groups of people whose main functions will be that of creating new know-how, we should deviate from the old pattern of sending individuals to good laboratories in developed countries because, once they come back, they are somehow diluted, they do not serve as the minimal critical mass for the crystallization of further functional groups. Perhaps we should consider something now tried at the Weizmann Institute, namely, the mobilization of small groups or teams who will get interested and integrated into specific projects in certain good laboratories and then, when they come back, can form nuclei around which further growth can develop.

In developed countries the achievements of technology, based on the scientific progress of the last few decades, have transformed the social structure within those societies in such a way that class conflicts, ideological conflicts, have been erased to a great extent.

Because these ideological differences have faded as modern industry and technology have improved the standard of living, political parties do not really differ about basic ideology, but rather about the basis of the implementation of means. They aim at the same goal. But the means are nothing but scientific means, technological means.

The choice of tomorrow will therefore not be between alternative ideologies but between alternative scientific approaches. Politicians will have to make this choice, which will be far harder than those to which they have been accustomed, because they will face a new world based on different categories of consideration. How to educate them to make these choices is a problem which I think ought to be considered.

We have made some attempts in this institute to try to educate politicians. We have mobilized members of parliament here to introduce them to some of the problems which we think they ought to consider in order to be capable, not so much of making decisions, but of realizing what they ought to know in order to make the decisions. I sincerely believe that this is one of the most crucial problems regarding the general question of decision-making in the world of tomorrow—and I do not speak of the far future.

Finally, I think that the politicians of tomorrow who are concerned with decision-making will face much harder problems than they have faced until now because, until this very day, science was concerned mostly with the changes in the environment. Technology has profoundly affected the environmental world in which we live. It hardly affected our own organism, apart from the prevention of disease and so on. However, the advancement of science during the last few decades, particularly of the biological sciences, has produced new tools which enable one today to direct developmental properties of organisms, to affect brain development, to affect organ development, and therefore to affect patterns of mental development. Methods which are now applicable to experimental animals will be applicable within a very short time to human organisms, and then we shall have tremendous tools, which will both be very dangerous indeed and yet have tremendous potentialities.

Then, of course, the question will arise: who will make decisions? How are we going to change ourselves? These will be crucial decisions because not only will we be able to change ourselves, but also by changing the genetic material, we will be able to affect future generations. Therefore the problem of educating those who will have to make decisions is now by far more crucial than ever before, simply because the ways to implement scientific achievements in human engineering are such that we will have to face, in a very concrete way, the question of which kind of men we would like to produce.

DISCUSSION

Professor Yehoshua (Israel) was very concerned about the pedagogical consequences of the increasing theorization of science. "Many fields of science," he said, "are becoming theoretical before our eyes." From the pedagogical point of view, this makes the problem far more complex; it is much harder to teach theory than to engage students in practical experiments. Miracles are being achieved in the United States, where some elements of a special theory of relativity are even being taught in some elementary schools. But it is hard to understand how this miracle is being done.

To illustrate that it is possible to teach third-graders the relativity of position and motion, *Dr. Herbert D. Thier* (United States) took two empty glass tumblers and two conference programs as his equipment. He demonstrated rapidly the relation of the objects to each other when he moved them about or kept them still, and assured his audience that children grasped the principles involved.

Further to the points raised by Professor Feldman, *Professor Arquimedes Caballero* (Mexico) stressed the need for education to keep up with the constant development of science; he said that Mexico had several centers to provide "refresher courses" for teachers.

Dr. Ademola Banjo (U.N. Economic Commission for Africa) saw three objectives of science teaching emerging from the papers and discussions. The first is to provide the student with an explanation of the physical world, to explain nature and how it works. The second is to inculcate in him an attitude of mind: the attitude of inquiry, of objectivity, and the habit of logical thought. These should be reinforced by the scientific method of observation, experimentation, formulation and testing of hypotheses. The third objective should be to show the uses of science in everyday life, the way in which it can change the environment through the production of new materials and articles, new techniques of production. The last aim is particularly important in developing lands, anxious to increase as rapidly as possible the production of their agriculture, crafts, and industries. This means teaching technology as well as science. Even if a student eventually concentrates on the classics, he should not leave school without understanding what goes on, and what is needed to increase production, on a farm or in a factory.

3

IS HUMANISTIC SCIENCE APPROPRIATE FOR A DEVELOPING COUNTRY?

By Fletcher G. Watson

Henry Lee Shattuck
Professor of Education,
Harvard University,
United States

To the question: "Is humanistic science appropriate to a developing country?" the immediate answer is probably a resounding NO. By definition a "developing country" has had an agricultural economy and now is striving to increase its industrial productivity. In addition to raw materials, adequate power sources, capital, and satisfactory transportation to and from foreign markets, such industrialization requires the continued availability of manpower having a wide range of technical skills. At the least-trained end of such a manpower range might be a general public capable of utilizing new mechanical devices and health services. At the next level would be skilled labor and technicians capable of installing new equipment and making reasonably complicated repairs, such as radio repairmen, auto mechanics, agricultural advisers, and public health agents. At the upper end of the ability range would be engineers, doctors, and planners who would select the types of industries and services to be created, decide upon their location, and design the details of the operations. In developing countries increasing numbers of people with these capabilities are rapidly needed to increase the country's industrial output and raise the general level of health. To achieve this goal, it seems that the science program in the schools should be oriented toward technology and industry.

However, we are considering a science program for all the children of the country of whom a very large percentage will not become skilled technicians. Yet we may hope that all the people will be involved to some degree in the decisions made about the development of their country. Therefore, we must ask whether a technologically oriented science program is appropriate for all the future citizens, who will include mothers, teachers, artists, businessmen, legislators, and voters. To achieve a general population which is able to utilize and maintain an increasing variety of technical devices, we can argue that all students should have some experience with the use and the maintenance of the devices becoming available in their country. Perhaps most important here would be a knowledge of how to use and maintain the equipment so that it is used productively, is not broken, and not used in a hazardous way. For this reason, we shall argue later that part of the early science program for all children should familiarize them with the technological, health, and agricultural materials that are likely to be commonplace in a country during the next decade or two. This proposition has been one of many influencing the choice of materials and experiences designed into the General Science program for

Forms I and II in Nigeria. Yet, even if the experiences with such mechanical and biological materials are extended into some study of the more general principles underlying their functioning, this would not be an adequate basis for designing a total science program for all children over many years of schooling.

Before we consider what else might be done we should recognize that at present the typical science program in the schools focuses upon the current state of scientific explanations, sometimes briefly considers the evolution of scientific concepts and theories, and is more appropriate for potential scientists than potential members of the general public. Some years ago Professor Joseph Schwab described these programs, which emphasize the known, as "a rhetoric of conclusions."[1] During recent years a major effort has been made in the U.S.A. to extend the purposes of science teaching so that students have some intellectual and emotional involvement in the creation and evaluation of scientific theories. That is, some attention is given to the process of knowing. This opens opportunities for individual creativity and arguments about the limits of data and of theories, encourages "open-ended investigations," and to some degree "allows every student to be a scientist." At least in part these efforts have intended to provide the student with an awareness of the intellectual and emotional difficulties of creating scientific knowledge, and therefore develop in the student some empathy toward the scientist as a creative person. Certainly these are desirable goals, but they are unnecessarily limited for future citizens living in a country where the change from an agricultural to a partially technological society is proceeding rapidly. Before we examine other possibilities we should ask: in what ways do science and technology enter the lives of people?

Knowledge of specific empirical results and generalized theories, like these gained through scientific investigation, can have two uses. One, which has interested and rewarded many of us, is an inner personal satisfaction of knowing. The knower feels that he can increasingly organize and comprehend the diverse phenomena he senses; that is, he can create some kind of personal order out of apparent chaos. In this form his knowledge is personally pleasing. A science program, and all of schooling, aims at developing this personal satisfaction in knowing. But the knowledge is not productive.

Knowledge becomes productive when the knower uses it to make decisions about the actions he can take. Such decisions occur on many levels. They may be personal, be within small groups (such as the family, the village or a business enterprise), or be for a larger group such as a whole country. But, irrespective of the size of the decision-making group, knowledge becomes useful when it is applied to the creation and selection of possible alternative actions needed to solve real problems.

Science and technology are useful in establishing what we "can do," but only to a limited degree, if at all, do they indicate what we "should do." Teaching science only in terms of its technical applications and theoretical generalizations without considering the social consequences of possible

---

[1] Joseph J. Schwab, *The Teaching of Science* (Cambridge, Mass.: Harvard University Press, 1962).

decisions will result and has already resulted to some extent, in a society in which the scientists are feared by those who must make decisions but do not themselves understand the potentialities and limitations of applying scientific and technical knowledge. In developing countries, where manpower, time, and capital are in short supply, wise decisions are critical. Each decision must maximize the social gain. One major mistake may irrevocably cripple the country's development. Yet rarely is such decision-making discussed, analyzed, and practiced in schools in any country of the world. This interface between knowledge and social action is of the utmost importance to each individual and to each country, particularly to rapidly developing countries. Instruction which relates scientific knowledge to people and to their decision-making is what I mean by a humanistic approach to science teaching.

In many countries, especially the developing countries, schooling for any individual child is likely to be relatively brief. If, therefore, we are to alert the whole future population to the nature of scientific knowledge and its use in decision-making, we should start as early as is practical in the primary schools. In many of the developing countries, however, there is little or no science offered in the primary schools. In the primary schools we should help the child become aware of the diversity in his environment, the possibilities of organizing or grouping various things and actions into more general types, and realizing that he can foresee the possible consequences of decisions that may be made. The context can be drawn from the commonly known local environment. My friends in the General Science program in Nigeria have cited an example they use in their unit on ecology. The story presented to the children is like this: The Chief of a village sees a hawk steal one of his chickens. The Chief becomes very angry at the hawk and orders the hunters of the village to kill all the hawks they can. What will happen? The students, with perhaps a little guided discovery from the teachers, realize that when the population of hawks is decreased the population of snakes will increase. A large population of snakes will decrease the population of mice. When there are few mice the insect population will rise rapidly, and the productivity on the farms will go down. Thus they have a five-step ecological food chain which ends up showing that the possible decision by the Chief could have disastrous effects upon the agricultural productivity of the village. In the primary schools the science program may stress a gradually expanding set of experiences with selected phenomena, getting to know about biotic and physical aspects of the world and how it acts, and how the decisions of individuals can lead to short-term and long-term consequences desirable or undesirable for all the citizens.

Because few primary-school teachers may be effective with any aspects of science, this initial phase may have to be postponed to the introductory forms of the secondary school. This is where we began in Nigeria, but already many of the experiences proposed for the first two years of the secondary school are being planned into a new science program for the upper years of the primary schools. Such an introductory program can extend over four or five years, develop a citizenry which is familiar with the characteristics and operations of their natural environment plus selected technological additions with which they will be living. But this does not comprise the basis for a total science program.

For older children who are beginning to choose careers, two types of science programs may be necessary. One for scientific and technologically oriented students may proceed similarly to programs now utilized in many schools. For the great majority of students who will not be involved in scientific or technological careers a second type of program will be more desirable. This can be a humanistic science focusing upon the wide use of scientific and technological information in decision-making. While such a program can take a variety of forms, one that will give the greatest relevance to the students is the utilization of case examples important to that country or region. Among general problems that may be considered are: the utilization of knowledge to increase food production, a consideration of the population expansion in the country, and the desirability of and possible procedures for limiting the number of births. Another example is the identification of desirable new industries and the selection of appropriate sites for their location. Certainly many biological topics dealing with the control of disease, which is always prevalent in the developing country in the form of nutritional, infectious, and parasitic diseases, are worthy of major study. This would result in changed health habits and cooperation with public health officers working on large area problems like the control of malaria or the tsetse fly. An appraisal of the natural resources of a country, such as availability of water, power, timber, soils, mines, oil, and human intelligence, will open up wide ranges for study and discussion.

Examination of these or other more relevant topics will involve the students in learning and appraising a large amount of technical information, understanding the significance of known scientific relationships, and considering the social significance of alternative decisions. Certainly in the United States the problems of pollution of the air and water by a great variety of man-made products is a clear example of the difficulties that may arise when industrial or agricultural decisions are made without any serious consideration of long-term consequences. Particularly important may be the differentiation between the consequences of small- and large-scale activities, such as a few woodburning fireplaces in contrast to the quantity of smoke and ash produced by the power plants and industries of a major industrial city.

Case studies appear to be especially useful because the examples can be developed locally rather than be imported and should be significant to the students. Study of a case should not be hurried; each case studied thoroughly may well take half a year. Careful selection of the cases should be made between those that deal with biological and physical sciences, although in many cases that distinction will rapidly blur because the consequences of biological decisions may have strong impact on the physical environment, and similarly decisions in the physical or technological environment may have strong impact on the biotic environment.

Such cases may be expanded to consider the whole range of decision-making by technically competent people, by industries, by governmental agencies, and by legislatures. Cases can also involve consideration of the complex of capabilities that have to be brought together to establish any industry, as for example risk capital, patents, raw materials, transportation systems in and out, power requirements, taxes, the diversity of manpower required, and a host of other topics.

Although the initial cases may most appropriately be drawn from the immediate environment, this should not exclude the possibility of exploration by older students of comparable cases in other countries and in times past. For example, the social impact of the steam engine may serve as a grim reminder of the creation of slums, incredible working and living conditions, and the virtual enslavement of the workers even as the steam engine was used to provide rapid transporation, much increased productivity, and the whole industrial revolution.

If such a case approach were adopted, a pedagogical revolution as well as a sharp change in the intent of science instruction would follow. Students would be expected to work on their own or in small research teams in the laboratory and field, in the library, in local industries and in the halls of government to gather relevant data and seek alternate decisions. Students would become increasingly responsible for their own knowledge and their own learning. Discussions and debates would be essential.

The role of the teacher would be drastically different than it is in most schools at the present time. Therefore, once a general program of study comprising perhaps various optional units or blocks of study had been laid out and some basic resource material suggested to the teachers, much effort would be needed to retrain the present teachers and to train the oncoming generations of new teachers. It would be unrealistic not to make clear that the training of large numbers of teachers capable of working in an open manner with students trying to investigate problems significant to them will perhaps be the greatest single limitation on the utilization of the approach suggested. However, the problems of appropriate science education for developing countries are crucial. Many of the more developed countries which have had ineffective science programs are now groping their way toward a humanistic approach to science as a socially significant enterprise. The developing countries, where major educational changes may be easier to achieve, can lead the world in evolving a new program of humanistic science.

DISCUSSION

Speaking about the themes in his paper, Professor Watson focused attention on the importance of decision-making. Deep concern has been expressed for teaching science as a pure intellectual activity. This is exceedingly useful and important: it affects literature and a country's total culture. To cite one example, Newtonian mechanics influenced poetry and the arts as well as science. But knowledge of science—and even technology—affects directly only a small number of people, although the results, of course, affect everybody. What affects everybody are the questions: How do you make choices? What are the bases for your choices? Do you evaluate the consequences of your choices?

Children should be taught to assemble information from the best possible sources, not just to rely on their own knowledge; to balance alternatives and to weigh their advantages and disadvantages; to weigh the possible results of their choices. For instance, the building of the Aswan Dam produced a lot of power; it also produced a lot of silt behind the dam. What happened downstream, as a result? In California, farmers killed pests by the indiscriminate use of DDT. But DDT does not break down: it lies on the trees, it gets into the soil. The rain carried the DDT into the rivers and thence down to San Francisco Bay, which is now polluted. The decision to use DDT was obviously made in an unscientific way, without any attempt to evaluate the consequences.

Dr. Peter Strevens (Great Britain) thought that it is very important to humanize the teaching of science, to provide through the science syllabus some of those aspects of the civilized citizen, of the mature and responsible member of society, which in previous educational generations were not seen to be necessarily a major hallmark of science. Indeed, such training was usually incorporated in the humanities and appropriated by the teachers of literature as being their main function. It is very interesting at this juncture of history to see science teaching taking on this type of education as one of its duties and to see it attempting to improve long-range decision-making.

The Rev. Joseph Elstgeest (Tanzania) took issue with Professor Watson's statement that "few primary-school teachers may be effective in any aspects of science," and the consequent conclusion that initial phases of his science program might have to be postponed until the introductory forms of the secondary school. Primary-school teachers, even though they may not be professional scientists or even science graduates, can still be effective teachers of science, if they are given the opportunity to develop themselves. They can be trained to develop the right approach.

But *Dr. Ademola Banjo* (UNECA) disagreed with Father Elstgeest. The evaluations required of the teacher for Professor Watson's purposes need a very sophisticated knowledge of science and its effects, not normally found in primary-school teachers. Furthermore, the attempt to introduce such ideas at primary school level may confuse the children. Teachers at the primary-school level should only try to teach the children something of the spirit of science, the idea of looking for evidence, and so on. What is important, with regard to all education as well as science education, is that both teachers and children should get away from the authoritarian approach of the teacher who dictates what sort of evaluations or answers he wants; instead, the children should be encouraged to think for themselves, to form independent opinions.

Taking up Professor Watson's point about decision-making, *Mr. Peter Inocent Mwombela* (Tanzania) wondered how people can be taught to make decisions when they do not know the consequences of their decisions. For example, Professor Watson quoted the example of DDT used by Californian farmers polluting San Francisco Bay: what if the people charged with making decisions simply did not know what the effect of the DDT would be?

Replying to the discussion, Professor Watson said that there is no such thing as teaching a class: there is only helping a learner to learn. The teacher should function as a sort of referee, while the pupils explore problems from their own environment that interest them. What should be included in the package they learn will vary from country to country. The important thing is that the teacher should guide them in an approach, not try to instill facts. This applies also to the questions about making decisions: of course, wrong decisions will be made, but the decision-makers should at least be trained to try to estimate the consequences of their acts. History alone can provide the ultimate answers about decisions, but at least children should learn to approach a problem by evaluating all the known factors and possible consequences involved. They must learn to ask: What happens? And then, what happens next?

PART II

SURVEYS OF SCIENCE EDUCATION
IN THE DEVELOPING STATES

4

A SURVEY OF
SCIENCE EDUCATION
PROBLEMS IN ASIA

By Pradisth Cheosakul

Deputy Secretary-General,
National Research Council,
Thailand

The advancement of science has had far-reaching impact on the life in Asia, which consists mostly of developing countries that derive their main incomes from agriculture. Those countries usually do not have enough financial means for their national development. Since they are also burdened by a population explosion, they have to increase their incomes by introduction of both modern techniques for agricultural production and industrial uses of their natural resources. To attain this objective calls for the application of science and technology, the success of which depends on the creation of a favorable environment for the promotion of scientific research, the improvement of science education to increase scientific manpower, and the establishment of a definite science policy related to economic planning.

In the beginning private scientific societies and associations were established so as to bring science and technology into the economics of the developing countries—for example, the Ceylon Association for the Advancement of Science, the Malayan Scientific Association, the Pakistan Association for the Advancement of Science, and the Science Society of Thailand. All these bodies have the same purpose, to promote and support science.

Later, when private efforts to promote science and technology proved insufficient despite receipt of some financial aid from the governments and foreign foundations, national research councils or the like were established as civil service agencies for advising the governments in scientific matters, especially research. Among this type of research agencies in Asia are the Academia Sinica of the National Republic of China, the Israel Academy of Sciences and Humanities, the National Science Development Board of the Philippines, and the National Research Council of Thailand.

Since most of the national research councils have advisory functions and give grants-in-aid to qualified researchers but do not conduct research work themselves, it is necessary to create additional machineries for the implementation of national scientific programs. A chain of scientific organizations for direct engagement in scientific research and development has therefore come into existence all over Asia. The majority of these research organizations have encountered serious difficulty in the recruitment of sufficient competent scientists to pursue their programs owing to two important factors: the lack of incentive and the shortage of scientific manpower.

In an attempt to attract talented scientists into research, one research organization after another has been granted or created with an autonomous status independent of civil service regulations so that the research scientists can be properly compensated for their service. Typical autonomous research organizations of the developing countries in the Economic Commission for Asia and the Far East (ECAFE) region are the Council of Scientific and Industrial Research (CSIR) of India, the Korea Institute of Science and Technology (KIST), the Singapore Institute of Standards and Industrial Research (SISIR), and the Applied Scientific Research Corporation of Thailand (ASRCT).

Recognizing the urgent need for trained scientists, some scientific societies and associations have contributed both directly and indirectly to the cause of science education. For instance, the Science Society of Thailand is actively engaged in attracting young people of talent to pursue a scientific career. It provides them with encouragement and support by means of the following activities:

1.   Publication of *Science* magazine, containing articles useful to students of different levels in their appreciation of science.
2.   Establishment of the Science Club of Thailand to stimulate the interest of students in science.
3.   Organization of Science Fairs for secondary-school students in order to persuade them to spend their spare time in out-of-school scientific activities. In 1968 an Asian Science Fair was held in Bangkok under the joint sponsorship of the Thai government and UNESCO. It has been agreed that the fair will be organized annually in member countries on a rotational basis.
4.   Science lecture tours undertaken by scientists of the society at the request of schools throughout the kingdom in order to stimulate the interest of students in the study of science.
5.   Summer institutes for science teachers run by the Science Teachers Committee of the society, which provide refresher courses in different disciplines of science such as astronomy, biology, chemistry, physics, and nuclear science.
6.   Translation of scientific textbooks such as the materials issued by the Physical Science Study Committee, Biological Sciences and Curriculum Study, and Chemical Education Material Study. The society has also completed the translation of an encyclopedia from English into Thai for secondary schools.
7.   Science Talent Search for outstanding secondary school graduates in order to award them scholarships for the study of basic science in a local university, each with an annual stipend of 5,000 baht ($250) for a period of four years.

Besides supporting and coordinating research activities of government agencies as well as private enterprises, some national research councils play a significant role in science education. The National Science Development Board of the Philippines serves as a unique example of research agencies which pay close attention to science education. One of its important functions is to upgrade science education in the Philippines as follows:

1. To strengthen the educational system so as to maintain a steady supply of scientists and technologists
2. To encourage studies in basic science
3. To set up a program for the effective training of scientists and technologists
4. To grant scholarships for the study of mathematics, science, technology, and science teaching
5. To recommend necessary measures for making the educational system an effective instrument for the advancement of science.

As a modest contribution to science education in Thailand in particular, and Asia in general, the National Research Council of Thailand cooperated with UNESCO to conduct a Pilot Project for Chemistry Teaching in Asia as a regional arrangement from October 1965 to July 1966. Through the courtesy of the Faculty of Science, Chulalongkorn University in Bangkok, the seminar and training under the project were held in the Chemical Technology Building of the university. The objective of this project is to develop through research the subject matter and equipment suitable for Asian students at the upper secondary-school level so as to keep up with the progress in this field and to meet the requirement of the local conditions.

During Phase I of the project stoichiometry, including a small part of the topic on energy and structure, formed the main theme of investigation. Dr. Laurence E. Strong, who is Professor of Chemistry at Earlham College, Indiana, U.S.A., and was formerly in charge of the work on the Chemical Bond Approach, served as the first director of the project. In the course of the 10 months 3 staff members, 5 consultants, and 19 participants from 16 countries under the sponsorship of UNESCO participated in the project. Whenever the situation permits, arrangements have been made for the university chemists and secondary-school chemistry teachers to work together at the project.

From October 1966 to December 1967 Dr. Edward C. Watton, Professor of Chemistry, University of New South Wales, Australia, succeeded Dr. Strong as the second director of the project. During Phase II of the project under the direction of Dr. Watton action was taken to convert the regional project into a national one. Despite the change of its status the project has heretofore been open to Asian educators involved in chemistry teaching. As a consequence foreign participants sponsored by UNESCO came to join the project from time to time. After the departure of Dr. Watton in December 1967 UNESCO assigned Dr. Jaroslov Zyka, Professor of Chemistry and Head of the Analytical Chemistry Department at Charles University, Prague, Czechoslovakia, as the third director of the project. UNDP and UNESCO agreed to provide Thailand, under the Technical Assistance Program, with the service of Dr. Zyka to guide further the Project for Chemistry Teaching for 1969 and that of another expert to conduct the Project of Physics Teaching at least through 1970.

In the beginning of 1969 a two-man study team provided by UNDP and UNESCO came to examine the experience of the UNESCO-Thai Pilot Project. It submitted an outline of the future full-scale science teaching improvement program under the title, "National Institute for Improvement of Teaching in Science and Technology in Thailand," which may be supported by the United

Nations Special Fund. Having approved the recommendation in the outline, UNDP and UNESCO are now sending a second team of experts to draft a request for technical assistance from the United Nations Special Fund for the establishment of the proposed institute. It is envisaged that the outcome of this project will form a strong foundation for future education in science and will set a fine precedent for other developing countries.

For the purpose of strengthening science education in Asian countries, the first Regional Workshop on UNESCO/UNICEF-Assisted Projects in Science Education in Asia was held in Bangkok from November 4 to 18, 1968. Information on and experiences in the implementation of science teaching projects were exchanged. The workshop repeatedly emphasized that while science education could provide future scientists and technicians for national development, it should also serve as an important part of the students' general preparation for their way of living in society. Students should be exposed to scientific ideas as early as possible in their students lives, because many of them discontinued their study at various stages below the tertiary level of education.

Research on science teaching, science-curriculum development, and science-teacher training received high priority in the deliberation of the workshop. It was recognized that regional centers where research projects such as the Thai/UNESCO Project for Chemistry Teaching are undertaken have made very significant findings in methodology and techniques for teaching science. At the same time active centers for curriculum development in Asia should be built up so that all the necessary conditions—student background, local language, and educational system—can be taken into consideration in working out a science teaching syllabus suitable for the schools in each member country. A collective, cooperative, and planned effort for science-teaching research and science-curriculum development should be made by all sectors dealing with science, e.g., schools, teachers' colleges, universities, teachers, professors, research scientists, industrial scientists, science teaching supervisors, and administrators.

Since the quality of the teachers may limit the type of approach, the level of instruction, and the degree of flexibility allowable in a curriculum, the workshop suggested that the teachers take appropriate pre-service training and upgrade it by frequent in-service training. The workshop also stressed the importance of equipment in science education and recognized the following general principles for assistance in establishing a science equipment project:

1. The assistance part should be arranged in such a way that it is self-liquidating.
2. The national part should be so planned that it becomes self-perpetuating. With regard to the national part, the following aspects of the project came under consideration:
   a. Local manufacture of equipment
   b. Supply and distribution of equipment
   c. Maintenance and repair of equipment

As a guide for the member countries in Asia the workshop proposed a prototype project on science-curriculum development which covered the following points:

1. The national program for science education
2. General objectives
3. Background and survey
4. Specific objectives
5. Plan for operations and scheduling
6. Establishment of organizational structure
7. Operational follow-up to organization.

One of the most important efforts to promote science education was made by a group of countries in Southeast Asia with the support of the United States. After a meeting in Bangkok on November 30, 1965, with Mr. Eugene R. Black, who represented the United States on a special aid mission, the ministers of education or their representatives from Laos, Malaysia, Philippines, Singapore, Thailand, and Vietnam set up the Southeast Asian Ministers of Education Organization (SEAMEO), which was joined later by Indonesia. SEAMEO in turn formed the Southeast Asian Ministers of Education Council (SEAMEC) and established a permanent headquarters under the name of Southeast Asian Ministers of Education Secretariat (SEAMES) in Bangkok with a director chosen by and responsible to SEAMEC.

During the historic meeting of the Southeast Asian Ministers of Education with Mr. Black some form of regional cooperation in selected fields of education was discussed. At first fifteen project areas were submitted to the member countries of SEAMEO for their consideration. Based on the favorable replies given by these countries in a subsequent survey, ten of the project areas were selected for drafting project proposals. Among the ten proposals was a project on "Regional Center for Education in Science and Mathematics (RECSAM)." At its second conference convened in Manila in November 1966, SEAMEC accepted the proposal for establishing the center at the Malayan Teachers' College, Penang, Malaysia. The center is one of the six SEAMEC projects which have been so far accepted.

As approved by SEAMEC the objective of the center is "to help the participating countries in improving the teaching of science and mathematics in the region in order to lay the foundations for meeting the technically and scientifically trained manpower requirements of the region. It is proposed to start initially at the elementary and secondary levels, and to involve teacher training institutions, colleges of education, and faculties of universities as may be necessary in implementing the program." The center will not compete in any way with existing institutions or programs of member countries; instead, it will function only to complement and supplement them.

The cost of the RECSAM project for the period July 1, 1971, to June 30, 1975, has been set at US $8,145,900. In the first year of the interim period from July 1, 1968 to June 30, 1969, the United States contributed US $125,000 to the project, whereas Malaysia provided it with service and facilities worth US $46,600. It is anticipated that in the second year of the interim period the United States will donate US $165,600 to the project, while Malaysia will support it with service and facilities worth US $92,150.

Aware of the increasing demand for scientific and technical manpower in many countries or areas lying within or bordering the Pacific region, the

Council of the Pacific Science Association during the Eleventh Congress held in
Tokyo from August 22 to September 10, 1966, appointed a new Standing
Committee on Science Education in the hope of encouraging more youngsters
to study science. During the Inter-Congress Meeting of the Pacific Science
Association organized in Kuala Lumpur from May 5 to 9, 1969, the Standing
Committee convened under the chairmanship of Professor Bentley Glass,
Academic Vice-President of the State University of New York, and considered
a paper prepared by Professor Glass under the title "Science Education and the
Explosion of Scientific Knowledge."

In this paper are described the profound effects produced by the current
exponential increase of scientific knowledge upon science education in both
highly developed and newly developing countries. From these effects it is
possible to determine the scientific needs of the developing countries. The six
outstanding needs, according to Dr. Glass, are these:

1. To provide a good curriculum for training science teachers for
    the local educational system
2. To provide adequately for training sufficient numbers of science
    teachers
3. To provide science education centers to retrain science teachers
    continuously as a regular part of their annual duty
4. To send a sufficient number of the best students abroad to
    engage in advanced scientific study
5. To supply posts and research facilities in sufficient number and
    of sufficient attraction to bring most of these scientists home
    after training
6. To establish an agency to make a continuous study of the
    relevance of new scientific discoveries to the social and
    economic and health needs of their own country and culture.

After the Standing Committee had exchanged their views on all the six
points, it agreed to use them as a basis for further discussion and
recommendation at the Twelfth Pacific Science Congress to be held in Australia
in August 1971.

Besides the Southeast Asian Ministers of Education Organization and the
Pacific Science Association, the Association of Southeast Asian Institutions of
Higher Learning (ASAIHL) also contributes to the improvement of science
education in this region. ASAIHL, which was founded in 1956, consisted in
1968 of 52 member institutions in Burma, Hong Kong, Indonesia, Malaysia, the
Philippines, Singapore, Thailand, and Vietnam. Its objective is to promote the
economic, social, cultural, and civic welfare of the people of the Southeast
Asian region by the exchange of information, teachers, and students among
institutions of higher learning of the region and by suggestions for cooperative
action in the development of educational and research programs by such
institutions. Its Secretariat is located at Chulalongkorn University in Bangkok,
Thailand.

From time to time ASAIHL organizes conferences and seminars that are
beneficial to science education at the tertiary level. Worthy of mention are the

Seminars of Mathematics and the Physical and Natural Sciences at Saigon and Dalat in April 1967, on Basic Sciences in Southeast Asian Universities at Bangkok in July 1968, on Technological Education in Southeast Asia at Bangkok in 1969, and on Agriculture and Veterinary Science at Los Banos in 1969. In the Seminar on Basic Sciences education and research in sciences were discussed in relation to national development and regional cooperation.

Referring to the author's past experience in taking charge of the program on "Science Talent Search" in Thailand it is sad to say that most of the winners reject the scholarships when they find out that they are not allowed to study medicine or engineering but basic science, because in Thailand the income of a physician or an engineer is many times higher than that of a scientist.

As demonstrated in this case, no matter how much effort—both moral and financial—is put into science education, no substantial increase in the supply of basic scientists can be counted upon as long as insufficient incentive is given to the scientific profession. A bright young man will not be interested in entering the scientific profession if he does not see much of a future in it. He has to be pretty sure that he will eventually secure a good position after he has completed his studies. The position must pay him enough to take care of his family properly. Otherwise, he will leave his scientific profession and engage in some other business which does not make full use of his training.

In order to create a favorable atmosphere for the pursuit of scientific careers, which will in turn facilitate the application of science and technology to the national development, it is suggested that the developing countries in Asia extend appropriate recognition to the scientists and be guided by a definite science policy.

DISCUSSION

Dr. Lee Kum Tatt (Singapore) commented wryly that he comes from one of the smallest countries in the world — 224 square miles at high tide, and 227 at low tide. In this small area live two million people. They possess no natural resources; all they have are human beings. So they are forced to rely on science and technology, and they set out to promote science education accordingly. But he added a warning: in promoting education, one should never lose sight of the objective, the *application* of science and technology to economic development.

Since time was not on their side, the people anxious to promote science education in Singapore took certain urgent steps. First they formed an inter-ministerial council and invited the minister of finance to serve on it, to be responsible for getting the budget. Then they saw to it that there were incentives to people to establish factories, not just incentives to young people to study science, so as to be certain that there would be work for the scientists and engineers after they graduated. The policy worked: two years before they had thought they were training too many scientists and engineers, now it seems they will be short of such experts. The new problem they are facing is a lack of technicians, a need for technical education: unfortunately, the developing countries have inherited a tradition that a stigma attached to technical education. The academic schools enjoy high status; the rejects from them go to the trade schools. Singapore is trying to overcome this unfortunate attitude, and Dr. Tatt thinks they are succeeding. They are fortunate that the leader of the ruling party and the head of the Economic Development Board are scientists. This happy state of affairs results in close communication between various government departments involved in science and technology, something which is often sadly lacking in developing countries.

Dr. John Murray Wilson (British Council in India) said that innovations from other countries should be closely examined against the cultural and educational background of the country concerned.

Education has expanded enormously in the Indian subcontinent during the last 20 years. The demand is so great that the adequate training of teachers and building up an experienced cadre of inspectors has gone by the wayside. The results of this policy have been extremely unfortunate. On the other hand, India has introduced summer institutes where teachers are taught about their materials and do experiments. But there are no schools in which they can pass on to children what they have learned, where they can use modern programs. As a result, they are often frustrated.

5

INTEGRATION OF SCIENCE AND EDUCATION IN LATIN AMERICA

By Marcelo Alonso

Deputy Director, Department of Scientific Affairs, Organization of American States (Washington, D.C.)

Government policy, scientific infrastructure (by which I mean the educational, research and planning system), and productive sectors are not independent factors of development and they must interact properly among themselves to produce a coordinated and well-balanced steady "leap forward." Inadequate coordination among these three factors is one of the most serious maladies found in many developing countries. And to remedy this malady, a certain length of time is required, time which certainly we cannot afford to waste.

In general, countries in a region such as Latin America have several common historical and sociological elements which make collaboration among them possible and desirable. This collaboration is essential if development is to be achieved at a reasonable rate. This perhaps justifies now more than ever the need for regional organizations such as the OAS and OAU, which are becoming stronger and more influential every day.

We must recognize that, although in developed countries the scientific and technological infrastructure has grown parallel to the degree of development, and in some cases faster and in quantum jumps, with a strong feedback between science and education, in the developing countries the scientific and technological infrastructure is not adequate to the needs of development. Until very recently governments were not conscious of this serious deficiency. As a result the science component of education has been generally neglected in comparison with more traditional humanistic subjects. This neglect of science may be due to the traditional degree of dependence of developing countries on the developed countries for scientific and technological development and input.

In the specific case of Latin America, we find that until World War II, Latin American countries were basically exporters of raw materials and importers of manufactured products, an economic system which requires neither science nor technology of its own. Science and technology education which does not feed into the economic and social sectors is a luxury that no country can afford. In Latin America, therefore, science and technology were, with a few exceptions, utterly neglected. Universities were in general unconnected with the realities and needs of the communities in which they were located, research was minimal, and science was taught so that the newly initiated scientists could preach the gospel to the following generation of scientists with practically no effect outside this closed circle.

The conditions created by World War II produced a change in the economies of the Latin American countries. Governments set forth new national policies of industrialization aimed to replace imports. This industrialization, however, consisted mainly of local manufacture using imported technologies and equipment and in many instances some prime materials. Again there was no need for autonomous science and technology, which basically remained ignored by both government and industry. Even now, when this situation is improving rapidly, the Latin American countries expend on the average less than 0.3 percent of their GNP in science and technology, — only about 1/10th of the expenditures by the developed countries. But we cannot blame governments alone; scientists were unaware of the fact that they could contribute to the development of their societies and showed no interest in exploring the possibilities of making science and technology useful to the society in which they lived.

This lack of understanding of science and technology in the years immediately following World War II has proved to be very expensive for the Latin American people. The weakness of the science and technology infrastructure is one of the greatest limiting factors hindering the acceleration of Latin American development. I may affirm without hesitation, therefore, that one of the most pressing needs of Latin America is to develop a strong scientific infrastructure capable of creating and adapting knowledge, able to assist in its diffusion and application, and closely tied with a modern educational system. Fortunately Latin America is moving quickly in this direction. During the last fifteen years a number of national and regional projects on science education have been initiated, the expenditure on education has increased substantially, the number and quality of scientists and engineers is rapidly increasing, graduate level studies are proliferating in Latin American universities, and the quality and quantity of research increases continuously.

We shall now examine two interesting aspects of the interrelation between science and education in Latin America which show the efforts for substantial improvement and which we can call "Education for Science" and "Science for Education."

Education for Science

By this term we mean the place of science in the education curriculum at all levels.

Primary Education

The teaching of science education at the primary level has not yet reached a completely satisfactory situation in most Latin American countries. The relatively large rate of population increase in Latin America, which is of the order of 2.9 percent, with a rate of increase of the population in school age of

5.8 percent, has produced on the ministries of education a tremendous pressure demanding more resources such as schools, teachers, books, etc., which it is difficult to provide at the required rate with the resources presently available, in spite of the fact that governments are investing more and more in education every year. For example, in 1960 the total expenditure in education was about $900 million or about 18 percent of the average budget. In 1968 total expenditure was about $3,000 million or 23 percent of the budgets.

In the more specific area of science education in primary schools there is a real shortage of skilled teachers, adequate textbooks, and teaching materials and a disproportionately large number of students per teacher, which makes experimental work difficult. Some texts produced in the United States and elsewhere, such as the "new mathematics," have been translated into Spanish and are becoming more and more widely used. But, of course, the utilization of these new materials requires a change in teaching methods and better trained teachers, who can depart from the traditional dogmatic education and provide a more intuitive and independent participation by the student, and it takes time to train such teachers.

Several projects designed to improve the situation are under way but they are as yet limited. We may mention specifically the Centro de Perfeccionamiento de Profesores en Chile and the Brazilian Foundation for the Development of Science Education in Sao Paulo as examples of institutions actively engaged in national projects in science education at the primary level. At the regional level, under OAS sponsorship, a regional program for the improvement of curriculum and teaching materials in science at the primary school level has been initiated. The headquarters of this program is at the Instituto de Mejoramiento Profesional del Magisterio, in Venezuela. Its specific objectives are to improve science and mathematics teaching at the primary level through the production of reading materials prepared specifically for Latin American schools and adapting, whenever feasible, the materials produced elsewhere. Design and structure are very simple, inexpensive materials are used, and courses are organized for the preparation of teachers. The program is just beginning and it is not yet possible to evaluate its results.

Secondary Education

Although at the secondary or high-school level the problems related to science education are much the same as at the primary level, the situation in Latin America is relatively much better and very encouraging. Several effective national and regional programs are being developed and a relatively large amount of external aid has been provided for this purpose. Listed below are some of the institutions more active in this field:

Argentina: The Ministry of Education in collaboration with the National Research Council has established a National Institute for the Improvement of Science Education. This institute conducts regular seminars and short-term courses for Argentinian teachers in collaboration with several Argentinian universities.

Brazil: The Brazilian Foundation for the Development of Science Education in Sao Paulo, which is a private institution, has specialized in the production of laboratory material and kits with the collaboration of the Ministry of Education. In addition, six centers for science education have been established in Recife, Bahia, Porto Alegre, Rio de Janeiro, Belo Horizonte, and Sao Paulo.

Chile: The Ministry of Education runs a Programa de Perfeccionamiento de Profesores which, besides conducting summer institutes, is developing educational material.

Colombia: The Foundation for the Promotion of Education has been sponsoring summer institutes, the production of educational material and equipment, and science fairs.

Mexico: Although there is no specific institution in charge of activities for improving science teachers, several programs have been organized by the National University and the Ministry of Education.

Central America: Although there is no specific institution in charge of a unified program, there are several groups, such as GEMEC in Honduras, involved in these activities.

Uruguay: The Institute of Philosophy, Science and Letters, which is a private institution of university level for the preparation of professors in those areas, is conducting a series of seminars and academic-year institutes for the improvement of science teachers. They have tried to adapt some materials published elsewhere and to design and manufacture scientific equipment.

Peru: The Institute for the Promotion of Mathematics Education at the National University of Engineering, and the Institute for the Promotion of Biology Education at the University of Cayetano Heredia, have been very active in science education at secondary level.

Venezuela: Both the Pedagogical Institute and the Instituto de Mejoramiento Profesional del Magisterio of the Ministry of Education are conducting activities related to the improvement of science education.

Both the U.S. National Science Foundation and the Ford Foundation, as well as UNESCO and OAS, have assisted in several ways these national activities.

In addition to the national programs we have mentioned, several regional programs have been carried out:

1.   *Summer Institutes in the U.S.* Under the joint sponsorship of the OAS and the National Science Foundation more than 500 science teachers have participated in summer institutes conducted in the United States in the last eight years.

2.   *Regional Courses.* About 1,000 science teachers have been trained in about 25 regional courses conducted since 1961 under OAS sponsorship with the collaboration of several organizations such as NSF and the Ford Foundation.

3.   *UNESCO Pilot Project in Physics of Light.* This project, which was conducted at the University of Sao Paulo and to which the OAS

contributed some fellowships, has produced excellent material and kits relative to the physics of light. This material has been tried in several other places with great success.

4. *OAS Regional Program for the Improvement of Science Education.* This program, formerly called Project 212, with headquarters in Uruguay, has been replaced by one providing special assistance to the ministries of education and teachers' colleges as well as a program offering regional training courses, with headquarters in Argentina.

5. *Publications.* The OAS is producing a series of monographs written by Latin American scientists and covering different aspects of science suitable for high school physics teachers. The monographs are published in four series corresponding to mathematics, physics, chemistry, and biology. The total number already published is 23. Also, with the assistance of the NSF and OAS, the new curriculum materials produced in the U.S., such as PSSC, BSCS, Chem Study, and CBS, have been translated into Spanish and into Portuguese. In some cases, such as in the BSCS, the translation has been adapted to the local conditions of Latin America.

6. *Inter-American Conferences on Science Education.* Under the OAS sponsorship and with the collaboration of many other organizations a series of conferences on science education have been held: two in mathematics (Bogota and Lima) and one each in physics (Rio de Janeiro), chemistry (Buenos Aires), and biology (Costa Rica). These conferences have put Latin American leaders in science education in contact with those of other regions of the world, promoting the exchange of ideas and experiences. As a result of this conference several of the national projects mentioned above have been initiated.

Perhaps the two most serious problems for the improvement of science education at the secondary level are the lack of a sufficient number of properly trained teachers and of adequate laboratory equipment. Although most of the programs that have been established tend to correct the first aspect, the one related to the local design and production of inexpensive and simple laboratory equipment using readily available materials is still in the beginning stage, and only in a few selected countries such as Argentina, Brazil, and Colombia are effective programs going on. Another problem is the rigid curriculums, tightly controlled by the ministries of education, with more emphasis on the dogmatic aspects of science than on its human values, resulting in limited stimulus in independent and experimental work by the students. This is being corrected gradually through periodic revision of curriculums. Extracurricular activities such as the "science fairs," sponsored by Science Services, are contributing to stimulate students and teachers. Science fairs are held more or less regularly in Argentine, Brazil, Mexico, Uruguay, Chile, etc.

University Education for Scientists and Engineers

It is clear that science education at the university level has most impact on the economic development of a country. When a country produces good scientists and engineers well trained in research and with a capacity for innovation, sooner or later they make their impact on the industrial sector, even if this sector initially shows a lack of interest in both research and innovation. But it is precisely at this level that the situation in Latin America shows most contrast. There are in Latin America more than 400 universities, but only a few, perhaps less than 10 percent, are prepared to produce good scientists and engineers and have adequate facilities for experimental work and original research. Undoubtedly, there are in Latin America true centers of excellence which are relatively well equipped with a very well-trained full-time staff doing good research, but unfortunately the most common situation is that the universities have a part-time staff, old-fashioned educational methods, and inadequate libraries and experimental facilities. This results in a university educational system which is basically informative rather than formative and tends toward an outdated encyclopedism. Again it is interesting to recognize that in the last decade, and in spite of several unexpected complications in some countries, the quantity and quality of scientific and technological education and research in Latin American universities has improved tremendously. Education at, or equivalent to, graduate level is flourishing and the institutions granting a PhD. degree, although very few in number, have a quality comparable to the best institutions in the world.

Undoubtedly, university science education and research, because of the university's character, are more adaptable to a regional cooperative effort. In this connection it is worth mentioning a special and challenging program that was agreed upon by the member countries of the OAS at a meeting held in Uruguay in 1967. At that meeting the presidents of the member countries agreed to develop and strengthen national scientific and technological programs, to establish a regional program and multinational institutes for advanced training and research, to strengthen existing institutes of this kind in Latin America, and to promote the exchange and advancement of technological knowledge.

For that purpose the presidents approved a Regional Scientific and Technological Development Program "oriented toward the adoption of measures to promote scientific and technological research, teaching, and information; basic and advanced training of scientific personnel; and exchange of information. It shall promote intensively the transfer to, and adaptation by, the Latin American countries of knowledge and technologies originating in other regions."

Promoted by the Inter-American Council for Education, Science and Culture (now the Inter-American Cultural Council), one of the organs of the Inter-American System, the program is financed by the contributions of the member states and is primarily designed to stimulate centers such as universities and research institutes which have reached a level of excellence so that they can render a service to other member countries through what are called "multinational projects." These centers offer opportunities for advanced training in the graduate level and for participation in research projects of staff from other less developed universities.

Opportunities for graduate training and research are now offered to more than 600 Latin American scientists. These more advanced centers may receive visiting professors from elsewhere but at the same time they are supposed to send members of their own staff to other Latin American institutions to offer courses or to initiate research projects. More than 200 visiting professors will be available under this program and a substantial amount of money in the form of equipment is to be provided. Assistance is also available to organize scientific and technical meetings in Latin America. Multinational projects cover 18 areas, grouped into basic sciences, natural resources, and technological research.

Since the program is basically geared toward institutional development, those persons who participate in the multinational projects, once they complete their training or research programs, continue to receive assistance and guidance when they return to their home institutions. This is one of the most interesting and original features of the program. It is hoped that this program will strengthen the ties among scientists and engineers within the region. It is also expected that in a period of a few years a substantial number of Latin American centers will be recognized as places where students from other countries can go to receive their higher education instead of going to U.S. or European universities. It is also expected that regional cooperative research projects will contribute to the solutions of some of the crucial technological problems of the region, such as the utilization of raw materials and natural products.

University Science Education for Nonscientists

Although it has been traditional in most countries to provide as part of the university education of scientists and engineers a basic training in humanistic and cultural subjects, only recently the need has been recognized to provide the same background in modern science to persons following nonscientific subjects, such as lawyers, architects, physicians, public administrators, and so on. It is clear that the basic role of science and technology today, not only as a tool for development but as a basic cultural element in our everyday life, requires that persons in the nonscientific professions have a deeper understanding of the scientific method and its applications.

Needless to say, this is particularly important in the case of decision-making persons such as public leaders and the managerial class who must have an adequate appreciation of the scientific needs in their own countries or industries so that they can use correct judgement in deciding the magnitude of the required national or industrial effort in science and technology and its relative priority in regard to other sectors of economic planning. It is regretful that this area of science education has been the most neglected one not only in the developing countries but to some extent in the most developed countries. In Latin America certain universities have established "faculties of general studies" in which the students, regardless of their future plans, spend a year or two covering both scientific and humanistic subjects. Although this is an interesting idea it has not been effective enough. Even in the developed countries a sufficiently imaginative and attractive curriculum in modern science for nonscience students has yet to be developed.

Therefore we may conclude that at present in Latin America, the educational system does not provide an adequate science background for nonscience students. One effect of this situation is reflected in the relative official neglect of science as part of government activities.

It is encouraging, however, to recognize that there is a growing awareness at the governmental level of the need of adequate planning for science and technology. In this respect both OAS and UNESCO are providing technical assistance to the countries that request it for establishing the proper machinery for science planning and policy. Many countries have established effective national research councils; in one country a ministry of science has been considered and in another country a science policy-making post at the ministerial level has been established. These measures obviously will be reflected in an improved science education and research in such countries.

Science for Education

By this term we mean the utilization of some recent scientific and technological developments in the educational process. We may classify these modern educational technologies into two groups: those which promote the extension of education to a very large number of persons and those which accelerate the process of learning. The first group includes modern mass communication techniques such as television, radio, films, and mobile units. The second group includes programmed education, the use of computers, and a series of audio-visual techniques that combine classroom activities with self-instruction.

In Latin America, with a growing population that presses increasing demands on the educational system, with a serious shortage of teachers and classrooms, and with about 34 percent of the adult population illiterate, modern educational techniques are absolutely necessary. It is estimated that Latin America needs more than 350,000 new classrooms and an equal number of elementary school teachers to care for all the population of school age. Of course, the introduction of modern educational techniques in the Latin American school system is not an easy task. First of all, it requires a substantial capital investment; secondly, it is essential to have well-trained instructors and specialists to make better utilization of those techniques; finally, it is necessary to adapt the educational system to combine the traditional methods with more advanced modern techniques.

To accelerate the "technification" of education in Latin America a concerted effort by all the countries is required to develop and adapt materials and programs. So far, several projects are already on their way in about half a dozen countries. For example, in Colombia more than 400,000 children receive part of their education through television at the cost of less than 5 cents per student per hour, which is a very reasonable figure. Television is also used in the same country to train teachers in subjects such as the new mathematics.

To assist member countries in the "technification" of education, the OAS has established, as part of its Regional Program for Educational Development, two multinational projects geared toward the development of the technology of education. One project is on educational research, planning, innovation, and experimentation, and the other is on educational television and audio-visual methods. The project on television will use the excellent facilities existing in Argentina, Chile, Brazil, and Mexico, which have acquired much experience in using television for educational purposes at all levels.

I think, therefore, that I can close my presentation with a note of optimism: in spite of all the difficulties I have mentioned, unprecedented progress in science education has taken place in Latin America in the last ten years and more spectacular advances are expected to take place as a result of the increased efforts of the Latin American governments and institutions to improve education in general, and science education in particular, at all levels.

DISCUSSION

In his presentation Dr. Alonso stressed the importance of regional projects, as proved by the Latin American experience. People with similar ethnic and cultural backgrounds, and living within the same geographical area, have to get together to try to work out common solutions. Latin American scientists know that next door they have an institution to which they can go, or send their students. Integration and collaboration are of very great importance.

At the same time, projects have to be developed at the national level as well. The determination of the needs of each country is essentially a national exercise, and each country has to examine and reexamine its situation. Where problems are the same, duplication would be absurd: where they are different, separate action should be taken.

Professor Adolfo Rafael Camarena (Dominican Republic) reported that his country made 1969 the "Year of Education." Eighty-two institutes at various levels of learning were inaugurated.

Mexico, is greatly preoccupied with the problems of science education at all levels, said *Dr. Arquimedes Caballero* (Mexico). In elementary schools, 52 million textbooks have been distributed free to 8.5 million school children. The science textbooks are prepared by experts, and are designed to promote active interest in science: for every subject there are exercises, a workbook, suggested activities, all aimed at making the student express his own ideas. Every three years the textbooks are reviewed and revised by a group of expert educators and scientists. Refresher courses are run for teachers, and special institutes exist to train them. They also provide training for teachers in institutes of higher learning. The free textbooks given to pupils in elementary schools often form the only libraries in the homes of the poor people in cities or of inhabitants of

rural areas. Mexico allocates 28 percent of its national budget for
education—and very little for national defense.

Another happy country with no defense problems was Costa Rica, said *Sr.
Guillermo Malavassi.* With no army at all, his country devotes a major part of
its budget to education. But there is a difficulty: there are chronic
anachronisms in pedagogy, teaching is anywhere from 14 to 50 years behind
new discoveries.

6

INTEGRATION OF SCIENCE AND EDUCATION IN AFRICA

By Eugène Razafy

Director, Institut Supérieur de Recherche et de Formation Pédagogique, Malagasy Republic

A characteristic aspect of education in Africa and Madagascar is the fact that many pupils leave school at the primary age; another equally large part leaves at the fourth or fifth grades. This is a fairly serious problem which, I might add, the authorities are considering and for which a solution must be found if it is not to become a brake on development. In my opinion, as we shall see farther on, the integration of science and education could avert this danger. In any event, it is a problem that causes us at least to review the content of the curriculum.

In the French-speaking countries, at least, the educational system makes literary education a point of honor. There is no question here of belittling literature or classical education, but I sincerely think that the present context makes it advisable to review this content. One may truly say that the unprecedented progress of science in this twentieth century is such that it is rare today to find a subject to which science does not contribute. From sociology to psychology, from pedagogy to philosophy, from economics to linguistics, science intervenes and helps the relevant subject to develop. Moreover, our century is experiencing a scientific civilization, and in order to adapt this civilization to the developing countries, scientific cadres must be created: the part played by science in education must be comparable to its role in life and in the world. That is why this scientific training should not be confined to specialists but made available to the mass of the population, in order to establish the firm foundations of a modern society.

But the very success of science, its rapid evolution, has necessarily opened up a wide gap between scientists and the people. This is partly because the scientific world is immured in an esoteric language that eludes everyday understanding. One finds oneself in a paradoxical situation. We live in a very advanced scientific era, yet without the public understanding much about it. We live more and more in an unknown world; in other words, one becomes more and more incapable of acting on the environment in which one lives. One is merely subject to science and its environment.

The other consequence of the success of science is the divorce between science and scientific education. There is science in the making, which progresses, and on the other hand the science that is taught. It is almost impossible for traditional education to keep up with the pace of science—a fact that has caused this regrettable lag. The unfortunate consequences of this are clearly apparent: while clear and satisfactory theories are current in scientific circles, we persist in teaching schoolchildren outdated theories. The most striking instance is the teaching of mathematics, which has dropped so far behind that at present it is not reform that is needed, but a genuine revolution—at least in the eyes of the public. The methodology employed is faulty, because the overloaded curriculum, overcrowding in schools, insufficient material aids, and unspecialized premises compel the teaching staff to give lessons that are too verbal, or at best demonstrative.

Integration of Science as a Method

In view of the requirements of these African countries, should not the essential aim of education be to ensure adoption in the child of the scientific approach—an attitude that should remain permanent in his professional life and in his life as a citizen? Should not the habits of observation, of analysis, of experimentation be inculcated in him from an early age? The results of psychological research show that the child is capable of logical reasoning on a basis of the facts of his own world. It would thus seem desirable that, through all the curricular subjects dispensed, he be familiarized with logical thought. Such contact with the world of reasoning and logic, and such familiarization with simple scientific notions would already be an initiation to abstract concepts. Such initiation was formerly considered premature, but, as Piaget remarked, "Early initiation, well conducted, can only favor the development of the mind."

Training in the primary grades might thus be considered initiation into the working methods of the scientific approach. This would alleviate the problems of the developing countries as regards early school-leavers. Practically speaking, if they have not learned how to learn, the little knowledge they acquire would quickly be lost and what they take with them on leaving school would be negligible. Conversely, a "well run-in" working method, a scientific approach having become a reflex, would always help pupils in any situation. Moreover, the analytical and observing spirit would spur them to keep on learning. They would thus have acquired, as Piaget says, "not knowledge, but a potential of knowledge through a capacity for carrying out determinate operations."

We have said that the economic advancement of the developing countries depends on their future possibilities for training large contingents of scientists. But it is not enough to increase effectiveness; future scientists should primarily be trained in a manner making them capable of adaptation to the increasingly rapid changes in science. One must not train scientific men of yesterday or the day before yesterday, but scientific men of the future.

An aim thus conceived calls for new educational techniques, for it is beyond doubt that the method of approach is bound to influence the developing trend of the student's mind. Particularly the concept of practical work needs reviewing. With some exceptions, practical work was primarily aimed at illustrating the theoretical courses and putting lessons into concrete form. The only educational profit derived was of a technical nature, that of montage. One is content to verify the laws learned at the courses.

Again with the aim of having pupils acquire the scientific approach, it would perhaps be advisable to start from a problem. I would like to give an example, the better to illustrate my thought:

The object of study is interrelations between plants, the soil, and water. At present a certain amount of knowledge is communicated to the pupils as clearly as possible. The courses are then illustrated by means of practical work done by the pupils, or at least by a practical demonstration given by the teacher to the pupils. Teachers say: "A plant needs water because . . ." and give the various reasons. Practical experiments come later, in the way of confirmation.

It would perhaps be better to set the pupils a problem from the outset; helping them to analyze, put forward hypotheses, and draw conclusions, with the requisite precautions. In our instance, the sequence could be as follows:

Does the plant need water? Why? Might that be due to the fact that water is useful to it at every moment of its life? Does that mean that it needs a constant water supply in its organs?

Experiment (done by the pupils): Is there always water in plants?

Conclusion: There is water in plants.

Further hypotheses are formulated, e.g.: Is that water stable, or does it renew itself? The pupils should answer by resorting to experimentation and draw a conclusion, which might be: "A plant loses and absorbs water; therefore it constantly renews its water supply."

It readily follows that one can always multiply the hypotheses and work along the same lines each time, to arrive at the problem initially posed. One thus explains a principle that in some quarters is already termed "directed discovery."

Integration of Science in Knowledge Form

The precise aim that we have set ourselves should have its counterpart in a new curriculum. To avert divorce between education and the scientific world, as referred to heretofore, it would be desirable that the results of scientific research be integrated with education as quickly as possible. Such integration seems relatively feasible at university level, through the very fact that a faculty member is also a research worker. Integration at secondary and primary level involves much greater difficulties.

It requires more or less permanent curricular reform. The curriculum itself must be flexible enough to be capable of evolution *pari passu* with science. The knowledge dispensed should be modernized at all levels, for it is unthinkable that the scientific advances of the last thirty years should be restricted to higher education.

Obviously such content should be differentiated according to level; but there again, I think one should not fear to introduce certain ideas because the pupils have not in certain subjects (e.g. mathematics) attained the necessary level for the final enunciation. In actual fact, if we are to believe the educational psychologists, "The subconscious plays a very important part in the assimilation of an idea, but it requires time. It should thus be supplied early with material for reflection."

All this would require continuous cooperation between research workers and educational staff. The first-named should keep informed on the curriculum and on the current method in the schools; they should maintain permanent contact with the teachers, whom they should affranchise with the new ideas, helping them to present certain outdated theories from a new angle of approach.

It would require for teachers a continuous recycling and revising to date of their scientific knowledge, and primarily a capacity for renovation. This implies a new concept of teacher training. They should be convinced in particular as regards the influence of science on social changes, on individual ways of thought, ways of life, and attitudes. Teachers in the developing countries should never forget their role as active elements in the development of the country, through training its future citizens. They must train active, "available" citizens, able to act on their environment, that is, citizens who know the society in which they move, capable of keeping up with the evolution of the civilization amid which they live; citizens—we shall risk being repetitive—who do not merely endure our scientific civilization, but understand it and, if necessary, act on or influence it.

This need of information on recent ideas causes much difficulty for teachers often overloaded with correcting exercises of overcrowded classes. Other social activities also make heavy inroads on their available time; hence the need to arrange regular meetings between researchers and teachers, at which meetings the content and method of teaching would be thoroughly discussed. Nevertheless, such get-togethers must not evolve into one-way information sessions; they are profitable only in such measure as they are conductive to a dialogue between researchers and users.

In order to support these various efforts, we must succeed in solving the documentation problem, which is the heaviest handicap on the work of researchers and also of educational staff in African countries. This, we might add, is an international problem. Subscribing to the various specialized reviews would be no more than a partial solution; these reviews are so numerous that one cannot read them all. An effort should be made to centralize the scientific results for each subject, to file them under headings and to prepare index cards which would be diffused in all the countries, so that researchers can readily supply reference data for the articles in which they are interested. That is an enormous job of work, but it is worthwhile.

DISCUSSION

"In developing countries, economic underdevelopment, illiteracy, and the material conditions of life make the unsophisticated villager ignorant and therefore unappreciative of the major advances of society," said *Alhaji the Hon. Garba-Jahumpa* (The Gambia). He quoted the words of the late Reverend Solomon Caulker at the First Rehovot Conference: "Eight out of every ten babies die before they are one year old. Most of our people die of leprosy, malaria and undernourishment." The same conditions still obtain in most parts of Africa, and clearly the impact of science and technology upon such a society is very small. Original research of a fundamental nature, or knowledge of nuclear reactors and outer space, are irrelevant in the lives of such people—what they need is applied research geared to local conditions.

The Hon. Dr. V. O. S. Olunloyo (Nigeria) described conditions in his country, which has a population of 50 million. There is considerable diversity among the people, and formal educational activity varies somewhat from area to area. The people are educationally very much alive, very many of them want to go to school.

But it is not simple to provide education of quality in the quantity desired. The cost of giving even free primary school education would overwhelm a country like Nigeria. So they have to improve the economy. All things need to be done simultaneously—improving the economy, increasing the number of teachers, training them, improving the educational materials, so that the African countries can change in a world that is changing very fast.

The point of cost was endorsed by *Dr. Wadajo Mulugetta* (Ethiopia). He has been a member of a committee of experts appointed by the Ethiopian government to study the educational system of the country and to recommend urgent reforms. They came to the conclusion that, if they introduced the reforms they wanted, all public activity would have to stop—hospitals would have to close, road construction to cease, agricultural development to come to a standstill.

Another difficulty is that most of the population is rural; the proposed changes in science education are really designed for urban schools. For instance, the most simple apparatus deals with internal combustion engines and electrical equipment, such as few African students will ever see. Even the most simple gadget is outside the life and beyond the comprehension of the African child in the bush. He thought that reforms should be aimed at helping the child in the tiny village to become a more productive adult.

7 PLANNING SCIENCE EDUCATION

By C. O. Taiwo

Provost, College of Education,
University of Lagos,
Nigeria

Developing nations, in Africa and elsewhere, comprise various peoples with diverse languages, customs, and traditions. Their countries differ in size, physical features, climate, and vegetation. These differences are important and significant in any proposal for development. But in spite of this diversity, there are common characteristics. Most of the nations have an agricultural or rural economy. All of them have a high proporation of illiterate people and a per capita income which is at a mere subsistence level. They all desire political independence and, having achieved it, want social and economic freedom. All of them are in a hurry to bridge the gap between the developed nations and themselves. They see education as a big lever in their struggle for social and economic development and therefore devote a large proportion of their budget to the provision of education for their children. In the 1965-66 financial year, Western Nigeria approved an estimate of £7,239,000 for recurrent expenditure on education, out of a total of £24,211,000 for the whole region (now state). In 1960, the ratio was much higher. In all the developing countries, the goal is universal primary education.

Modern education in Nigeria dates back to the arrival of Christian missions in 1842 and was sponsored practically for the rest of the century by the Christian missions with the cooperation of overseas philanthropists and humanitarians. The aims and the means dictated nothing more than the rudiments of education. Science education had a late start and slow beginning.

Today, the importance of science is acknowledged by all developing nations. The news of any new scientific discovery or advance is received with considerable enthusiasm. The newspapers boost their sales by the inclusion of an account of the feat of the American astronauts. The universities weight their admissions in favor of the science undergraduates. In a number of states in the country, the secondary-school science teacher receives an extra allowance of £120 per annum, representing one-sixth of the minimum basic salary of a graduate teacher. Every country has either a science association or a science teachers' association or both, whose main preoccupation is curriculum development. These efforts reflect the importance attached to science as a potent factor in social and economic development.

The nations see science education as a means of providing the basis for suitable manpower in a modern society. They expect science education to make material contribution to life through improved agriculture, technology, and the scientific professions. There is a great need for the masses to have scientific knowledge so that they can understand new methods and techniques in agricultural production and take measures aimed at promoting good health and general well-being. Science education is needed as a firm basis for professions such as medicine, engineering, and architecture. There is a second though less obvious objective, the enrichment of individual human lives. There must be knowledge to dispel ignorance and break through degrading, impoverishing, superstitious beliefs.

There is often a wide gap between home environment and the school. At home the traditional ways and beliefs and the time-honored practices and values are often in conflict with the new ideas and values acquired at school. The home environment is so strong that science as taught in the schools has made little impact on the lives of many. This aspect of science education has received little attention. A number of people are beginning to wonder whether science has any contribution to make to spiritual and moral values.

One of the major problems of science education in a developing country is how to strike a balance between quantity and quality. Too few people are exposed to any science education. The large masses outside the formal education system are practically shut out. Nigeria with a population of 55 million in 1965 had only 3 million children in the primary schools, 210,000 in the secondary schools, 13,000 in the technical and vocational institutes, and 7,697 in the universities and comparable institutions. Applications for admission into the universities reflect a preponderance of arts students compared with science students. In 1965, there were in the five universities 968 undergraduates in science and 2,645 in arts, business, and social studies. Many secondary schools teach only a smattering of science and primary school science is still at an experimental stage.

The recent Conference on Education and Scientific and Technical Training in Relation to Development in Africa, indicates that the position in many African countries is not much different from the above picture. Each nation has to decide for itself where the emphasis should lie. But whatever that decision, the masses must have sufficient education to help them to live in the twentieth century. They must know enough to understand advice given for improvement in their occupations, civic duties, and personal health. There is at the same time a case for discovering and encouraging talents in science. Consideration should be given to providing centers of excellence in each country where students of promise in science can be given adequate pre-university training. These institutions, such as the Federal School of Science in Lagos, can provide recruiting pools to the universities and advanced teachers' colleges.

The cry for adaptation goes back to the Phelps-Stokes Commissions of 1921 and 1924 and beyond. It is acknowledged that curriculums should be adapted to the environment and the needs of the respective nations and their peoples. Continuing efforts by associations and individuals have achieved partial success; it is greatest perhaps in the field of biology. The environment of developing nations is partly urban and largely rural. In Nigeria, the ratio is approximately one to four. How deeply must teachers understand the environment in order to interpret it in terms of the school curriculums? This is a task to which many a foreign expert has turned with remarkable devotion, but the greater challenge is for the indigenous members of the developing nations. It is they who are the best interpreters of the environment and its influence. The attempts that are being made to revise the curriculums are hampered by lack of funds needed for research, trials, and experiments. Energy is dissipated by small, uncoordinated attempts. What is needed is massive operations under a team of experienced teachers drawn from the schools and the universities, with the opportunities of trials and re-trials.

Science teachers are in short supply and many of them need professional training and deeper knowledge. Unless the conditions of service of teachers are improved substantially, the best brains will not be attracted to the teaching profession and there will be no end to the drain from teaching to other lucrative but nonscience occupations. The advanced teachers' colleges, science colleges, and special or crash programs must be supplemented by attractive salaries and conditions comparable to those available in the public service. Teachers must be encouraged to train and the training should be in the best hands so that teachers may improve their teaching methods and techniques. Many colleges where primary-school teachers are trained have no facilities for science education and others are poorly equipped. The educational background of many students is low and needs to be raised. In a number of countries, the time has come for higher entry qualifications, equivalent to a good West African School Certificate.

If science is to be more than the passing on of information, children must have the opportunity to inquire and to experiment. Laboratory facilities must be adequate for individual experiments as well as group experimental projects. Sometimes the difficulty is the lack of amenities in the neighborhood of the school, such as electric power or piped water. This is especially true of the rural areas that are a long distance from cities. In other cases, there are no technicians to service the plants or machines. Orders for spare parts take a long time to be executed and meanwhile, more parts rust away. More thought should be given to the kind of equipment required so as to take into account the climate and the limited facilities for maintenance. Future plans for primary schools should include a science room and a library room.

In most developing countries, a foreign language is still the principal medium of instruction. Where the foreign language is the only medium of instruction from the start, effective teaching and learning are bound to be slow until there is some mastery of the language. In many countries, the local language is written and spoken by a large number of people. Such languages should be developed as media of instruction in those areas. Certain countries, Tanzania for example, use a local or adapted local language for teaching at the primary level. In the Western and the Lagos States of Nigeria, where the local language Yoruba has considerable literature in the humanities, efforts are being directed to the development of that language as a medium of instruction in science and mathematics. In all the countries, there will be for some time to come the need for a foreign language, which will be the second and working language. Both the first and the second languages should be learned well so as to ensure ease of communication.[1] Here radio and television, where available, should be used for the education of both school children and adults.

Planning is a new development in the activities of many developing countries. In the past, such important factors as reliable statistical data, the manpower requirement at the various levels, the probable effects on other services, and accurate information of the environment were not sufficiently taken into consideration. Such omissions led to unpleasant effects on the program or the economy of the nation. It is now recognized that planning in a ministry cannot be done in isolation from the overall planning of the nation. In each ministry of education there should be a planning unit comprising trained personnel who should work with the ministries involved to integrate education plans into the general development plan of the nation. In a country like Nigeria, where there are twelve states, there should be a state planning unit in each of the state ministries of education working with the national or central planning unit to secure unity in the overall planning and ensure the cooperation of the local communities. Advantage should be taken of foreign expertise in planning and of established institutions of educational planning such as the UNESCO Institute in Paris and its branch in Dakar.

In planning science education or any other form of education, the local people must be involved in the planning and all the media of information should be used to explain the implications of the scheme. Science education is a necessity in a developing nation moving from the traditional way of life into the modern age of science and technology. The people must know that science education is expensive and that if they desire it they must be prepared to make the sacrifice in rates and taxes. We ourselves must demonstrate the priority we accord science education by our own efforts before looking out for aid.

Planning is a waste of effort unless the plan is implemented. All the agencies involved in the implementation of science education should be consulted and their cooperation obtained. The universities and the teacher training colleges must step up the education of science teachers. Technical assistance in personnel and money will be needed to supplement local effort. As the plan progresses it should be assessed and modified in the light of any changes in the overall national plan or of experience acquired in the process of implementation.

DISCUSSION

Mr. Godfrey Eugene Lardner (UNECA) raised the question of the role of the social sciences in science education. "What the African region is engaged in is the socioeconomic transformation of African communities," he said.

---

[1] See Peter Strevens' paper, pp. 278-84, for further discussion of the language of instruction.

There is a need to consider the present state of education in sociology, psychology, and anthropology.

It would be impossible to transform whole national communities, to change attitudes and value systems and economies, without adequate expert advice on the social sciences. It is necessary to identify the agents of social change, to know the mechanics of inducing change, to determine what instruments will accelerate change. For example, in Israel highly trained professional women, experts in community development, were sent to work in Ethiopia wearing mini-skirts, without knowing that these offended the sense of propriety of the people. An agricultural expert induced some African farmers to use highly improved seeds, but gave no economic advice about marketing the products, or storing or processing them, and they went to waste; as a result, the farmers would never listen to him again. So science education must be planned to include the social sciences as well.

Dr. Wilton S. Dillon (United States) said that he wanted to qualify Mr. Lardner's unlimited enthusiasm for social scientists. The place of the social scientist is often not to control affairs or make decisions but to analyze social changes. But they can produce knowledge about social processes leading to certain objectives.

For example, modern industrialists who had set up factories in Virginia were advised that they should consult workers about the new machines. When Dr. Dillon described this experiment to an audience in Ghana, a dignified old man commented, "Yes, people do not like to be taken unaware."

Mr. Emanuel Waril (Sweden) said the need for social scientists as advisers is felt also in highly developed countries. In Sweden and Norway, workers feel that their abilities are not properly used, they are told at every step what to do, the only inducements offered to them are monetary. They are resentful because they receive no recognition of their intellectual ability, no status, no pride. It is essential to produce the right social environment to get people to work.

The point of inducements was taken up by *Dr. Kosonike Thomas* (Sierra Leone). It is hard to get people to become teachers by paying them more money, because of the shortage of money, as Professor Taiwo had indicated. One form of inducement is status, national status: teachers should be given knighthoods or other honors, other proofs that the community esteems them.

Dr. Sitali Mundia Silangwa (Zambia) pointed out that many more students want to be doctors than teachers. One way of diverting them to science teaching is to give bursaries at the university for potential teachers, but not for doctors.

In his reply, Professor Taiwo said that honors and bursaries are all very well, but that real status goes with salaries—if one really wants to raise the status of the teacher in the community, it is essential to pay him better.

8

UNESCO'S SCIENCE EDUCATION EXPERIENCE IN THE DEVELOPING COUNTRIES

By Stephen O. Awokoya

Director, Department of Science Teaching and Technological Education and Research, UNESCO (Paris)

The activities of UNESCO in the field of science education have passed through three evolutionary stages. The first period, between 1946 and 1962, may be regarded as the experimental stage during which the main lines of future development were laid down. The culminating activity of this period was the formulation in 1960 of a ten-year plan for natural science development, and the publication of a survey of the main trends of inquiry in the field of natural sciences, under the direction of Professor Pierre Auger.

The second stage in the evolution of the UNESCO program covers the period 1963-1968. It was ushered in by the United Nations Conference on the Application of Science and Technology for the Benefit of the Less Developed Countries (UNCSAT). This conference stirred the conscience of the world, and made the member states of UNESCO fully aware of their responsibilities. A period of accelerated expansion of activities began, involving assistance to member states in the formulation of scientific development policies and institutionalizing decision-making organs for the purpose, necessitating the expansion of scientific and technological institutions capable of meeting the economic demands of member States, compelling international financial organs to increase the scope of their assistance to developing countries, arousing the conscience of the world to the necessity of preserving man's environment in order to assure the survival of humanity, while promoting the rational utilization of natural resources. Undoubtedly, this second period of expansion has led to a quantitative growth in the activities of UNESCO and necessitated a rethinking as to the type of administrative structure that is adequate for this increased task.

The third period in the evolution may be regarded as beginning now. The provisions of the Fifteenth General Conference of UNESCO as regards scientific education and development are very much forward-looking. In the first place, it is now realized that proper progress can take place only if policies and plans are well formulated. In the second place, the promotion of the pure and applied sciences must proceed simultaneously at all levels of educational institutions. The quality of instruction must also be improved. New approaches must be utilized and technology itself must be incorporated in the educational process. Besides, the rate at which natural resources are being utilized makes it necessary for an intergovernmental organization like UNESCO to play, in association with the United Nations and other specialized agencies, a coordinating role in ensuring that man's natural resources may at once be preserved, utilized, and regenerated in perpetuity.

The Period of Experiment and Exploration (1946-1962)

The most pressing problem in the years 1946-1948 was that of rehabilitation in war-devastated areas. Many schools had to be reestablished and laboratories furnished. Offers of help came from many sources. UNESCO's Field Science Offices were largely occupied with the distribution of books and equipment of various sorts. Many displaced persons were given bursaries for scientific studies. Some research laboratories had to be rebuilt and reequipped.

In the year 1949, a request came from Ecuador for assistance in the organization of scientific and technological research. Very shortly afterwards, a Latin American conference on the development of science was held, which was subsequently to lead to the institutionalization of science policy and planning in Latin America. In order to increase UNESCO's capacity to advise member states, the Organization undertook a survey of National Research Councils in Austria, Belgium, the Federal Republic of Germany, India, Italy, Pakistan, Sweden, and Israel. Today, many member states of UNESCO have established special organs for the formulation of science policy and plans, for this is a prerequisite of systematic development.

The Field Science Offices were established during the first two or three years of UNESCO's existence in Latin America, the Middle East, and the Far East. Collaboration between UNESCO and the Science Council for Africa South of the Sahara was also established in 1950, beginning with a conference to which delegates were sent by South Africa, Portugal, France, Belgium, and the United Kingdom. At the international level, an advisory committee was set up to advise UNESCO on its international responsibility in the promotion of scientific education, training, and research. By this device, it was hoped that international cooperation in science would be promoted and the activities of the National Science Research Councils and centers could be properly assisted.

The ten-year plan formulated in 1960 represents in essence the lessons learned during the experimental and exploratory period. In that plan, UNESCO proposes to coordinate scientific activities at national and international levels as an essential factor of development. It also sees the importance of the application of science and technology to industrial development. Since then, the promotion of science and technology has been a major element in UNESCO's activities. This implies a commitment to the development of the basic sciences as well as the applied sciences and the promotion of activities ranging from the requirements of primary education to those of research.

This period also witnessed the recruitment of many science education advisers to assist member states in the development of science education and in the adaptation to local requirements. The 1962 conference at Abidjan in the Ivory Coast placed emphasis on teacher training and refresher courses, science equipment in secondary schools, and popularization of science.

Perhaps another major activity of the period, insofar as science policy and planning are concerned, is the historic Addis Ababa conference which places emphasis on the role of educational planning on the African continent. Although the targets set at the time have not been completely realized, they opened up visions of a glorious future to the participating member states and stimulated uninhibited expansion and development in many African states.

Popularization of Science and Its Implantation in Society

The need to popularize science as an essential ingredient of modern culture has never escaped attention. Only through such an activity can developing countries be stimulated to make the supreme effort that will abolish ignorance and promote development.

As a result of the activities conducted during the experimental and exploratory period, it is now known that an institutionalized machinery must be established for the popularization of science and the stimulation of interest in scientific and technological careers. Some of the activities that have been encouraged include the organization of science fairs, the holding of science exhibitions, the showing of science films, the establishment of science clubs, the creation of science museums, the holding of science weeks, the celebration of important events connected with great scientists or scientific discoveries, the award of scientific and technological prizes such as the Kalinga Prize and the Technology Prize, the publication of the magazine *Impact,* which deals with the impact of science on society, the holding of conferences on the public understanding of science, the publication of cheap, popular science books, the creation of associations of science writers and directors of science clubs, the utilization of the mass media for radio and television broadcasts, and the encouragement of the publication of popular science magazines in member states in order to increase interest in science. The faith of member states in these popularization activities has grown with the years until it is now recognized as part and parcel of the science education process. Properly organized, it merges into the permanent and continuous education of adults.

Science Information Service and Clearing-House Activities

The necessity for providing a science information service was evident even during the drafting of UNESCO's constitution. It is impossible to envisage scientific and technological education at the university level without an adequate science information service. Even at the junior and secondary school level, the clearing-house activities of UNESCO have increased in volume in recent years. The achievements that have been realized in the promotion of the science information service during the period of experimentation and exploration have today led to the study of the feasibility of a world science information system.

It is difficult to estimate the extent to which the information service provided by UNESCO during those years was of assistance in keeping many scientists relatively up to date. As development proceeds, however, the necessity for having national information services established has become increasingly apparent, to meet the needs not only of the scientists but also of teachers in primary and secondary schools.

Science Education in Primary Schools, Secondary Schools, and Teacher-Training Institutions

The exploratory and experimental activities which characterized science education in primary and secondary schools and teacher-training colleges during the first period of UNESCO's existence continue to this day. It was realized that no progress could be made in any of the developing member states without expanding facilities for teacher-training and improving the quality of science teachers through in-service training and such continuous educational activities as the publication of a Science Teaching Newsletter, which was started in September 1954.

Owing to the paucity of science equipment in the teaching laboratories of developing countries, UNESCO had to survey sources of supplies and furnish information to member states through the distribution of catalogs. Foreign exchange difficulties led to the creation of such facilities as UNESCO coupons and the proposal to secure international agreement on the elimination of customs duties on didactic science equipment.

The major publications of the period were the UNESCO Source Books for Science Teachers, the Handbooks for Science Teaching in Tropical Schools, and the ten UNESCO manuals for mathematics, general science, physics, chemistry, biology, and rural and household science. First published in 1956, the source books had nine impressions by 1960 and were completely revised in 1961. No other publication of UNESCO has enjoyed comparable sales. The teachers' handbooks for science in tropical areas were also quite successful, as they were all written by experts with long experience of the conditions obtaining in those countries. The generation of indigenous teachers trained with those manuals has now initiated training programs in the teachers' respective countries. It was also during this period that UNESCO prepared a report on the place of geology, geography, biology, agriculture, chemistry, meteorology, and astronomy in general education—a precursor of the present integrated approach to science teaching.

It is in the preparation of laboratory equipment that UNESCO's activities during the early years showed considerable imagination. Simple manuals to give guidance in the design and manufacture of equipment for school laboratories were published. Science workshops were also encouraged to assist in making science kits and laboratory apparatus. A set of 76 drawings on the construction of laboratory equipment and simple visual aids was published and made available to developing countries. These activities might not have been large in volume, but they preached a philosophy of self-sufficiency and creativity and encouraged an approach to science teaching which had a salutary effect in countries where complete dependence on imported apparatus meant that science could not be taught if foreign exchange were scarce.

Higher Education and Research in the Basic Sciences

In the developing countries, higher education and research in the basic sciences have always been very limited; consequently, not much could have been done in those areas of the world during the initial stages of UNESCO's existence.

The crowning activity in the field of scientific research in the advanced countries was the publication of a survey on the main trends of inquiry in the field of natural sciences, supervised by Professor Pierre Auger. This was indeed a major undertaking involving 255 specialists, all the UN specialized agencies, 24 member states, 7 intergovernmental organizations and 19 nongovernmental organizations. The complete survey, submitted to the Secretary-General of the United Nations on January 10, 1961, was very widely distributed. The significance of the survey can be found not only in the coverage but also in the recommendations concerning scientific research, the dissemination of scientific knowledge, and the application of such knowledge for peaceful ends. For the first time it made available in a single volume the main trends in the fundamental sciences of mathematics, physics, chemistry, and biology. This review of the administrative and organizational structure for the promotion of science was based on a survey of existing national organs and brought into prominence the significance of scientific and technological manpower, national investment in scientific and technological research, the creation of research institutions, the dissemination of results and their application, and the role of international scientific organizations, both governmental and nongovernmental.

This survey is the culminating product of the first phase in the field of international action in scientific education, research, and development. The United Nations Conference on the Application of Science and Technology which took place in Geneva in 1963 may be regarded as a follow-up to the guidelines embodied in this historic publication.

Higher Education, Research, and Development in the Applied and Environmental Sciences

The United Nations Conference on the Application of Science and Technology for the Benefit of the Less Developed Countries (UNCSAT) marked the beginning of an era. UNCSAT emphasized in the first place the significance of policy formulation and planning in the field of science and technology, industrial development, urbanization, and ruralization. Secondly, it emphasized the importance of human resources development, the control of the explosive growth of population, the necessity of public health and good nutrition, and the inevitability of training scientific and technological manpower.

Thirdly, UNCSAT opened the eyes of the member states to the ways in which different sectors of the economy could be advanced. These include the conservation and exploitation of natural resources and the development of agriculture, industries, transport, and communication. The impetus which UNCSAT gave to development was universal and represented the beginning of an era for the developing countries of the world, who unfortunately have limited capacities for utilizing most of the findings of the conference for the acceleration of their rates of development.

The environmental sciences are those which deal with the lithosphere (earth's crust), hydrosphere (oceans and rivers), biosphere (plants and animals), atmosphere and outer space, which is rapidly becoming a part of man's environment. The amount of education concerning man's environment promoted in primary and secondary schools and undergraduate classes has always been limited. Recent innovations in the content of science education have recognized, however, the importance of instruction on man's environment as a basis for scientific education. Postgraduate activities are numerous, and during the period under review UNESCO has promoted many of them.

The magnitude of the needs of developing countries showed, within the first three years of UNESCO's existence, that no impact could be made on development without channeling into it a substantial amount of external aid. By 1952, technical assistance started to flow into the developing countries for the establishment of institutes of technology and the development of science faculties. The volume of assistance was small, however, and the fields limited. This led to a demand for more substantial assistance and to the creation of the United Nations Special Fund. Some of the projects started by the Special Fund in its early stages were the Middle East Technical University in Turkey, the Power Engineering Research Organization in India, the Documentation Center in Mexico, and the Central Mechnical Engineering Research Institute in India.

By 1960 the United Nations Technical Assistance and Special Fund programs appeared fairly well established, but the volume of aid needed to be substantially increased. The development which later took place was a recognition by member states and the international financing bodies that substantial international investment must be made if the developing countries were ever to narrow the gap between their level of development and that of the advanced nations of the world.

The Period of Expansion and Development (1963-1969)

The period of expansion and development may be said to begin in 1963. In preparation for this period, the recommendations embodied in the Auger Report, in the ten-year development plan formulated in 1960, and in the findings of the United Nations Conference on the Application of Science and Technology for the Benefit of the Less Developed Countries (UNCSAT) are most significant. The recommendations of UNCSAT constituted the turning point in the expansion of UNESCO's program, the main lines of which were already indicated and further elaborated during the conference.

During the following period, international funds flowed into scientific and technological development, leading to an unprecedented expansion in the number of national policy-making bodies and planning organizations, higher technical institutions, engineering faculties, technical and vocational establishments, multi-disciplinary research centers and programs of development in the fields of geology, earthquake engineering, natural resources, hydrosphere, oceanography, space, geophysics, etc.

The main lines of development clearly indicated at the beginning of this period were:

1. Expansion and development of government policy-making and planning organs.
2. Expansion and development of institutional machineries for the advancement of basic science education and research.
3. Expansion and development of institutions for training in the applied sciences to promote economic development.
4. International research and development in the field of environmental sciences.

Government Policy-Making and Planning Organs

The realization that policy formulation, systematic planning, and determination of priorities make development easier has led many member states of UNESCO to embark on the creation of central organs for the formulation of plans and policies. To assist governments in this regard, UNESCO undertook many country surveys in order to carry out a comparative study of national scientific research organizations, policy-making bodies, planning ministries, etc. The results of these surveys were published in separate volumes covering Europe and North America, Asia, Latin America, the Arab States, and Africa. Assistance was given to member states through scientific advisers who helped in the establishment of policy-making bodies and planning institutions. Fellowships were given to science administrators in many countries in order that they might study the existing structure of administration in the advanced countries. A study has also been undertaken on the migration of scientists and technologists from a number of developing countries—notably Argentina, India, and the UAR—with a view to elucidating the factors conducive to this "brain drain."

Regional development of policies and plans has also been of considerable importance during this same period. Meetings of experts connected with scientific policies have been organized in Asia, Africa, Latin America, Europe, and the Arab States. International activities connected with science policy and planning have been expanded during the past several years. The culminating activity in this regard is the formulation of the World Plan of Action, which is expected to create a framework for the activities of the United Nations system and to indicate the guidelines for future activities.

The stimulation of interest in science and technology which began during the exploratory and experimental period continues to increase in volume. It is true to say that science is being implanted in developing countries to an ever greater extent as an important element of social culture. It is no exaggeration to say that scientific leadership in the developing countries is increasingly conscious of the importance of public awareness of the necessity for scientific and technological growth if their nations are to respond adequately to the challenge of the age. UNESCO's quarterly magazine *Impact,* depicting the effect of science on modern society, continues to influence the thought of scientific and political leaders throughout the world. The Kalinga Prize and the UNESCO Technology Prize are competed for by more countries every year. More science clubs and fairs are run by member states and the earlier necessity for mobile fairs has decreased. More science museums have been created. The movement of visiting professors to developing countries to give specialized lectures and stimulate their colleagues abroad has also increased in volume.

All developing countries want to industrialize and exploit their natural resources for their own benefit. In order to define the factors that influence development—leadership, legislation, manpower, capital funds, research, transfer of technology, market entrepreneurship—UNESCO has undertaken special studies with a view to identifying those factors and to disseminating the results to developing countries. The studies relevant to the mobilization of trained manpower include the one on the access of women to scientific and technical careers. In many developing countries, this reservoir of manpower, which is at least 50 percent of the working population, remains untapped.

Institutions for the Advancement of the Basic Sciences

The expansion and development of institutions for the advancement of the basic sciences has proceeded most rapidly since 1963. UNESCO has been able to stimulate member states to make the necessary investment and to assist in the creation of model institutions based on the best modern ideas. In this regard, a major activity was the collection, analysis, and dissemination of information on basic science teaching. The results of this analysis are published in a series of books known as the *New Trends,* covering the areas of the basic sciences, such as physics, chemistry, biology, and mathematics, on levels ranging from primary school to university. The quality of science instruction will tend to rise through this advice, which brings to the attention of teachers throughout the world contemporary innovations in the teaching of science.

Science teaching in primary schools received varying degrees of attention during the exploratory and experimental period. In recent years, however, many member states have shown considerable interest in the introduction of science in their primary school curriculums. Many notable scientists in the developed countries have devoted a great deal of time to developing materials for use in primary school science. Noteworthy in this respect are the African Primary School Program of the Educational Development Center of the United States, the Nuffield Foundation's "Science 5/13" program, and the applied science program of IBECC (Brazilian Institute of Education, Science and Culture). UNICEF and UNESCO have combined to produce a list of possible equipment for use in primary school science, the so-called Eve's List.

A program of integrated science recently begun by UNESCO is expected to incorporate the main ideas in many of the programs going on in different parts of the world. Through this program children in primary schools will be introduced to the scientific exploration of their environment and to scientific experimentation relating to their daily needs in food, housing, clothing, health, transport, and communications. They will also have their games and play enriched in such a manner as to lead them to discover some of the principles of modern science. The exciting possibilities of primary school science have yet to unfold in the years that lie ahead. There is no doubt, however, that expansion and development will proceed side by side.

Science teaching in secondary schools has also expanded and developed a great deal in recent years. UNESCO's pilot projects in physics, chemistry, biology, and mathematics have endeavored to incorporate many of the principles involved in the curriculum development activities of many countries. In order to stimulate the adoption of new techniques in science teaching in secondary schools, in-service training has been intensified in member states and the training of secondary-school teachers in science has been increased through the establishment of advanced teacher-training colleges. National study groups have been formed and regional seminars organized.

The thrust for modernization of content and approach, drawing on major curriculum reform projects throughout the world, continues to increase. University professors, secondary-school teachers, ministers of education, administrators, artists, programmers, and technicians have formed teams for secondary-school curriculum development. The teaching commissions of ICSU continue to give advice on these innovations. It is reasonable to hope that the modernization of content and methods in secondary-school science teaching will lead to such a transformation that the product of secondary schools will in the near future be completely different from their predecessors.

Science teaching at university level has also received considerable attention. Source books on the teaching of basic sciences during the first year of university studies have been prepared. Films suitable for the teaching of basic sciences in universities have been brought to the attention of many member states through the collaboration of UNESCO with the International Science Film Association. Surveys of university curriculums and teaching methods have been undertaken in Czechoslovakia, France, the Federal Republic of Germany, the United Kingdom, the U.S.A., and the U.S.S.R., in order to assist the universities in developing countries to know the latest trends.

The most significant development of the period is, however, the expansion of UNESCO's activities in the development of basic science faculties at universities of member states. Many missions have been sent to member states to advise on the development of science faculties. A major innovation of recent years has been the establishment of national science teaching improvement centers, which are expected to develop effective science programs, including new teaching materials, through the collaboration of university scholars, science teachers, and administrators. One such center is being established in

Israel, another in Brazil, and many more are expected to be set up in the next few years in order to provide the institutional machinery for the injection of scientific innovations into the education system.

Institutions for Training in Applied Sciences

The expansion and development of institutions for the training of engineers and technicians has received its greatest impetus since 1963. The number of United Nations Special Fund projects administered by UNESCO in this field has risen from 25 to 60. They include research establishments, university faculties, technical colleges, and agricultural institutions. Centers for the development of standards and instrumentation have been created, and consultants have been made available to member states to assist in the establishment of research institutions. The number of postgraduate courses in the applied sciences has been increased with the assistance of advanced states; these include hydraulic engineering, chemical engineering, automation, and hydrology.

Engineering and technological education at universities had phenomenal development during this period. In 1963 there were only six Special Fund projects in this field, but by 1965 they had risen to over 51, and in 1968 this figure had increased to 61, including the higher technical institutions. This rapid growth necessitated a hard look into the subject of engineering education and training. Meetings of experts were organized to examine the elements of effective education and training of engineers and technologists. A major conference on this subject took place in 1968 and was attended by some 280 participants. The conference considered the general requirements of an engineering educational system, the programming of engineering schools, the changing role of the engineer in society, the access of women to engineering education, long-term needs for engineers, and the methodology of engineering education.

During the period under consideration, the training of technicians also expanded. There is, however, a tendency for member states to convert technical institutes into technological universities, even though their needs for design engineers are much smaller than for technicians. This often leads to unemployment of the graduates, owing to the fact that engineers are overproduced while the supply of technicians remains inadequate. The situation is, however, being kept under continuous study and there is hope for improvement.

Agricultural education and training in developing countries has not always received adequate emphasis, even though many of these countries depend largely on agriculture. In collaboration with FAO and ILO, member states are being assisted in developing agricultural education. A World Conference on Agricultural Education is scheduled to take place in 1970 under the joint sponsorship of FAO, ILO, and UNESCO. International courses for the training of teachers and specialists in agriculture are organized in Switzerland under UNESCO's auspices. A pilot project on rural education in primary schools has also been organized in Africa. The volume of assistance given to member states by UNESCO could be increased. A fair evaluation of the total amount of international aid in this field can only be obtained by adding together what is available through FAO, ILO, and other agencies.

Advisory missions to member states on educational development continue to increase. They often lead to the identification of projects and to general counsel on the conditions necessary for the promotion of science and technology. The most critical factor in the promotion of science and technology in developing countries is the generation of a cadre of competent high-level manpower. For this reason, the greatest emphasis is given by UNESCO to educational training in school and out of school. The training must be continuous and life-long if obsolescence is to be avoided. Furthermore, the conditions of service must be attractive and professional manpower must be organized in such a way that they may influence the government decision-making bodies and contribute their maximum to scientific and technological development. It was for this reason that a World Federation of Engineering Organizations was created under UNESCO's sponsorship in March 1968.

Environmental Sciences

Although UNESCO has always shown the greatest interest in the environmental sciences from the first years of its existence, the necessity for concentrated effort continues to increase owing to the expanding nature of man's environment, the growth of population, the need for surveys, research, training, conservation, and utilization of natural resources. Activities in the environmental sciences have been restricted to research and training. Ecological studies have been promoted over the years and integrated surveys of natural resources undertaken. A notable example is the review of the natural resources of Africa, published at the request of the UN Economic Commission for Africa; this study now forms Volume I of a new series on natural resources.

Some of the earlier efforts of UNESCO in promoting education in the environmental sciences include such publications as *Mother Nature*—a notebook for primary and secondary schools in Sudan and Sahara, and *Conservation of Nature and Natural Resources in Modern African States*. The publications of tomorrow on man's environment will probably range through a study of the soil, the earth's mantle, the hydrosphere, the biosphere, the atmosphere, and outer space.

The Period of Comprehensive Development (1970-   )

One may be allowed to speculate on the perspectives of science education development for the future and the role which UNESCO can play vis-à-vis the developing countries. The main trends are clear in the current program, especially as regards science policy and planning, basic, applied, and environmental sciences, international assistance, and cooperation on an expanding scale. Above all, there should be no longer any illusion about the dominant role that political and governmental action will play in future. Not to recognize this is to be naive and to ignore the most potent power in national, regional and international cooperation and development.

Science Policy and Planning

The setting up of science policy-making and planning organs that many nations have embarked upon will continue feverishly in Africa, Latin America, and Asia. The activities of these bodies will increase, science statistics will be collected and analyzed, legislations enacted, documentation service promoted, scientific institutions established, national funds invested in research and human resource development, natural resources inventory taken, mechanisms created for the effective transfer of technology from laboratory to production enterprises, national development telescoped into shorter periods of time.

Both in national and regional development, the developing regions will find it difficult to pull themselves up by their boot straps. But organize they must, in order to succeed in the struggle for survival in the technological age. What is more, they must avail themselves of the large reservoir of international goodwill represented by various schemes of bilateral and multilateral assistance. Any excessive inward looking that tends to promote extreme nationalism or regionalism is potentially dangerous for the peace of the world and may slow down development. Regional policy and planning are inevitable during the next decade, but their potentiality for disrupting world peace must be transformed through international action into powerful instruments for the promotion of international understanding and cooperation in science. Those responsible for the direction of regional science policy and planning in developed and developing countries have therefore grave responsibilities.

Basic and Applied Sciences

It seems fairly certain that educational activities in the coming years will be seriously affected by incipient changes in the structure of knowledge. The traditional boundaries between pure and applied sciences are breaking down. Even those which existed between the physical sciences are vanishing, while the life sciences are rapidly becoming multidisciplinary studies. What the structure will be is too early to predict. Already, however, the primary and secondary schools are devoting themselves to specific units of instruction and adopting a multidisciplinary approach. The so-called integrated science for primary and junior secondary schools is a move in this direction. It will enable the pupils to learn about the science of things above us, around us and below us; to study the science that governs food, housing, clothing, health, transport, and communication; to experiment with the soil, plants, animals, water, air, and sunlight. The research institutions, by the same token, are becoming multidisciplinary, but oriented towards some specific demands.

The traditional divisions into primary, secondary, and tertiary levels are also changing. For many countries where education is compulsory up to 15 or 16, the distinction between primary and secondary hardly exists any more. The content of science education in mathematics, physics, chemistry, biology, geology, and astronomy at the primary and secondary levels has been so transformed in recent years that people who left school only twenty years ago may not be able to follow some of the instruction now being given to pupils, especially in mathematics and physics. A transfer of curriculum topics is proceeding from universities to secondary and primary schools and from secondary to primary, while some topics are being completely eliminated. This innovation of content is the most noticeable feature of the past few years. The example set by PSSC has been followed in many parts of the world and will continue in many nations. Many National Science Improvement Centers will be set up in the coming years to reconstitute not only the content of science education but also its methodology. UNESCO is assisting many developing countries in this venture.

The mounting interest in the study of man's environment will probably be intensified during the next decade, and this will be reflected in the science teaching of primary and secondary schools and of the universities. A multidisciplinary study and investigation of man's environment—the lithosphere, hydrosphere, biosphere, atmosphere, and outer space—will have a dominant place in UNESCO's international program of research, education, and training.

The explosive growth in science has necessitated a re-examination of the methodology of science teaching. Undoubtedly, the innovative activities will expand with the growth of National Science Improvement Centers leading to the design of new equipment, application of the psychology of the learning process, use of the mass media, audio-visual material, exploratory techniques, programmed texts, computer-assisted instruction, and various other devices that now appear rather unorthodox. In all these innovations, present-day technology is being built into the methodology of instruction. More and more of these activities will take place in the next decade, Because the school period is much too short for the amount of knowledge that has to be imparted, the machinery for continuous and permanent science education out of school will also expand in order to avoid the obsolescence which rapidly becomes the lot of scientists isolated from their colleagues in other parts of the world.

Already the amount of knowledge imparted by indirect and unscheduled routes has reached a level that calls into question the efficacy of the traditional method, and UNESCO is accordingly committed to finding out how the use of the mass media can effectively supplement the education process by ensuring at once its continuity and permanence. The increasing volume of innovations throughout the world makes it imperative for UNESCO to continue to expand its clearing-house functions, its surveys of current practices, its comparative analysis of their effectiveness, the dissemination of the findings, and the promotion of documentation and library facilities.

DISCUSSION

In concluding his survey, Chief Awokoya said bluntly that the developing countries have to organize themselves, to put their houses in order, or they may be left too far behind the developed lands. The developing countries are in the grip of fear—fear that they will never close the widening gap between them and more fortunate countries, fear that they will forfeit their right to exist. But there is an enormous reservoir of good will in the world, and they must use the international assistance that is available. Mankind's greatest efforts have been made in response to challenge. It is up to the developing countries to meet the challenge by organizing in every way, by planning, by creating regional and national institutions, by developing basic sciences and applied sciences, by adopting a multidisciplinary approach, by transforming science and technology into production.

Professor Gerald Holton (United States) urged the developing countries not to develop scientific inferiority feelings; with courage, with funding, with leadership, with a willingness to listen to local people, with an openness to a variety of modes of experimentation, they can vastly improve science education in their own territories, largely from their own resources. In some respects, as regards science education, the so-called underdeveloped countries have a more developed outlook and more local initiative than the United States, where physics teachers are struggling against overwhelming job problems.

"I stress local initiative," said Professor Holton, "because it will develop self-respect, and because science education is not a science—it is still to a great extent an art." The next real advances in the field may come, not from Boston or London or Moscow, but from a country like Brazil, or Thailand, or Israel.

One of the functions of UNESCO, as is clear from Chief Awokoya's address, is that of a marriage broker, bringing together different groups. This activity of the agency should be greatly expanded and intensified. Millions of dollars, and years of man-hours, are being expended in the United States on curriculum development; Dr. Holton thought the Americans had a few interesting answers to share with others. More effort should be made to send groups on limited missions to developing countries, from which similar groups can be brought to the United States.

He warned against the indiscriminate use of new education gadgets; UNESCO should help to see that they are adequately examined before they are forced upon educational systems. UNESCO can also encourage authors of textbooks, and groups, to think internationally, in terms of the one world of science, and to use examples outside their own parochial settings.

Dr. Julius Gikonyo Kiano (Kenya) felt that there is no need for the developing countries to feel pessimistic; they are already finding answers to many of their problems. He was happy to note that UNESCO emphasizes the element of applied knowledge as well as research in basic sciences. It is very important that a child should get an education enabling him or her to do something.

One important field that he thought UNESCO had been neglecting is adult education. There is not enough reading material for adults; he hoped that in its next budget UNESCO would include provision for publications for libraries outside the classrooms.

The idea of regional conferences, mentioned by various speakers, is an excellent one; he was pleased to be able to report that ministers of education from all over Africa had met in 1968 in Nairobi, in a conference on education and science teaching and technical teaching in Africa (CESTA). The idea of sharing facilities was strongly supported by most of the participants.

PART **III**

**CHILDREN'S NEEDS AND OPPORTUNITIES
FOR LEARNING**

9

THE NATURE
OF LEARNING
IN CHILDHOOD

By Jerome S. Bruner

Center for Cognitive Studies,
Harvard University,
United States

In speaking of the nature of learning in childhood and its relationship to the development of nations, I would like to stand back and approach the matter initially from the broad perspective of evolutionary theory. For we must bear well in mind at the outset the biological function of culture as a way of enabling and amplifying the powers of the human hand, human senses, and the human mind.

Let me consider first the evolutionary significance and species-specific nature of human learning. Obviously, it differs in two massively different ways from learning elsewhere in the primate series. The first has to do with the capacity of Homo sapiens to receive and to translate knowledge in a linguistic form. This permits man to convert knowledge into a form that renders it highly transmissible. Language not only permits an enormous condensation of knowledge, but permits us to turn the knowledge into hypothetical forms so that we may consider alternatives without having to act them out in the form of trial and error. The possession of the gift of language also provides a way of transmitting knowledge—some knowledge—without direct encounter with nature. Thus society and culture serve to provide a buffer between man and nature as well as a storehouse of techniques for coping with contingencies created by nature—techniques to be learned in advance of encounter.

The second major characteristic of human learning is the openness of human skill. There is a great flexibility about how we learn things. Learning to do things one way, we seem to be able to do them almost automatically in a wide variety of ways. Thus, we develop the ability not only to use our inherited limbs, senses, muscles, and reason but also to amplify and assist them with tools and such powerful prosthetic devices as microscopes, computers, and even such extraordinary sources of power as slow nuclear fission. Closer inspection of the development of human skill suggests that in its nature it may have a syntax that differentiates it as much from primate agility as human language is distinguished from the calls of higher apes. Human skill is constructed of a set of combinable sub-routines that can be put together in much the same way as we put together sentences.

But there is also a third characteristic of human learning that is more continuous with primate evolution, though just as important. It has to do with the nonspecificity of what is learned by humans and higher apes. Not only does man learn specific things—be they facts or skills or abstractions—he also seems

91

to learn how to learn. He learns strategies for eliminating errors faster; he learns to organize information; he learns to anticipate; he learns to compensate for poor conditions and to exploit good ones.

Man's brain is probably an obstetrical compromise in evolutionary history. It begins with bipedalism. Evolutionary selection for bipedalism involved two contradictory requirements. On the one hand, there was selection of those hominids capable of using the freed hands intelligently. On the other, there was a seletion of those with strong, thick pelvic girdles, achieved in hominid bipeds by a closing down of the birth canal. Greater intelligence meant a bigger brain; better locomotion meant a smaller birth canal. The compromise appears to have been a big brain that began in the form of great immaturity—likely a selection of members of the species with more fetal characteristics. In any case, the result was a long period of immaturity with surprising freedom from preemptive precocity—that form of early maturing that decreases the growth of any further plasticity or flexibility in what is learned. What evolved was a species enormously sensitive to environmental variability and equipped to develop skills that would take advantage of what had been stored up not only in the gene pool of the species, but also in that uniquely human pool of knowledge and technique called human culture. It is in this last sense that the society as a whole rather than the immediate nuclear family must take responsibility for its young, since no parent knows all there is to be known in the culture pool and, indeed, few know much. Such is the division of labor and its effect on man.

Let me return for a moment to what I referred to earlier as nonspecific learning, for it is a form of learning that is well advanced before the child ever gets to a school. It is compounded of many things of great importance that constitute the so-called hidden curriculum provided by the home, the neighborhood, and immediate surrounding culture. It involves attitudes and values as well as strategies of learning and thinking. To begin with, there is early inculcated some deep attitudes about the use of mind: is it for thinking things through on one's own, or is it to register upon and store the authoritative word handed down? Does it carry with it a sense of hope about the possiblity of solving problems, or does it portray nature and man as subject to fate, caprice, and fortuity?

How are these subtle points of view transmitted to a small child? They surely relate to the quality and tone of early interaction between the infant and mother. Our work at Harvard University has underlined the number and variety of ways the child can pick up knowledge of his environment and its consistency or lack of consistency. The infant early learns to respond accordingly. Where one sees the early patterning most vividly is in deprived social surroundings. The child of the depressed slum may suffer not only a reduction in energy and zest from malnutrition, but also a decline in his willingness to try to solve problems and, eventually, in his ability to solve them. In his development we find a variety of measurable deficits by the age of three: reduced capacity for sustained attention and for distributing attention, reduced range in linguistic usage, reduced imagery, declining confidence in ability to delay reward in the hope that further effort will get him a greater one.

In consequence, there develops by age three not only a deficit in measured intelligence, but even a decline in intelligence relative to the more fortunate child. For not only has the child from a blighted cultural background failed to master the elementary skills, he has also failed to develop the means for linking himself with the powerful amplifiers provided by human culture: ways of using language to help one think, of using forms of logic and mathematics to help one find deeper order in surface confusion, forms of myth and characterization to help one penetrate the nature of the society in which one lives. There is a popular if obscure phrase among pedagogical theorists: learning readiness. It used to be thought that such school readiness was principally a function of maturation of the nervous system, and indeed there are, as we shall see, some important maturational milestones. But a good part of readiness is made by the child's history interacting with his maturing capacities.

Let me cite a few specifics. Hess and Shipman in the United States and Bernstein in England have shown the extent to which the slum child fails to develop fully elaborated language. Dialogue is limited to present and palpable objects or events—what Bernstein speaks of as a restricted linguistic code rather than an elaborated one. Mischel has shown in a series of brilliant investigations that the child of a slum or of a depressed area undergoing rapid and disruptive social change (such as in urbanized West Indian islands) will not forego a small reward now for a bigger reward later. In consequence, he will persevere less at problem solving, try out fewer solutions, take out less time for the sake of mastery. Again, Deutsch and others have shown that if one takes the academically least successful children from any given socioeconomic stratum, they are likely to be the ones with fewest episodes of conversation with parents.

But richness of opportunity to learn may have an even more direct effect on the growth of human capacities. Perforce many of the relevant studies have been done on animals since they require forms of intervention that are not permissible in human experimentation. Krech and Rosenzweig, working along with Calvin, have found that opportunities for learning in the immature animal affect the cycle of acetyl choline and cholinesterase crucial in synaptic transmission. They have also found that such early learning not only increases the growth of branching dendritic processes in the brain but also seems to produce spur-type growths along axons. And at a more functional level, Harlow has reported that macaques who have had an opportunity for early learning show less deficit following lesions to the cerebral cortex, and also a superior recovery of function.

Thus far we have discussed deficit—evidence from socially induced pathology in the early life of the child. We know curiously little about the more positive side—how to create optimum situations for learning, how to bring to full expression the human potential. We shall come to that finally and hazard some guesses. Before we do, however, there are some other matters that must concern us.

The first concerns the child's growing conception or representation of the world around him. In preparing materials to aid the child's learning, the curriculum must fit into the child's available modes of knowing, his representations. At the outset, the child's approach to the world is in terms of action and the development and realization of sensorimotor skill. He knows by knowing how to, and his knowledge expresses itself in the organization and guidance of action. In time and gradually, this form of learning is supplemented by a capacity to summarize events and actions in the coin of imagery. There is a concreteness and perception-bound quality of the child's intelligence during the years, say, between three and seven, that contrasts vividly with the deeper-lying, vivid fantasies that also characterize the child. Knowledge at this stage is spotty, ragged, and fractional, and tends to deal with very few features of things at any one time. Eventually, thought and problem-solving come to embrace concepts, to deal with more logical operations, with possibilities taken in combination rather than with events taken singly and in fragments. The details are complex and the controversies that exist about these matters real, but the general outline is reasonably plain. By the time the child is well into school, he is capable of knowing things through action, through image, and through symbolic-linguistic representation.

What is required, as the child progresses, is opportunity to exercise his growing and maturing capacities—not to "speed him up" through the course of development, but to give him easy control over and confidence in his abilities to cope. Where these are not so mastered and where confidence fails to develop, we have the child who defends himself from the threat of failure inherent in learning. It is when this happens that we encounter the learning block, the school phobia, the chronic underachiever. It would seem, moreover, that the growth of learning is organized much like a set of prerequisites where the mastery of one skill or one conception either frees the child to move on to a next one, that is, provides a set of components that will be organized as a subsequent skill matures, or provides the means by which the child comes to comprehend a new relationship.

In general, learning itself is its own reward, as it moves through a cycle of skill growth and consolidation. And much of learning in natural, apprentice-like situations has this property of intrinsic reward. Various writers in the past decade, referring more specifically to primate learning including that of man, have postulated what have come to be called "effectence motives" that impel the organism toward mastery and satisfaction of curiosity for its own sake. I do not know whether much is served by postulating such a drive, but that satisfaction is gained from such effectence achievement is beyond question.

Why then do we need other forms of extrinsic reward? Let me make plain that extrinsic reward—be it in the form of praise, grades, prizes, or whatnot—have little direct effect on what one learns save in highly restricted situations. What is crucial to learning is knowledge of results and the possiblity of using error for correction. That is a matter of information rather than of commerce in prizes or approbation. Mastering an equation, a sentence in a foreign tongue, or a bodily skill depends only indirectly upon the prize one gets after the episode is over. Extrinsic reward, rather, directs attention and sustains it and above all else indicates that what one has learned matters to somebody else—notably, to the society of which one is a member.

What is crucial about intrinsically motivated learning is that it must be buttressed by knowledge of results as it goes along—which schools, for example, often do not provide. But intrinsically motivated learning can also be supported by providing materials to be learned that are themselves capable of leading to insights and skills that can then be parlayed into deeper insights and more powerful skills. The great disciplines of learning have precisely this structure, and that is one of the most powerful pedagogical reasons why they are worth teaching. There are plenty of practical reasons, obviously. As you all know, there is now a world-wide movement reforming curriculum in the schools of many countries much along these lines. One of the mottoes of this effort is that any subject can be taught to any child at any age in some form that is interesting and honest. This means, basically, that one can readily start a child on his or her way with some early version of a more complex notion or skill rendered in the form of an exercise in manipulation or in imagery before the idea or subject is given in its more complex form, embodied in a highly abstract, symbolic notation. What this guarantees, of course, is that the child can then go on to as much depth and precision as he can master. He is, then, becoming deeply involved in his culture.

In fact, schools are improving, though they are doing so neither fast enough nor with enough regard for the child whose home background leaves him deficient in the hidden curriculum with which we began this discussion. Experience in many developing nations, particularly in Africa, underlines the importance of preparing the child in the home setting for school. And, indeed, it is of deep importance in these developing areas that in the elementary schools particularly there should not be a slavish imitation of the European school pattern.

Our task is not so much that of adapting the Western school to new conditions elsewhere, but rather of inventing new means for relating flexible human capacities to the challenges and requirements of developing societies. We must not limit ourselves to the school as the sole instrument of education, for it has represented a very small part of the process of preparing human beings for the challenge of change. It is the very conception of growth itself and how we assist it through the life cycle of the human being that is now the issue. Perinatal care, toys in the nursery, opportunity for early application of what one has learned, the restructuring of work to match one's age—these are as important in the broad picture as curriculums, teachers, and textbooks.

DISCUSSION

Discussing his paper, Dr. Bruner contended that it is difficult to teach a child to think scientifically, if he comes from a highly traditional cultural background—a tribal, medieval, or similar background. This might seem to be a surprising proposition; after all, is not science a great, open technique for asking questions in a form that might be described as tangible, so that it can be easily adopted by anyone? The difficulty arises because children in the more highly developed societies receive an enormous amount of prior training suitable for the task of learning scientific thinking, long before they ever go near a schoolroom. They have toys such as blocks that fit, gears that fit, screwdrivers that fit, to aid them in the learning process.

Then there is the use of hypothetical language: e.g., "I have nothing in my hand now, but what might I have had in my hand if somebody had come along just now with several things, and I had taken one of them?" This is standard chatter in the scientific domain. Children from middle-class intellectual homes in a Western society pick up this type of talk and thinking without any conscious effort on their part. Children from so-called culturally deprived homes—Dr. Bruner objects to the phrase "culturally deprived" because it seems to imply that all that is needed is a special dosage of a vitamin called culture—have difficulty handling this mode of language.

Another difficulty that culturally deprived children have is in using what has been called "the expanded code of language", as compared to its indexing function: the latter is, for example, to identify something as "that ashtray," while the former includes grasping all the associations and connotations in regard to something.

All these things are learned out of school, in the home and the society in which the child is reared. If people wait until the child goes to school before providing him with the preliminary conditioning, they run the risk of creating a failure situation, in which the child will feel out of touch.

Professor Alexandra Poljakoff-Mayber (Israel) noted that children in Israel coming from very traditional homes encounter considerable difficulty in learning science. This is probably due to their growing up in surroundings where there is always a central authority, and it is self-evident and accepted that this authority is always right, has to be right, can never be wrong. The old-fashioned type of teacher fits into this pattern, but the new type, teaching science as a personal experience for the pupil and urging him to do experiments and judge results for himself, shatters the concept of an omniscient authority.

Dr. Gina Rivka (Israel) endorsed Dr. Bruner's view that learning begins long before the child reaches the schoolroom. In Jerusalem they have experimented to find which mother succeeds in educating her children, and which does not. It was found that even uneducated mothers can educate their infants, if they set about it in the right way. The aim should be to educate the mothers how to educate their young.

An optimistic note was struck by *Dr. Julius Gikonyo Kiano* (Kenya), who thought that Dr. Bruner was exaggerating the difficulties of children in what he called tribal and medieval groups. The impact of Western societies has been so strong that these tribal cultures have been thoroughly disturbed; the children are not "culture-bound." They certainly still have problems, but cultural predetermination is no longer a major obstacle.

In the light of Dr. Bruner's remarks, *Mr. Evelly Selai Mohapi* (Lesotho), urged the developed countries to give aid to the developing lands back at the nursery-school level. Every village should be provided with a nursery school, and this school should have modern toys and equipment. Thus a new generation will be raised that will know more than its parents. Time is not on the side of Africa, and waiting till the parents are able to educate their children will take far too long.

In his reply, Dr. Bruner agreed that the early years of infancy are of great importance in the child's life. Some experiments have shown that already at 18 months infants reflect the different levels of their parents in the confidence they display in manipulating objects and in playing. He agrees that the mother should be trained to be an adequate partner in the growth enterprise of the child. He derives considerable hope from a new interdisciplinary approach to the child—biology, linguistics, pediatrics, biochemistry, pedagogy, and other interested sciences are being brought together to serve the nurture, growth, and education of children.

10 SCIENCE AND EDUCATION: THE PROPER BALANCE

By David Samuel

*Weizmann Institute
of Science,
Israel*

The past decade has witnessed the growth and development of an unusual partnership—an alliance between successful professional scientists and all those who are primarily concerned with the process of education itself: ministers and their staffs, local educational authorities, school principals, and teachers. Obviously, many practising scientists are also concerned with education; it is, in fact, our experience that productive and imaginative research workers are inevitably good teachers—at least, at the university level. It is not at all certain, however, that all scientists instinctively understand the problems of teaching in school or fully grasp the day-to-day difficulties and tensions of the classroom. For this reason, it is wise that science educators have borrowed from science the concept of a *model system* of trial and revision on a small sample.

Although the initial urge for experimentation in science education may have come from the men in the laboratories, it was the teachers who encouraged, adapted, and implemented many of these projects and who bore the brunt of the benign revolution. By testing and evaluating each project, by suggesting new systems of teaching, and, above all, by submitting with good grace and forbearance to what were (and still are, in many cases) experiments in learning, they played a vital and essential role.

As a result of this teamwork, an entire repertoire of projects, in all the well-known scientific subjects and in several new interdisciplinary ones, have concentrated mainly at the high-school level. This level was considered, at the start, to be the most critical; it is in secondary-school classrooms that future cadres of scientists and technologists will be found. And it is here that nations can start to overcome the development gap. In many ways, this age group turned out to be the easiest to tackle because of the relatively small number of selected students involved with a strong motivation and with more experienced teachers.

These days, however, a new trend has become discernible in the teaching of science, or, I should perhaps say, of scientific concepts, at the elementary school level. This means the introduction, at an early age, of the understanding of numerical relationships, of relative sizes, of evidence and uncertainty, of the limitations of experiments, the properties of matter, and the idea of growth—these are but examples. Today's concern with pre-high school teaching matters everywhere, but it matters most in the emerging nations. For these nations, the problems of education in general and science teaching in particular are greater, more challenging, and more urgent. The formation of scientific concepts at an early age, is, I believe, the overriding educational problem for the next decade, the education of those, at any level, who are not scientifically bent, who are not fascinated by numbers, or machines, or crystals, or snails, but who are still eager to know what goes on in science, and who may, one day, themselves have to make decisions on scientific matters. Training these children is no less important than the training of the future technologists.

One important consideration, a dilemma of which we are all well aware, is whether to stick with the purists, teaching a few select scientific principles elegantly (though this elegance is often appreciated only by experienced scientists), or to plump for "relevance"—that overworked word used so much by students—and teach future citizens how to cope with the complexities of day-to-day engineering and popular medicine.

The pendulum has swung between these educational alternatives for quite some time and will no doubt continue to do so, and we shall end up, I imagine, with a compromise. Perhaps a mixture of the two possibilities—*relevance that is elegant*—will be the best solution. By this I mean that, at least for those who are approaching the end of high school, science courses should include, instead of merely more mathematics, elements of computer techniques; instead of more physics, perhaps astrophysics; instead of more biology, animal and human behavior; and instead of more chemistry, something about our environment.

In Israel, we are still looking for the right balance in this, as in many other fields. Perhaps we are fortunate that we live in a middle-sized country, in a land too small to be self-sufficient but large enough for us to have to try to be self-sufficient, large enough to have to try out different educational approaches on a small but manageable scale. We are still in the throes of evaluating the results of various pilot projects, and we shall probably continue to do so for years to come; for once started, the process of improvement must go on. It has been said that in many ways this is still a developing country, its population ranges over a wide spectrum of origins and upbringing, its language is difficult and unique, its survival dependent on its own efforts. Under such circumstances imitation is no solution. We have tried to translate other people's schemes for science in school, but we have learnt, as others have learnt, that our science education must be tailored to *our* classrooms, to *our* teachers and to *our* children. We had various projects for doing this; some of them were amateurish and even in conflict with each other. Today we have managed to coordinate these efforts, to have them evaluated by a central body—The Israel Science Teaching Center.

Although much has been done, there is still much to do. Recently I added a question to a routine chemistry questionnaire directed at sixteen-year-olds majoring in science. What do chemistry graduates do for a living? we asked. I am sad to report that practically no one had any idea what a modern chemist does or how he does it. If we want to ensure the flow of talented youngsters interested in a scientific career, we must teach them what is being done in the world outside, and to what end.

DISCUSSION

Dr. Fletcher G. Watson (United States) said that five factors are of critical importance in engineering large-scale changes in the education of children.

The first necessity is to have competent and enthusiastic people. Secondly, there is the factor of time: every new educational effort involves a long time, at least five years; the project has to be planned, developed, reappraised, and produced for large-scale use. Thirdly, teachers have to be thoroughly retrained in how to use the new courses: this process takes many years, costs more than the initial cost of the course, and should be instituted as soon as the first course activities are started. In the United States the cost of teacher training is estimated at five times the cost of the initial course development. The fourth essential is a strong evaluation program; it is essential to conduct continuous research on how the course is turning out. The fifth factor is money—without enough money for the project to be planned, developed, staffed, and researched, it should not be started. The frustration and bitterness will be less if the project is not begun than if it fails through lack of means. A positive political environment is also important; no educational reform is possible if the ministers of education and their representatives are hostile to it.

Dr. Jerome S. Bruner (United States) warned against what he calls "the education of prestige." Andrew Schenfield has written about "The Politics of Prestige"—the cost to Great Britain of carrying out a foreign policy on the premise that it was a Great Power. Similarly, a Nigerian neurologist-psychiatrist has discussed the "Medicine of Prestige"—having a large number of beds in a hospital. In the case of education, the passion for prestige expresses itself in a worship of so-called "general education." There is a danger of general education becoming a sacred cow in developing countries; we should take a new look at "vocational education" in the deepest sense of the term. The nature of society and of work are changing; vocational education involves an education, not only in the use of a particular machine, but also in the nature of the social organization.

Harvard, M.I.T., and Berkeley are organizing a cooperative venture of anthropologists and biologists to study Man. Developing countries should think in new terms like these, not merely adopt traditional goals like general education.

11 GOALS, MEANS, AND STRATEGY IN ADVANCING SCIENCE EDUCATION

By Uri Haber-Schaim

Physical Science Group,
Education Development Center,
United States

Why should science be studied in schools? What do we expect it to contribute toward the general education of the student and his becoming a responsible member of his society? The answers to these questions may vary from country to country and from time to time within a country. Even in a given country at a given time, the answers may depend on the age and interest of the students. But in all cases the answers to these questions, if they are taken seriously, determine the content as well as the means and the strategy of implementing programs in science education.

Unfortunately, all too often the questions are not even asked. When they are asked, the answers are found mostly in prefaces to textbooks and guidelines published by ministries of education, and ignored everywhere else. For example, the rationale for a course in biology may contain statements such as "to make the student familiar with fauna and flora of his area and develop an appreciation and understanding for the living world." The textbook the student uses, however, may be devoted largely to plants and animals in other parts of the world, or contain a great deal of technical material in molecular biology. In the classroom the student divides his time between listening to his teacher's lecture and being quizzed on his assignments. In physics the rationale may sound like this: "To develop an understanding of the basic principles of physics and of their application to technology, and an appreciation of the unity of physics." Yet in reality the physics course is divided into airtight units such as heat, light, and mechanics. The student is drilled in solving a variety of artifical problems; if he is lucky enough to have access to a laboratory, he is told exactly what to do there and what results are expected.

I have not done sufficient research to be able to explain exactly how the educational systems in so many countries get into such a sad situation. However, from my own observations I am inclined to believe that the three most important factors are:

1. Examinations, and in particular externally administered examinations, become the master rather than the servant of education.
2. The guidelines to schools are primarily expressed in terms of syllabi—lists of topics and numbers of class hours per topic. Over the years topics are added to but rarely taken off the list. This makes the syllabus unrealistic.
3. There is a complete separation between goals, content, and methodology in the planning of education and in the preparation of teachers.

I think that these three factors also explain why it takes a combination of people inside and outside the educational establishment to start reform movements such as are represented at this conference. It takes the outsiders to diagnose the trouble and to carry out attempts to provide a cure, and it takes the insiders to have the changes accepted. The last twelve years have seen the development in various countries of a number of large-scale projects in science education from kindergarten through college. Many of the participants in this conference are likely to be called upon to make decisions on the advancement of science education in their own countries. Is it best to import programs from other countries? Should local adaptations be made—and if so, what kind? Should programs be developed locally, nationally, or internationally on a regional basis? How does one go about it? The answers to these questions will depend on the technical and financial resources of the country, its cultural values, and other factors. I cannot provide them. I can only try to suggest a few items for a "check-list" to be included in the decision-making process.

Defining Goals

First of all, there has to be a clear picture of the educational goals, not only in terms of subject matter but also in terms of attitudes, skills, and cultural values. The last-named have the largest effect on what goes on in the classroom. If it is considered of primary importance that the teacher, as a representative of the adult world, appear as the infallible master, he has to run a taut class. He will see to it that no questions arise to which he does not know the answer; he will make it clear to the students that doing this his way is the best route to success. The students will get the message fast, and will soon learn to write down what the teacher expects from them rather than what they saw or measured or reasoned out in their own experiments.

If, on the other hand, it is considered most important that all the incentive to learn come from within the individual student, the teacher must stay in the background and try to encourage each student to get interested in the things available in the classroom.

If it is agreed that going to school has to serve the exclusive function of pumping knowledge into all students in the most efficient way, then the school must be provided with a large number of little cubicles where each student can study at his own pace (with or without a computer or a programmed text) and never be slowed down by a poorer student or pushed by a better one.

If it is considered important that students learn to express their observations clearly and defend their conclusions, and also to listen to differing values expressed by others, then the opportunity for such class discussions must be provided.

On the more professional side, if it is desired that students learn primarily to apply knowledge to immediate problems of the community, the biology may be slanted toward hygiene and the physics toward shopwork.

If for a certain age group it is decided that the human aspects of the development of science are important, then the students must be provided with open-ended laboratory experiments which do not settle questions right away, and also with historical reading materials about critical issues in the development of science.

In short, the goals—the real ones, not necessarily the proclaimed ones—are intimately connected with what goes on in the classroom. If we want to set new goals we have to translate them into concrete programs and provide all the necessary means to implement them.

Among the means I distinguish three categories: software and hardware, teacher education, and ways to measure student and teacher achievement. I would like to concentrate on the last two categories, because they pose the hardest problems when it comes to strategy.

One of the common features of recent programs in science education is that the role of the teacher in the classroom is different from what it was before. Therefore, when new programs are to be implemented, two problems must be solved: the re-education of the teacher in the schools and the proper preparation of future teachers. The magnitude of these problems depends partly, of course, on the size of the country, but not on that alone.

A great deal depends on the attitude of the persons concerned with the change. I am happy to report that in my experience the vast majority of science teachers are eager to grow professionally and to improve their teaching habits as well as their command of the subject matter.

Things get a little tougher when it comes to the teachers of teachers—that is, to college professors. By far the greatest problem may be to convince the people in charge of matriculation examinations or university entrance examinations to alter their standards. In the last analysis, however, this is a problem in human engineering, and there are ways to solve it.

The administering of tests is usually the prerogative of government, and governments, like big industrial units, function best with smooth and standardized procedures. They are not built for innovation. A drastic change introduced at once on a large scale may prove to be a calamity. To connect the research and development stage with the large-scale production stage, industry developed the pilot stage. This is the stage in which troubles can be spotted and eliminated—or, if necessary, the whole product may be discarded without disastrous financial loss. The same is true in advancing education. It is only natural that the people who carry executive responsiblity will be reluctant to authorize the large-scale implementation of new programs even if they look attractive. They should be, because too many things may go wrong.

Using Pilot Schools

Here is where the introduction of pilot classes or whole pilot schools becomes so important. There is no great risk taken if a few schools are allowed to try out new programs. However, such tryouts can produce useful information for the purpose of further decision-making only if these pilot schools are freed from all the usual constraints, including the standard examinations. Pilot schools must be allowed to use tests developed specifically for the new program, and if the programs themselves do not call for formal testing they should be excused from them altogether.

To avoid the feeling of loss of authority on the part of the people normally in charge of examinations, it is best to get them personally involved in the monitoring of the pilot activities. They will then have firsthand knowledge of the new program, and moreover will have had a hand in applying the new tests. If the new program is then adopted, the new tests will naturally replace the old.

The importance of having the leading persons of the testing agencies on board any new program cannot be overstated. Only in this way will the examinations become servants and not masters of education.

Pilot schools should also be freed from the standard number of subjects per year and the standard number of hours devoted to such subjects per week. At present there are two well-interconnected systems in operation: the European system with many subjects per year stretched over several years with few hours per week, and the American system with a few one-year courses with a relatively large number of hours per week. If no school is allowed to experiment with the scheduling, how can developing countries find out for themselves which system suits their purposes better, or whether perhaps a compromise between the two is better than either of them?

Pilot schools are, of course, indispensable for the original development of programs. I would like to point out that they are just as important when it comes to importing programs from other countries. It is often said that no program should be imported without adaptation. But the difficulty is to know what adaptations to make. In biology, adaptation to local fauna and flora comes immediately to mind. In physics or chemistry the situation is not so simple: after all, Newton's Law is the same in all countries. The best way to find out what adaptations are necessary is to try out new materials unchanged on a small scale and monitor the results. Then there is a basis for decision on changes, whether in content, methodology, or apparatus.

In order to avoid any misunderstanding, I should point out that by "pilot schools" I do not mean elite schools which are selected permanently for experimentation. Pilot schools must offer a representative sample of the schools of the country, and different schools can take part in different pilot activities.

To sum up, I believe that the most important aid to the advancement of science education is the establishment of pilot programs in schools where government innovative groups can work together free from constraints in order to develop solutions to educational problems and provide the responsible authorities with the necessary input to make the right decisions.

DISCUSSION

Dr. Augustus Caine (Liberia) welcomed the idea of a model school or experimental school, but he wondered how a developing country should set about selecting such a school. If such a school is to function outside the requirements of the curriculum and the syllabus, as Dr. Haber-Schaim suggested, what will become of the students? Will they be exempt from the normal requirements of the school system? If so, what will become of them eventually?

Analyzing the aims of science education in the developing countries, *Dr. Ademola Banjo* (UNECA) said that speakers had seen these as cultural and utilitarian. The cultural aim is to teach an understanding of the new society, and the use of the scientific method; the utilitarian one is to prepare students for work in professions or vocations. He suggested the addition of a third aim, teaching what he called the culture of production—the connection between science and production. Biology goes with animal and crop raising, physics and chemistry with industrialization; even if the student does not become a biologist, a physicist, or a chemist, he should understand the relationship between science and production.

Mr. Evelly Selai Mohapi (Lesotho) took up Dr. Haber-Schaim's plea that they should ignore that shibboleth, the examination system. This is an exciting proposal, but one should not forget that there exists, at least in his country and most African countries, an Examination Council. This is not composed of scientists. They work out a syllabus and a curriculum, they expect classes to come up to a standard in a stated time, and they demand results in examinations. What is more, schools are judged by how well or badly their pupils fare in the examinations set by the Examination Council and its examiners. So where can the experiments in education be fitted in to the system?

Then there is the question of teachers. Many of the teachers in some countries simply will not change their methods, nor is it easy to get them to attend retraining courses.

Dr. Isaias Raw (Brazil) agreed that it is essential to get more freedom from the examination system. It is particularly distressing that the standards set in these examinations are imports from England or France, and have no bearing on the real standards or needs of the country concerned.

Dr. Fernando Raul Romero (Peru) said that the developing countries have skipped many stages in history, and have inherited an educational system formulated for urban, industrial societies, and not rural societies like theirs. Nevertheless, it is dangerous to divorce themselves from European systems they have adopted, even though these do not correspond to their own reality. At the same time, African educators preoccupied with end-of-year school examinations should worry less about the formal aspects of education. Education has to satisfy human, economic, and social needs.

Dr. Arthur H. Livermore (United States) discussed the problem of how to find out if students have learned what is expected of them when the new curriculums are used. Under traditional teaching methods, science consists of a body of facts which the students learn; they are asked questions, and, if they recall the facts, this proves that they have learned what was expected of them. It is possible to check on students under what Dr. Livermore calls "the science in process approach." Teachers are given a list of tasks to assign to the children to see if they understand what they are doing. For example, a nine-year-old child may be asked to demonstrate the displacement of water by air with a drinking glass and a bowl of water. Such an exercise will make it possible to see if the student has mastered the skills required of him. It is possible to work out objectively what is wanted of the children, and what evidence can be accepted as an indication that they are developing in the way that was wanted by the framers of the new curriculum.

Replying to the discussion, Dr. Haber-Schaim agreed that the selection of pilot schools is not easy. He could not give concrete guidelines; he could only say that, in his experience in several countries, the first criterion used is always eagerness and willingness to participate.

To excuse students in pilot schools from fulfilling standard curriculum requirements is a fundamental necessity for reform to succeed; the problem has been solved in several countries by their arranging special, parallel examinations. Sometimes, compromises are found. If the worst comes to the worst, examination councils should be overruled.

He concluded: "Anything you do in your countries will come to a halt unless students can be freed, and schools can be freed, from these boundaries and barriers. I don't see any way around this."

12

SPECIAL OPPORTUNITIES FOR SCIENCE TEACHING IN DEVELOPING COUNTRIES

By Jack S. Goldstein

Physics Department,
Brandeis University, and
Chairman, Steering Committee,
African Primary Science Program,
Education Development Center,
United States

African classrooms across the continent, in spite of very large cultural, social, and economic differences, have much in common. Typically, they are empty of anything that would be easily recognized as scientific equipment; in fact, they are frequently empty of all those things we normally associate with the classroom environment, including even books and writing materials. On the other hand, they do contain, in common with classrooms in more developed countries, teachers and children who are eager to learn and understand.

Western visitors in African classrooms are often struck by the apparent docility shown by the children, whom they see in a completely passive role. Children and teachers alike are unwilling to enter into new and strange learning situations, particularly in the presence of visitors, including school inspectors. It is safer to rely on rote learning techniques even if they are based on old-fashioned concepts and methods and even if they contain a high proportion of irrelevant factual information. But every time the barriers of shyness, anxiety, and insecurity can be overcome, the teacher may well be inundated with a flood of questions about almost anything imaginable.

What the Child Wants to Know

I recently was privileged to listen to just such a barrage of questions from a group of fifth and sixth grade students in Malawi who had just completed a rather standard lesson in chemistry. A free question period was declared, and although the teacher had expected questions on the previous lesson, here are the first two questions put by the students:

"Why is there color in the sun early in the morning and again in the evening, but not at midday?"

"Why does it stop raining after you see a rainbow?"

For many teachers of fifth and sixth grade children, the questions may appear to be totally irrelevant to the lesson at hand. And yet they had arisen directly out of the lesson; the children had made an easy jump from observing chemical changes of color to the somewhat more vital and immediate role that color changes play in their lives. The teacher had a much more difficult time making that jump, because he knew that the rainbow and the colors of the sunset are not chemically induced; but of course the children did *not* know that, and they were eager to find out.

The questions themselves are significant, because they demonstrate that even without special encouragement, children are sensitive observers of nature and they want explanations of what they see. The African child feels this curiosity as much as any other child. His curiosity, like that of children everywhere, is focused on his immediate environment; but whereas the western child's environment contains many manufactured artifacts such as transistor radios and television sets, the African child is more likely to be curious about those things that we tend to classify as primary natural phenomena. This can be, of course, an immense advantage in the teaching of science at the primary level. Children cannot learn much about the insides of transistor radios, but perhaps the rainbow can be explained with nothing more than sunlight and a water prism—direct experiments within the reach of any African classroom.

It is important to recognize that the child's curiosity about his environment must be satisfied in one way or another. If satisfactory experiences tending to "explain" are not available in the context of the classroom, then other kinds of explanations will be found elsewhere by the child. There always exists a vast body of folklore, with animistic explanations for everything. This is of course true of Europe and America as well as Africa. What can we call the typical explanation (to a child) of how a radio works except a new form of western folklore? Surely, the typical explanation received by the western child is as believable to him as would be any other fairy story. Unless the explanation can be coupled with a direct appeal to a child's *experience*, or with activities that broaden and enrich that first-hand experience, it will not be different from the unthinking reliance on higher authority that we so deplore when we see it in someone else's society, on the grounds that it kills initiative and eliminates patterns of exploratory behavior. It does not matter that we can argue that our explanation of the radio is "factually" correct. What matters is that the child must understand that facts are verifiable, that experiments can be performed to confirm or deny a postulate.

Of course I do not suggest that a fifth grader can or should understand the principles of the transistor radio. That is a very difficult thing to explain at any level. But it seems to me that it is valid for a teacher to say to the child, when necessary, that it is too soon to try to answer such questions, provided at the same time, possibly through some very simple experiments, he emphasizes the point that these matters are *eventually* to be understood.

I have, of course, chosen an extreme case of advanced technology, but not a far-fetched one. The child who asks about the rainbow is also asking a very difficult question. Experiments with a water prism will not "explain" chromatic dispersion, but will bring the child to understand a little better what is happening, and above all, that these phenomena which so provoke his curiosity, are *natural* phenomena, to be understood, perhaps more fully later, but nevertheless, *to be understood*. For it is certain that one of the most important outcomes of learning is the set of actions taken on the basis of one's understanding of nature. If the African child does not come to understand the role of the nature of the soil, of fertilizers, of irrigation, he may well grow up believing in and acting on the premise that good crops result from the proper sacrifice of chickens.

I hope, therefore, that it is clear that I do not propose simply the substitution of one set of beliefs for another even if the second set of beliefs is more "correct" than the first. I have wanted to emphasize the word "understanding," which ought to be synonymous with the word "learning." Nevertheless, in much of the world, learning still implies some sort of rote process. That is certainly the simple substitution of one set of beliefs for another, and seems to me to be the most unlikely to produce creative, thinking individuals. Creative people will certainly continue to appear; but how much better if their creativity is stimulated and enhanced by their educational experiences.

It becomes necessary, therefore, for all of us to think out once again, as well as we are able, the nature of the scientific process. We must seek to identify, in the materials we introduce into schools, the fundamental processes of data collection, development of manual skills, organization of data, hypothesizing, testing of and prediction from hypotheses, with its attendant evaluation of errors, and the estimation of probability. Perhaps this is not a complete list; perhaps others would break down the scientific process in other ways. It would be inappropriate to digress here on the philosophy of the scientific process. For us, in the African Education Program, it has been a useful working list of concepts, although I am quick to admit that there are some activities that are hard to classify according to such a simple scheme and yet seem very important.

But it is surely obvious that however, the scientific process is analyzed, it has to be taught in the context of national needs and priorities. Africa is still largely rural; she has serious problems relating to agriculture and to public health, to name only two areas. At the same time Africa seeks to close the technological gap between the West and herself. It is essential that wherever possible the processes of scientific thinking be taught using relevant materials as the vehicle. Sometimes the relevance is difficult to see because it is less immediate. The study of the pendulum, or of the constellations, or of magnets, may not appear to be directly relevant. I am not sure that children will grow up to be better farmers for having such knowledge, although I think they will; but I think it is important for children to grow up with the knowledge that all of the things around him are inherently understandable by human beings.

Fortunately, much of what children need to know can be put into a clearly relevant context. The scientific study of soils, of mosquitoes and flies, of rainfall and sunshine, or of animal behavior are all examples of contexts that are directly and obviously relevant to national goals and priorities, and yet provide ample scope for the introduction and exploration of scientific ways of thinking.

Any program which has as its goals those that I have rather loosely described, and which attempts to reach those goals by encouraging free (and sometimes frustrating) inquiry into the natural world, puts a tremendous burden on the teacher, and also on the system within which the teacher is obliged to work. I want, therefore, to address myself briefly to the question of what the teacher needs to know and understand.

What the Teacher Should Know

Let me assume a not untypical situation: a teacher with a primary school teacher's certificate and two or three years at a teacher training college. With what intellectual equipment can he be provided in order to deal with the complex set of problems that will inevitably be presented by any thinking child?

It seems to me that there are two desirable attributes of a teacher's behavior which can be and must be reinforced at every opportunity. One is the wisdom *not* to provide a child with a ready-made answer when it happens that the teacher knows the answer to a question. Children must be encouraged, always, to seek ways of asking their questions of nature, rather than of the teacher. This should not be construed as a charge to the teacher to be silent; frequently the best answer to a question from a child is *another* question from the teacher, but so framed as to suggest to the child a way of attacking the problem.

The second attribute which we must encourage teachers to display is the willingness to say "I don't know" when in fact the teacher does not know. Again, this must be done in the most constructive way possible. "I don't know, but let's see how we might find out"—or "I don't know but let's try an experiment and see."

I do not imagine that saying "I don't know" is any easy thing for a teacher to do. Neither is it easy to maintain discreet silence when the teacher is knowledgeable. But teachers *can* understand and appreciate this approach to teaching, especially if they have experienced it as students in teacher training colleges and institutes.

Finally, I wish to make an additional point. The nature of science, or of the scientific approach to knowledge, lies firmly in the domain of a nation's scientists. Unless those who are engaged in science on a daily basis—university scientists, industrial scientists, etc.—participate in the business of science education, they must not be surprised if what the children learn is not science at all. Only if a nation's scientists are willing to join hands with its educationists will the ultimate product be a thinking human being.

PART IV

TECHNOLOGICAL, VOCATIONAL, AND
OUT-OF-SCHOOL EDUCATION

PART IV

TECHNOLOGICAL, VOCATIONAL, AND
OUT-OF-SCHOOL EDUCATION

13

SCIENCE AND TECHNOLOGY IN PRIMARY AND SECONDARY SCHOOL CURRICULUMS

By Arthur H. Livermore

Deputy Director of Education,
American Association for the
Advancement of Science,
United States

Scientific ' and technological education in the primary and secondary schools of any country should be molded by the current social and economic conditions of the country as well as by its developmental goals. This is, perhaps, obvious to science educators. However, I believe that it is a point that must be kept continually in mind when we are thinking about science and technological education in developing states.

There are two parts to this paper. First, I shall describe the nature of some of the new science education programs in the United States and attempt to show how they are related to the social and economic condition of the country. Second, I shall suggest directions which science curriculum development might take in developing countries.

Primary and Secondary Programs in the United States

Until a little more than ten years ago science education in the United States had changed very little for several decades. During those decades the social and economic condition of the country changed dramatically. Nuclear energy was harnessed for military and industrial use. The television industry burgeoned. High-speed computers became commonplace. The chemical industry produced a host of new products—plastics, antibiotics, insecticides, alloys—that improved the quality of life, but at the same time introduced problems such as air and water pollution. Medical technology progressed to the point where major infectious diseases could be controlled and human organs could be replaced.

But most students at the time they finished high school, though they were aware in a vague way of the impact of science and technology on their way of life, did not understand the nature of the scientific process and were ill prepared to make judgments related to scientific activities that were required of them as citizens. Should fluoride be added to the water supply of their town? Should a nuclear power station be constructed near their city? Should the use of DDT be controlled by government agencies?

Elementary-School Curriculums

A major concern of the groups that set out to develop new science programs for the elementary schools was to increase the scientific literacy of the general public. The Commission on Science Education of the American Association for the Advancement of Science, which developed Science—A Process Approach, has said in one of its publications that they wish to help a citizen to "understand the ways of science and scientists . . . to possess what some have called scientific literacy—to be able to read about science in newspapers or elsewhere, and to make responsible judgments about what he reads or hears."[1] Similar positions have been taken by the developers of the Science Curriculum Improvement Project (SCIS), the Elementary Science Study (ESS), and the Minnesota Mathematics and Science (Minnemast) program.

The four science education programs just mentioned are for children in primary and elementary school from kindergarten through grades six or eight. They are four of a number of elementary science programs that have been prepared by different groups of scientists, science educators, and teachers with funds provided by the National Science Foundation. The funds spent to date total several million dollars.

Although each of the groups that have developed new science programs for elementary schools have the same final goal—developing scientifically literate citizens—they have adopted different approaches to this goal. The difference is mainly in the amount of structure built into the program. Of the major new programs the Elementary Science Study is the least structured and Science—A Process Approach the most.

The similarities of the new programs are more significant than the differences. In every case they reject the traditional mode of teaching elementary science, which is centered on a textbook and which emphasizes memorizing scientific facts and concepts with little concern for understanding. Instead, the new programs are centered on investigation of simple scientific systems, on constructing testable questions about the systems, and on designing and carrying out investigations to seek answers to the questons: that is, on actively engaging in the scientific enterprise.

Elementary Science Study (ESS), the least structured of the new elementary school programs, consists of a group of units, each of which provides science activities that can be used in the classroom over a span of several days. Some of the topics suggest the range of science content: Balance Boards, Shadows, Micro Gardening, Kitchen Physics, Batteries and Bulbs, and Mealworms. The mealworm unit is a good example of how an ESS unit is taught. Each child is given an open box which has in it a pile of bran and several mealworms. The children observe the movements of the mealworms for

---

[1] Robert M. Gagné, *The Psychological Bases of Science—A Process Approach* (AAAS miscellaneous publication 65-8), p. 2.

several minutes, and then (with as little direction from the teacher as possible) construct questions that might be answered by further manipulation. Where in the box does a mealworm spend most of the time? How can you make a mealworm back up? How does a mealworm find the pile of bran? The children design their own investigations, carry them out, collect data, and use the data to answer their questions.

The Elementary Science Study requires the teacher to take quite a different role from the traditional didactic one. No longer is the teacher the source of answers to questions. Instead, he stimulates questions, guides, parries questions with question, and gives assistance only when assistance is needed. This is a difficult role for many teachers, since they have not been trained for it. This is a problem not only for the ESS teacher, but for teachers in other programs as well. We shall return to it later.

The major thrust of the Science Curriculum Improvement Study (SCIS) is developing the child's understanding of scientific concepts. In the early grades the concepts are simple. What is an object? What is a system? What is meant by interaction of systems? Later in the program concepts of force and energy, chemical interaction, and biological systems and interactions are introduced.

Another program similar to SCIS is in an early stage of development. This is the Conceptually Oriented Program in Elementary Science (COPES) which is directed by Dr. Morris Shamos of the Department of Physics, New York University.

The program that I have been associated with for the past six years is Science—A Process Approach, the elementary science program of the Commission on Science Education of the American Association for the Advancement of Science. The philosophy of this program is twofold: first, that the activities of a scientist comprise a complex set of activities such as observing, measuring, inferring, interpreting data, and many others; second, that skill in these activities can be developed in young children.

The activities of the scientists are what are called the processes of science in Science—A Process Approach. For each process, those who developed the program have constructed a hierarchy of skills which children should develop starting with simple ones in kindergarten and terminating with more complex ones in later grades. In the kindergarten material, for example, the children learn to make observations using sight, hearing, touch, odor, and taste. In later grades they make observations of the field around a magnet and of systems such as semipermeable membranes, fermentation of sugar by yeast, and steel wool rusting.

The program for each of the seven years of Science—A Process Approach consists of approximately twenty-five exercises. For each exercise there is a lesson plan for the teacher and a kit of materials and equipment for the children to use. The lesson plan for each exercise begins with a statement of objectives. The objectives are statements of what behaviors and skills the children should be able to exhibit after they have engaged in the activities of the exercise. For each exercise the teacher is provided with a set of evaluation materials which he can use to determine whether or not the behaviors stated in the objectives have been attained. Clearly stated behavioral objectives and evaluation are an integral part of the whole Science—A Process Approach program.

I have already said that all of the major new science programs for the elementary grades are centered on investigation of simple scientific systems, on constructing testable questions about the systems, and on designing and carrying out investigations to seek answers to the questions. If a program is to attain these goals, each classroom must be equipped with sufficient materials so that the children can individually or in small groups work with the equipment. This requirement has produced a major change in the elementary-school classroom where formerly science was taught from books. Now arrangements must be made for procuring and storing a considerable volume of materials and equipment. Each of the major new elementary-school science programs have developed kits of equipment and supplies. These are available from commercial suppliers. It is possible for local school systems to put together their own kits, but in most cases the schools find that it is more satisfactory to purchase the ones that are commercially available.

Before I leave the subject of elementary-school science and move on to the higher grades, I want to say a word about teacher training. For the most part elementary-school teachers in the United States have not had very much training in science. What training they have had is very likely to have been through survey courses in which the teacher was not required to do any work in the laboratory. For this reason the average elementary-school teacher is somewhat hesitant about using a science program which requires him to supervise the activities of children who are doing simple laboratory work. It is, therefore, not only desirable but almost imperative that a school system introducing one of the new programs provide some in-service training for the teachers who will be using it. We have developed a set of training sessions for teachers who are planning to use Science—A Process Approach. These sessions are similar to the exercises for children but are pitched at a more sophisticated level. Many school systems are using this program to train their teachers either in summer workshops or in weekly sessions throughout the school year.

Certainly the new elementary school science programs suggest that there should be changes in the pre-service science education of teachers. There is a great deal of discussion in the United States about this need and some suggestions for changes have already been published. However, the road to change is long and the journey down it has only just begun.

Junior High School Curriculums

Now let me turn to the developments in science education in the junior high school grades seven, eight, and nine. Children in these grades range in age from approximately thirteen to fifteen. The junior high school programs are similar to the elementary ones in requiring the children to carry out investigations. The investigations are, of course, more complex and in most cases require a science laboratory. This is in contrast to the elementary-school programs, where the investigations are carried out in the standard classroom.

Most of the junior high school programs that have been developed so far have emphasized the physical sciences or the earth sciences. These are Introductory Physical Science (IPS), developed by the Educational Development Corporation; Time, Space, and Matter (TSM), developed by a group at Princeton University; and Investigating the Earth, developed by the Earth Science Curriculum Project (ESCP) at the University of Colorado. Each of these programs has been produced commercially and is having a considerable impact on science education in the United States.

The fourth program is still being developed by a group at Florida State University. This is a three-year sequential program called Intermediate Science Curriculum Study (ISCS). It begins in the seventh grade with investigations of physical systems. In the eighth grade chemical systems and in the ninth grade physical, chemical, and biological systems are investigated. It is clear that there is a need for more biological material for junior high school science. Junior high school science teachers report that children in their classes have a great interest in biology, particularly physiology, and so it would seem that a program to develop more materials in biology for junior high school years would be desirable. The Biological Science Curriculum Study, which produced the high-school biology program that I will discuss later, has done a survey of needs in biology for the junior high school. However, up to the present time no funds have been available to bring together a writing group to produce a junior high school biology program.

Secondary-School Curriculums

Although I am discussing the new high-school science program last, they were actually the first programs to be developed. Each of the new programs was prepared by a group of university professors working closely with high-school science teachers. The major impetus for developing the new programs was to update high-school science. University professors had become increasingly concerned about the out-of-date science that was being taught in high schools. Much of it had to be unlearned when the students entered college. The goal of each of the high-school science groups was then twofold: first, to be sure that what the science students learned in high school was modern; second, to provide a better background for beginning science courses in the colleges. Work on the new biology, chemistry, and physics programs began in the middle and late 1950's. Each of the programs has been published commercially and is being used in schools.

The biology materials produced by Biological Science Curriculum Study (BSCS) are probably most widely used. The biology group produced three different programs known as the green version, the yellow version, and the blue version—each of which takes a somewhat different approach. The green version approaches biology through ecology, the yellow version is centered on the cell, and the blue version has molecular biology as its major thrust. Each of these programs puts much emphasis on investigations in the laboratory. This is also true of the physics and chemistry programs that will be discussed later.

Traditional biology programs in the United States suffered from a curious deficiency. They did not include any discussion of evolution or of human reproduction. These deficiencies resulted mainly from the activities of fundamentalist groups who found evolution a threat to their religious beliefs, and human reproduction a topic not discussed in polite society. BSCS has been quite successful in overcoming these barriers in most parts of the United States—not, however, without considerable effort in some states.

Two high-school chemistry programs were prepared by different groups. The Chemical Education Materials Study (CHEM Study), has had the greatest impact on the teaching of high-school chemistry. Recently the rights to the material were sold to three publishers who have just released their own versions of the program. The Chemical Bond Approach (CBA) program, Chemical Systems, is still in its original version and probably will not be revised. Although both CHEM Study and CBA moved considerably away from the traditional high school chemistry program, CBA moved farther and introduced more radical changes than did CHEM Study. It is for this reason that CHEM Study has been more popular than CBA with high-school chemistry teachers.

The first high-school science program to be produced was the program of the Physical Science Study Committee (PSSC). This began in 1956. Like the biology and chemistry programs, PSSC has produced a modern physics program. They also have produced special pieces of equipment for teaching it. The program is generally considered to be quite difficult by both high-school teachers and high-school students.

Enrollments in high-school physics have been dropping over the past ten years or more. This decrease in the enrollment in physics was, to a great extent, the stimulus for the production of a new physics program which, while modern, incorporated something of the history of physics and also modern implications of physics for society—the hope being that this type of course would attract into the program more students who do not intend to be science majors. This program, Project Physics, has just recently been published commercially. It is too early to know whether the decreasing trend in physics enrollment will be significantly affected by Project Physics.

Restoration of Technology

The goal of the high-school curriculum groups—to modernize high-school science education—was admirable. However, in doing this they removed from the high-school programs virtually all reference to technology, especially in chemistry and physics. There is a growing concern in the United States that science education has moved too far away from technology and in a sense has isolated itself from society. One group with this concern has developed a high-school science program called the Man-Made World. This program does not fit into any of the standard science slots in the high-school science curriculum, and for this reason it will probably be some time before it has any impact on high-school science education.

I think that the new elementary science programs have provided a pattern which may make it possible to restore modern technology to the science program in grades K-12, while at the same time retaining the spirit and the content of modern science. If we take Science—A Process Approach as an example, the science content of each of the exercises is chosen not specifically for the sake of content, but to use content from different fields of science as a vehicle for developing skills in using science processes. It is therefore not only feasible but desirable to develop skills in measuring or classifying, for example, with content for biological, physical, and earth sciences. It is also entirely feasible and certainly deisrable to use technological topics to develop these skills.

I see no reason why technology should not be reintroduced into the junior high school science programs as well. Technological topics should not replace modern scientific concepts in the science program, but should be used as a vehicle to introduce scientific concepts. Doing this would produce citizens who are not only literate concerning the nature of the scientific enterprise but also aware of the interactions of science and society.

Science and Technology Programs in Developing Countries

Now let me turn to the second part of my paper—suggested directions that education in science and technology might take in developing countries. First I want to reemphasize my belief that scientific and technological education in any country should be molded by the present and projected economic and social conditions of the country. It is economically wasteful and individually frustrating to educate individuals for jobs that do not exist in a country that is basically agricultural and in which there is no prospect of developing a significant industry in the near future. The major thrust of science education should be toward agriculture and the technologies associated with it.

Another factor that is a prime concern in developing a science technology program for a developing country is the number of years of schooling that a child receives. In an industrialized country where a large percentage of the children remain in school for 12 or 13 years one can afford to spend time on topics that may have little bearing on an individual's future career. In a country where most children leave school at the end of third grade this luxury cannot be afforded.

All of this suggests that in designing a science and technology education program in a developing country great care should be given to state specifically and in behavioral terms what the objectives of the program should be before starting to develop it. What specific behaviors and skills does the child need to have at the time he leaves school in order to be an effective and productive citizen of the country? His science experience in school then should be designed to develop these behaviors.

What I have just been saying leads me to a caveat about adopting science programs that have been developed for another country. There is, I am afraid, a great tendency throughout the world to translate and introduce into schools programs that have been developed in industrial countries such as the United States and Great Britain. Good as these programs may be for the countries in which they were developed, it is highly improbable that they will be very useful in developing states. I think that the developing states would do well to use the general philosophies and methods that have been found successful in teaching science in the new programs, but should develop the science and technological content that are needed in their own countries. The maxim might be: it is better to adapt than to adopt. Scientists and science educators from developed countries can help those in developing states to prepare programs that will be useful provided they are careful to recognize that the needs of the developing states may be quite different from the needs of the countries from which they come.

I should like to close on a point that is of personal interest and concern to me. I have heard many scientists both from industrial countries and from developing states express concern about the unscientific mode of thinking of the majority of the people. This usually leads to an expression of opinion that improving the science education of the people will remove their superstitions and cultural taboos. It does not seem to me that this is necessarily the role of science education. I think that in the long run science education may produce such changes, but I do not believe that this should be a major goal.

In this connection I have been very much interested in the work that Francis Dart and Panna Lal Pradken did in Nepal. They found that not only were there cultural differences in the way in which children in Nepal learned scientific concepts as compared to children in other countries, but also that scientific concepts were used in parallel with traditional cultural explanations of phenomena such as thunder and lightning. The scientific concepts did not supplant the traditional explanation. The authors proposed "that science be presented as a 'second culture,' complementing that already present rather than replacing it . . . . An implacable, either/or approach . . . invites conflict both within the student's own mind and between him and his elders in the community."[2]

To summarize, let me list what I think are the major points of concern in developing a science and technology education program for a developing country. *First*, the economic and social needs of the country should be examined. *Second*, the skills and knowledge that a child should have when he leaves school to make him an effective and productive citizen should be considered. *Third*, the desired skills and knowledge should be stated in detail and the science and technology program developed with these goals in mind. *Fourth*, programs developed in other countries should be adapted but not adopted without modification. *Fifth*, scientists and science educators from industrial countries should, if they are called upon for assistance by developing countries, keep clearly in mind that the scientific and technological requirements of the developing country may be quite different from the

[2] Francis E. Dart and Panna Lal Pradken, "Cross-Cultural Teaching of Science," *Science*, 155 (1967), 649-56.

requirements of their own country and that the culture of the developing country may require a different approach to science education than the approaches that are effective in an industrial society.

DISCUSSION

Dr. Augustus Caine (Liberia) noted that Dr. Livermore seems to be urging a revolution against textbook teaching in science.... that is, against following up predetermined experiments in textbooks. But he does not see why the student should not follow up an experiment laid out in a textbook, why he should not go'through the procedures to see if the postulated results do ensue. This can teach him the concept of collecting data, analyzing data, and following through to conclusions, and after that he can do his own experiments.

A warning on placing too much stress on scientific literacy and relevance to the social and economic development of a country was given by *Rev. Joseph Elstgeest* (Tanzania). Matter that falls within this objective may simply be boring to the children. The important thing is to let them discover what they want to discover.

Dr. Wadajo Mulugetta (Ethiopia) was perturbed because most of the talk has been about what are fundamentally urban schools, suitable for an urban society, and not for rural villages. Furthermore, few students in African schools remain for more than three or four years.

If very few students go on to enter secondary schools, said *Dr. Fatma Varis* (Turkey), pupils should be introduced into specialized areas of education at a much younger age than is customary. The present tendency is to favor giving a general education in early years. The question of when students should be channeled into special branches of education will vary from country to country, according to its special needs.

Dr. Robert H. Maybury (UNESCO) said that 90 percent of students will leave school after four, five or six years, many of them to slip back into villages and rural life. In such circumstances, the relevant education is an education in creative design—meaning, first, identification with or recognition of a problem relevant to the individual in his environment—his food, his health, the trees, the ground, the air, the water—and secondly, strategies learned for creatively employing resources that lie at hand—materials, technology, processes. Thus he can be taught to design solutions to his problems. Dr. Maybury believes that a school curriculum framed with these objectives in mind can offer very exciting possibilities.

In his reply to the discussion, Dr. Livermore explained to Dr. Caine that the aim of the reformed curriculums is to reduce the amount of help the student gets from textbooks or from teachers. It is far better to give them materials and let them ask questions, pose hypotheses, work out answers.

14 PREVOCATIONAL AND TECHNICAL EDUCATION IN PRIMARY AND SECONDARY SCHOOLS

By Meir Avigad

Director, Department of Vocational
and Technical Education, Ministry
of Education and Culture,
Israel

It is important for a developing industry in a developing country like Israel to be provided with capital and machines, but if there is no skilled manpower available to work these machines industry cannot realize its aims.

The intellectual and technical level of the technicians and workers in a developing technology, and in consequence their capability for adapting themselves rapidly to new methods of production, is a crucial point in developing modern industry and in keeping the labor force at full employment. To attain those aims we have to create in elementary and secondary schools a coordinated curriculum where vocational and general education reinforce each other. Under this system, no student is rejected outright at any stage of his education, though he may be directed at least temporarily to more limited objectives when there is reason to believe that his personal choice of a career offers little probability of success.

The introduction of vocational and technical studies in elementary and secondary schools is of greatest importance in preparing the youngster in a technological career, because we have found that graduates of academic secondary schools were not willing to become skilled workers or technicians, and that if they have to work in this field, lacking other possibilities, they become frustrated.

Therefore, propagating a complete secondary academic education and only afterwards training for a job, especially a technical trade, does not constitute a satisfactory solution. In any case this type of education is not possible for the majority of students, as we know from experience and statistics: only about 25 to 40 percent of youth are able, at least at this stage, to graduate successfully from a secondary school with a matriculation examination. The others generally become drop-outs.

Prevocational and technical education in primary and secondary schools is helping to solve those problems, for this kind of education and training makes it possible to realize two aims: (1) training for a trade in the student's adult life, and (2) giving the student a general education, which is of utmost importance to society and for his further development in technology. We found that the practical work done by the student in the school shop gives him self-assurance and ensures an equal standing at school. This newly found self-assurance develops a powerful motivation to study and to enlarge his knowledge—even in the field of general studies, which do not seem to have any connection with his training.

The General Education System in Israel

Israel has universal, free, and compulsory primary education to age 14. Secondary education is not governed by law. It is neither compulsory nor free. The main types of secondary schools open to students who have completed a primary education are: general academic, academic agricultural, special religious academic, agricultural, industrial vocational, technical vocational, nautical, and nautical academic. There are other formal opportunities for training in schools for practical nursing, commercial subjects, or apprentice training. Most schools, especially the academic ones, are four-year schools; however, there are also three- and two-year vocational schools.

Even though secondary schools are not compulsory or free, about 85 percent of the elementary school graduates enroll in them. About 55 percent of these students enroll in general academic schools, 35 percent in vocational-technical schools, and 10 percent in agricultural, nautical, and other schools.

Since secondary-school tuition fees are high, a "graded tuition" system was established. The government and local authorities pay the entire tuition of about 40 percent of the students in secondary schools. Fifty percent of the students pay only partial tuition. The criteria for governmental support is the economic condition of the parents. The government ties its tuition support to the possibility of guiding and directing the student to a specific type of school according to his intellectual abilities and aptitudes.

Of those who do not enroll in secondary schools or drop out after initial studies, about 70 percent start to work as apprentices. Under the Apprenticeship Law they are released from work one day a week to study in special apprentice schools, supervised by the Ministry of Labor.

Prevocational and Technical Education in Israel

In the mid-1950's prevocational education was introduced into the seventh and eighth grades of the primary school, which grades now include over 20 percent of the pupils, on the basis of some six to eight hours per week. Our general idea of setting up this prevocational education is expressed very clearly by the recommendation concerning vocational training by the International Labor Organization:

> Prevocational preparation should provide young persons who have not yet entered employment with an introduction to a variety of forms of work; it should not be pursued to the detriment of general education, nor should it replace the first phase of actual training.
>
> The prevocational preparation should include such general and practical instruction appropriate to the ages of the young persons as are calculated—

1. To continue and supplement the education already received.
2. To give an idea of and develop a taste and esteem for practical work and develop an interest in training.
3. To disclose vocational interests and aptitudes and thus assist in vocational guidance.
4. To facilitate future vocational adjustment.

More than 75 percent of the seventh- and eighth-grade pupils carried on in their vocational training either as apprentices or at a technical high school. During the school year 1965, principals of all elementary schools were prevocational classes had been instituted were required to give their opinion about the value of such classes in terms of their contribution to the educational and scholastic attainments of their pupils. The answers showed that prevocational education had a positive influence on scholastic attainments as well as on general educational achievements. The effect on cleanliness, sense of order, and perseverance was especially pointed out.

Taking into account the success we had with prevocational education in the seventh and eighth grade with the 20 percent of the pupils who received it, we decided in this reform to give all the students in the junior high school (seventh, eighth, and ninth grade) prevocational education.

The vocational and technical school network, which is spread all over the country today, is the outcome of a development that has continued for approximately 40 years. The first schools came into being hand in hand with the first steps of industry, and both industry and the vocational schools have been progressing almost side by side. Hence, vocational schools have been helping in supplying industry with the required skilled manpower.

During the twenty years that have passed since establishment of the state of Israel, the number of pupils in vocational and technical schools has increased nearly 25 times and amounts now to nearly 50,000 pupils, which is about 35 percent of all the pupils in secondary education. Five years ago the proportion of academic secondary education was 78 percent as against 22 percent in vocational education. Our aim is to give to at least 50 percent of all secondary-school pupils some kind of technical education, and that we shall attain within the next four years.

The state encourages and assists vocational and technical education because of its economic importance as well as for the part it plays in ensuring secondary education for all. This attitude is manifested in the financial support given by the government. Whereas, for example, in the year 1960 the government subsidy amounted to 10 percent of the general expenditure of the schools, it is now 60 percent, and this percentage is constantly increasing.

Apprenticeship and Vocational Schools

Graduates of primary schools can also learn a craft by apprenticeship. This system has been improved in the last 15 years and is now legally supervised by the Ministry of Labor. However, although the absolute number of apprentices is increasing, in proportion to the number of applicants for vocational schools it is nevertheless on the wane. Fewer and fewer boys are attracted by the possibility of learning a trade while working despite the financial gain incurred. It seems that the rise of the standard of living and the endeavor to progress socially and vocationally are largely responsible for this change.

About 40 different occupations are now offered in Israeli vocational and technical schools. Of those the most common ones are: metal work, electricity, electronics, automechanics, carpentry, draftsmanship, office work, fashion trades, and home economics. With regard to most of the vocations the same craft may be learned according to different syllabuses, which vary in length of study period and standard of requirements. The purpose of those variations is to adapt schools to the different abilities of pupils. Normal study periods are two to four years, and in schools where technicians are trained even five years.

We are now standardizing the study periods of all students up to four years irrespective of the standard of requirements in the different syllabuses. This development stems from the desire to adapt schools to pupils and minimize the drop-out of pupils during their study period.

In recent years a new scheme for the establishment of a system of relatively large comprehensive schools has been adopted. They are set up at present only in new development areas which are inhabited mostly by new immigrants. Great efforts are made to equip them with the best available facilities for vocational-technical education. They will offer several vocational-technical options according to the needs of students and the community.

The detailed curriculums in vocational and technical schools differ according to area of specialization and duration of studies, but there is a general pattern of time allocation in all options.

Pupils of vocational schools study on the average, about 45 hours a week, i.e., 7-8 hours a day. Till now about 60 percent of the time was devoted to vocational training, either theoretical or practical, and the rest to general studies, composed of the humanities, the sciences, a foreign language, and physical training. This proportion will be changed beginning with the next school year, and only 50 percent will be devoted to vocational education training and the other 50 percent to general studies.

The practical training takes place in the school workshops and consists of exercises as well as production. The ministry is giving special attention to the development of production in the schools and we have set up a special production center, the purpose of which is to help schools obtain orders from outside. The aim is to create in the schoolshop the same conditions as in industry.

A follow-up carried out in 1965 with graduates who terminated their training in technical trades ten years earlier found 39.2 percent working in the trade learned, 16.7 percent working in similar occupations, 15.3 percent working as engineers, and 28.8 percent not working in the trade learned. The follow-up also showed that the greater part of those who graduated from four-year courses were actually working as technicians and foremen. This led the Ministry of Education and Culture to plan for the transformation of the four-year vocational schools to schools having programs of four and a half years' duration preparing technicians and a program of six years' duration preparing higher technicians.

When entering work, graduates of three- or four-year courses are considered skilled workers of initial grade, but according to arrangements with employers and trade unions, they are eligible to advance quickly in professional grading after passing proficiency tests. Graduates of two-year courses, however, are not yet considered skilled workers and must complete their training as apprentices.

Graduates of the four-year courses who have successfully passed special additional examinations in general subjects are eligible to apply for admittance to the Technion-Institute of Technology in Haifa. The above-mentioned follow-up indicates that a considerable number (15 percent) were admitted to the Technion and graduated as engineers.

Vocational school teachers may be classified according to the different kinds of studies. General subjects are taught by academically trained teachers as in other secondary schools. Trade instruction, however, is generally given by two types of teachers: first, instructors who teach practical work in the workshop and related theoretical subjects. These are mostly graduates of four-year courses, who have practiced their trade in industry for several years and have then been given extensive theoretic proficiency courses to train them for their present profession. The other type is composed of teachers who teach theoretical technical subjects not directly connected with practical work. These teachers are engineers or technicians. There are, of course, instructors who teach only practical work, but their impact is dwindling as schools prefer to employ skilled workers who are capable of teaching elementary theoretical subjects, which has proved beneficial to both practice and theory.

All these types of teaching personnel must be pedagogically trained before receiving certificates. This training is given by the educational departments of the universities for general teachers, by the Technion Department of Education for teachers of advanced technical subjects, and by the Government Institute for the Training of Vocational Teachers for vocational instructors.

Technical and Vocational Education in Developing Countries

In light of Israel's experience, I make the following recommendations: (1) Technical and vocational education should be treated as a part of general education in primary and post-primary schools. (2) For students who do not intend to go on immediately to further studies, i.e., to a university, the curriculum should be on the basis of 60 percent general studies and 40 percent technical training, especially in the last two years of the secondary school.

As machinery is becoming more sophisticated and time of skilled labor is becoming more expensive than ever the task of on-the-job training is becoming more difficult and expensive. The classical on-the-job apprenticeship, with part-time released instruction, will gradually be diminished or disappear entirely. Therefore industry is looking for bright young men who have a general education at high school level together with a sound basic technical education and training from a technical high school, which will enable them to adapt themselves quickly to changing technological conditions.

DISCUSSION

Dr. Herbert D. Thier (United States) agreed with Mr. Avigad that it is a delightful idea to give an eighth-grader some feel for electronics, if it can be done. One great problem is the lack of prestige of technical or vocational education; there is a general assumption that the only children who seek such education are those who fail in other schools. This is a great pity, because society is becoming increasingly technological, and efforts should be made to get all types of children to realize that technology provides a real alternative to the printed page as an educational medium.

Dr. Lee Kum Tatt (Singapore) agreed that in most developing countries white-collar jobs are considered the most glamorous. But not everybody can be a general, or even a captain: only a few people can become doctors and engineers. The moment a boy goes to a trade school or a vocational school or a technical school, he is practically committed to the life of a technician when he grows up. The answer is obviously to make this life seem a very good one, both to the boy and his parents. How is this to be done? In Singapore, where there is an abundance of white-collar workers and a shortage of technicians, the government announced it would not employ any more clerical workers. The parents had to decide whether to gamble on their children succeeding in the intense competition to get into academic life, or to let him seek the certain rewards of a technician's existence. The parents got the message—the number of children in vocational and technical schools rose from 10 percent to 33 percent. Of course, this policy is only possible when there is sufficient industry to create a demand for technicians, and technicians are needed to build up industry.

15 TECHNOLOGICAL EDUCATION OF SKILLED WORKERS

By P. F. Harburger

Head of the Department for Youth
and Vocational Education,
Ministry of Labor,
Israel

Planning and Coordination
of Vocational and General Education

Since in the labor market of a highly populated and underindustrialized country the educational requirements of skilled workers are normally low, and since the need for middle- and top-level personnel is comparatively limited, we may safely say that most industrialization projects should not be delayed because of a low level of formal general education. This is not said as an attempt to deny that educational preparation is without importance to the acquisition of working skills. It is meant as a warning against unnecessary delays in the execution of important schemes. These schemes should take into account the available labor force and its characteristics, but on principle their fundamental viability should not be judged from this point of view for two reasons:

First, there are many examples in low-literacy-rate countries such as India and Pakistan of highly qualified jobs being held by illiterate workers who have received systematic training on the job, whereas in more industrialized countries a primary-school education or even a high-school education would be considered as a minimum requirement of entry into training. The Indian skilled worker may nevertheless be as highly skilled as his American or Scandinavian or German counterpart.

Secondly, from the standpoint of industrialization, what has to be reached by general education is not always advanced literacy or the skilled application of arithmetic—it is often general guidance toward a way of life as an industrial worker. This guidance is by no means a simple job, as it has to change attitudes of people most of whom grew up in a simple agricultural society. It is difficult because this society is penetrated already by right and wrong ideas of progress and social values, and the informal, incidental kind of guidance to which young citizens are exposed often works in a direction which in the end proves disastrous to themselves and to society.

General education can have an important role to play in countering the effects of this situation by supplying pupils at all levels of education with genuine information about skills, jobs, industrial developments, income prospects, etc., and by fostering values which are not only desirable and attainable by them but also useful for their country. These values have to take the place of many superstitions and social and religious prejudices and have to overcome those cultural inhibitions which prevent the citizen from occupying the place in a progressive economic society which is most suitable for him and most productive for his country.

Because as in countries with low literacy rates there is sometimes little chance that those with the longest formal education will stay in the job for which they were trained, formal education should be in these countries a criterion of minor weight in the selection of candidates for most of the ordinary jobs in industry.

It is recommended that general vocational education should be planned and organized in a way which makes a smooth flow from one level to another as easy as possible for those who are able and want to go up the ladder. There are many reasons·for such an approach. It increases the flexibility of the system on the whole and makes quick adaptation to changed situations possible. Furthermore, it meets the aspirations of students who would not be willing to start industrial training without the prospect of advancement. Thus, it may extend selection possibilities and contribute to more efficient training and attainment of higher job qualifications.

Blind alleys may exist in the relation of education to employment. One of the reasons why we later lay heavy stress on on-the-job training is that it is extremely unlikely that an enterprise will train its own workers for nonexistent jobs, whereas any school and any training center is in permanent danger of opening up or perpetuating "blind alleys," thereby not only wasting material means, which probably are scarce, and qualified teachers, who are hard to find, but discrediting vocational education and training in the eyes of unemployable graduates and the public.

As far as institutional vocational education is indispensible, it should be planned in permanent consultation between governmental agencies and industry, and real vocational education should be done on as broad a basis as seems economically reasonable. Unreliable manpower forecasts and unstable economic and technological situations can deprive the best training scheme of its meaning if it is narrow enough to make a man unemployable whenever a change in the use of materials, machinery, tools, or processes take place. Very often it may be cheap but shortsighted to train, e.g., a gas welder without giving him simultaneously basic knowledge of metal benchwork. In many cases one should train woodworkers, not carpenters and cabinetmakers as separate craftsmen. Flexibility and mobility—occupational and social—of skilled workers are great assets under fluctuating conditions.

In countries lacking in natural resources and with a low rate of literacy no effort should be spared to develop the available human resources in any possible way. One of the most promising ways—and this may later help in the process of industrialization—is to train people for making better, more progressive, but not too sophisticated use of their soil and to train single overall craftsmen in villages for jobs which are currently performed on a low level. In each village, there might be one man trained for building and woodworking and another for metalwork and pipe-fitting. Such a scheme would help develop human potentials, raise the standard of living of the villagers, and at the same time prepare future industrial workers.

Whatever the educational plan may be, coordination among all concerned is indispensable. "All concerned" means that in most cases governmental initiative should bring together from the very beginning economic and manpower specialists in charge of planning, primary, secondary, and higher education planners, employers, and workers, the last two probably as representatives of their organizations.

In human resources development, in education and vocational training, nothing can be successfully achieved without the confidence of those concerned—the job-seekers, the employers, the apprentices. If after heavy failures this confidence is lost, it is a gigantic task to win future candidates for training.

Therefore, no effort should be spared by those in charge of vocational education and training to secure early information on industrialization projects—national, regional, local, and individual. Without this no realistic plan of action can be designed. There are, on the other hand, plenty of examples which prove that detailed information at an early stage can lead to timely preparation of the needed manpower without gaps and dead ends. On a national scale there should be a plan of operation with the purpose of integrating organizationally and chronologically primary and secondary education, vocational guidance and vocational education institutions, instructors' and teachers' training, and cooperation of employers, foremen, other workers, trade unions, and governmental agencies.

Special problems arise in the training of future employees abroad, especially in the high echelons. Because there is a lack of such persons in most developed countries and because living and income conditions there are attractive for young men from a developing country, many of them do not return to their homeland and the heavy investment is lost. In the light of this danger, it may be possible that the training abroad of older workers who leave a family with children at home is a more promising venture in spite of the shorter productive life ahead of them.

Sometimes those trainees who return from abroad have acquired knowledge which is of little use to their country in its present stage of development or are unable to adjust their new knowledge to conditions at home. No specific advice can be given in this respect. Very careful selection of the training curriculum and the place of training may help, as well as continuous contact between the sending authority and the training institution abroad.

One general conclusion may be drawn: whatever can be done in a satisfactory way in the region itself (even temporarily with the aid of foreign experts) is preferable. This rule applies to a much lesser degree to graduate engineers than to other types of workers.

Methods of Vocational Education

In-Service Training

Because most of the countries which have to intensify their efforts toward industrialization are low in investment capital and taxation income, any training should be tied as much as possible to real work, real production; it should produce values besides the vocational and educational ones, i.e., it should help in the formation of capital.

This seems especially valid in the training of semiskilled workers. Such training can be done efficiently and economically only on the job. Semiskilled work is limited in range and depth, and any deviation of training from the real production process makes it unrealistic, artificial, and aimless. Therefore the training of semiskilled workers should be left to the enterprise and its management; public agencies, governments, or international assistance organizations should be satisfied with advising, helping, and subsidizing the plant's efforts.

The question of training skilled workers is somehow different and demands different answers. Training on the job by other experienced skilled workers, is generally the most efficient and economical way. In countries where economic, industrial, and technological forecasts are often not available, or are unreliable because of an unstable economic and political situation, any training for the open labor market is in danger of missing its goal. An exception to this rule may be the training of skilled maintenance workers on a rather broad technical basis, which is possible and sometimes vital in countries planning industrialization involving small and medium-size enterprises and with a wide scattering of branches of production and craft services. The common features of maintenance occupations, together with limited training possibilities for high skills in small working places, make institutional training unavoidable, in such cases, and it will often be the efficient way for getting the desired results.

Another reason for recommending training under real life conditions is the mentality of most undereducated people, especially of adults with a restricted life experience. Because of their limited ability to make abstractions and work toward long-deferred goals, their motivation for being trained relies on immediate realization of a material value, by seeing a useful product in the stages of its creation and by getting paid for being a partner in its production.

It is necessary to see in each older worker and even more in each foreman a potential instructor of new workers. That means that actually each worker should, as part of his training, get acquainted with simple job instruction methods. Larger firms with many foremen responsible for training young apprentices and new adult workers should establish training courses within their own organization; small and medium-sized firms have to depend upon institutional training organized by government or public bodies.

Because it cannot be expected that each workshop or plant will from the beginning have at its disposal suitable staff for efficient instruction, it is recommended that mobile instructors visit the working places where training schemes are carried out, for advising those in charge. This advice should not bear the character of inspection and supervision, which might be resented by many of those who are most in need of advice. These mobile instructors should be as qualified in vocational education as in technology.

A similar arrangement would be helpful in the modernization of agriculture and rural crafts. The villagers could be instructed "on-the-job" by mobile instructors, visiting each village at intervals and staying as long as necessary for bringing the trainee up to the next step of skill and knowledge—this may vary from two hours to two days. Tools unknown to the villagers should be supplied by public agencies through the mobile instructors.

The success of on-the-job training seems to be the more doubtful the less manipulative the skills are that certain occupations demand. E.g., in many developed countries technical drawing is taught either institutionally or on the job, whereas real technicians' training for any level depends so much upon theoretical instruction and laboratory work that it can generally successfully be done in an institution only.

It is assumed that on-the-job training is not only less expensive than institutional education, but much easier to organize, as existing facilities, equipment, personnel, and work orders may be used for training purposes. On the other hand, a number of difficulties are inherent in the system itself: employers are sometimes reluctant to embark on the adventure of on-the-job training. They are afraid of direct and indirect loses (time invested by foremen and other workers, spoiled material, wages paid to trainees without getting proper compensation, etc.). Employers should be made aware of successful training by other, similar firms. For this purpose, meetings can be convened in which the convinced and the doubtful exchange views; visits to plants where on-the-job training is succeeding can be arranged. Public funds should be made available to compensate employers for losses incurred by on-the-job training.

In some cases older workers are unwilling to transfer their special knowledge and skills to younger or new men. If this atmosphere cannot be changed by explanatory and educational means, a special training bonus may help to improve the situation. This is especially necessary and justified when the worker-instructor himself works on a piecework basis and is afraid he will lose some of his income by teaching.

One advantage which smaller firms may have over large enterprises in on-the-job training may be the more intimate atmosphere possible there, which is favorable for educational processes. On the other hand, they may not be able to train craft apprentices in all the aspects of their trade, for lack of highly skilled adult workers from whom the youngsters could learn, for lack of equipment, and/or for lack of differentiated orders for work. This last danger—one-sided work—is even more present in large factories, and one could say that in spite of the difficulties most craft apprentices and skilled craftsmen gets their vocational training in workshops and small factories, whereas the training place for semiskilled workers is the large factory.

The problem of training workers for new factories is solved in different ways. On-the-job training can be done, if the newly erected plant has a rather extended running-in period which can be used for training as well; or if the workers who are setting up the building, installing gas, water and electricity, and mounting the equipment are in this stage getting a kind of on-the-job training which is close to the demands of their future work in the factory; or if another firm agrees to train the new workers in its own premises. This will generally happen only in nationalized industries or within an industrial concern. An agreement with the suppliers of new equipment may include an obligation to train people. In most cases the management of the new plant will have to have recourse to the graduates of institutional training—its own or an outside institution.

Employers, especially in developing countries, are not always aware of the consequences and sometimes prefer to put the whole burden of training on the shoulders of government, which trains only for the open labor market. The graduate of a government course or vocational school bears all the positive and negative signs of a "general" or an "average" craftsman, and in order to be useful, he has to be somewhat overqualified for his actual job.

The dominating role of on-the-job training in vocational education, as we find it realized in most European countries, where 75 to 90 percent of young trainees learn on-the-job and only 10 to 25 percent in full-time institutions, leaves to these institutions mainly the task of technicians' training. Only certain skills have to be taught mainly in vocational schools—e.g., electronics even on the subtechnician's level, and technical drawing.

Summing up this point, one may say that all semiskilled and much skilled training can efficiently be done on the job; that vocational full-time schools should be reserved for some few trades, and that technicians' and engineers' training in all levels has to be done institutionally, in technical schools or colleges.

Sandwich Systems of Vocational Training

In cases where on-the-job training as an exclusive method seems inefficient, one can provide a kind of sandwich system, supplementing the in-service part by partial formal instruction. This becomes necessary when theory is a large part of training and can hardly be taught in the workshop in an efficient way, or when the use of teaching aids is so extensive that investment in special facilities and equipment is necessary, or when demonstrations and experiments which cannot be performed in the workshop are required.

In those cases in which a sandwich system seems applicable, the formal part of training should, as much as possible, be given on the premises of the work place and the teaching staff should include employees of the firm, if they are qualified to do an acceptable job.

In alternating between practical on-the-job training and formal training, too-short periods seem to be a disturbing factor in the workshop and inadvisable from an educational point of view. Generally, it may be said that shorter periods than a week are difficult to organise and are apt to interrupt the trainee's work in too early a stage. Whenever it is possible, a maximum degree of integration of the different parts of a sandwich system should be reached eventually by part-time formal education after hours of work or, preferably, as part of the weekly work and during working hours.

In some cases partial classroom teaching was introduced by management not so much because objective training needs required it but to make on-the-job training more attractive, or to assist insecure workers to overcome their doubts. Some Brazilian plants, for example, demonstrated to their new female workers, who were in training for semiskilled work, the importance of their work and showed the employer's interest in them by giving part of their training under classroom conditions.

With growing realization of the inadequacy of exclusive formal institutional training, with increasing experience of the inefficiency of exclusive on-the-job training, sandwich systems are becoming more and more popular. Their application includes in fact almost all occupations and all levels of qualifications. It is now generally agreed that a young apprentice is not adult enough for learning a trade without extending his general education as well. A skilled worker, according to modern concepts, should understand what he is supposed to do; on the other hand, modern technology is developing so fast that purely institutional education can hardly keep up with the quick changes that are imperative in the factory. The complexity of modern production processes, together with new educational views, gives much impetus to sandwich systems of vocational education and makes mere bookish learning as obsolete as the old classical apprenticeship system, based on trial and error.

Institutional Vocational Education

There are a number of occupations which can hardly be taught on the job with partial formal instruction in classroom, laboratory, or apprentices' workshop. For these occupations, full-time institutional education in vocational schools, trade schools, or training centers is the expensive but indispensable means of preparing industrial personnel.

There is always a danger that the acknowledgment of this fact may perpetuate a philosophy that tends to develop its own life, independent from the purpose which should be served. Institutions may have their own inertia, and vested interests will also sometimes play a decisive role in their existence. Not only are they expensive to set up and to maintain, but the attempt to follow-up with rapidly developing technology—without which they certainly cannot have much hope to fulfill their purpose—turns their administration easily into a permanent struggle between the teaching staff on one side, who know the needs, and the masters of material resources on the other, who are not able to keep pace with them. In the long run the headmaster often has to give in, and his school continues training people for nonexistent jobs or with tools and machinery that are quickly becoming obsolete. Another weak spot in the character of vocational education institutions is their susceptibility to social pressure, public opinion, fashion, and the goodwill of benefactors.

For example, social pressure and public opinion may force a vocational school to strive toward matriculation at the expense of the vocational training which is its real function. Fashion in occupational preferences by young people may induce an institution to develop its motor mechanic department, although it is already turning out more skilled workers than are absorbed by the labor market, instead of its carpenter shop; a benefactor may attach to his vital contribution strings which have a lot to do with his personal priorities or emotions, but little to do with the labor market. These dangers, which are practically nonexistent in on-the-job training and almost nonexistent in sandwich systems, should be kept in mind before decisions are made.

As the investment in setting up vocational education institutions is high, they should, whenever the need arises, be run in shifts, which will serve to lower the per-capita costs. For example, basic vocational training can be given in morning and afternoon shifts and supplementary training for upgrading in evening classes. In this way best use can be made of facilities, staff, and programs.

Wherever there are different vocational problems to be solved by institutional training, the multipurpose institution seems to be the most economic solution. Even from a psychological, educational, and social standpoint, the meeting of workers and employees from different occupations, different skill levels, and different working places is a desirable factor. From the aspect of optimal size a multipurpose center serves its pupils generally better than a one-sided, specialized, often small institution. Only beyond a certain number of pupils, classes, teachers, and programs can such an institution reasonably have all the many and expensive facilities which make a modern center efficient and attractive (library, laboratories, dining hall, auditorium, etc.).

Vocational schools and training centers should produce goods and not restrict themselves to exercises. A near-to-life attitude in vocational education and training is essential in institutions. Motivation, the necessity to make schools more like plants, in character, and the high costs justify training by producing.

Institutional training is the best method to teach many middle- and top-level occupations, where the theoretical part of job content is relatively large, and extensive use of laboratories is sometimes indicated. The training of skilled maintenance workers often has to be done institutionally as it seldom can be done in an economic way by the factory itself. Very few factories in developing countries are big enough to require, at one time, a sufficient number of maintenance workers of the same type to make in-service training practicable. Public subsidies would have to be so heavy that it is often cheaper to train this kind of skilled worker in schools or training centers.

Small and medium-sized enterprises need an overall employee who has a reasonable knowledge of many things. He should primarily be a craftsman—preferably a mechanic or metalworker, perhaps even an electrician or plumber—who gets additional instruction in a training center in those areas that are unfamiliar to him. Large factories which need many specialized maintenance workers will get mechanics, machinists, electricians, etc., from the labor market and give them highly specialized further training for their own equipment.

In the near future, a new type of maintenance worker will be needed in increasing proportions: the man who is highly skilled in the mechanical as well as the electrical and pneumatic-hydraulic side of modern machinery. His training demands much theoretical instruction, supported by the use of audio-visual aids and three-dimensional models. This kind of vocational education will, to a large part, be possible in special training institutions only.

DISCUSSION

Mr. Harburger said that a very fashionable phrase in education is "learning by doing"—activating the pupil, not having teacher-oriented education. Vocational education is in a better position to apply the phrase because it involves doing real things, concrete things, making things that are needed. And the principle is applied to the fullest extent in on-the-job training.

There are social advantages as well as economic in on-the-job training: it makes the craftsman's life seem more meaningful, it attracts youth from white-collar jobs, it strengthens social equality. But, as Mr. Harburger's paper makes clear, he does not believe in one solution, but in a variety of solutions.

Mr. Emanuel Waril (Sweden) fully endorsed Mr. Harburger's views, although he prefers the phrase "concentrated training" to "on-the-job training." This type of education gives a boy a marketable skill within a matter of hours, whereas education in a vocational school involves weeks or even months before he is able to earn anything. Furthermore, concentrated training gives him the motivation of knowing he is learning in the place where he can expect to be employed.

While agreeing with Mr. Harburger in principle about on-the-job training, *Dr. Ademola Banjo* (UNECA) noted certain difficulties about applying the concept in developing countries. He assumes that what is meant is not just putting a man to work, but training him, teaching him, at the same time as he is shown how to work. The difficulty is that there was a lack of uniformity in industries and factories in developing countries: one man may do a very good job on a lathe; his fellow-worker may be far less skillful; a man working in another factory not skilled at all. So the system cannot be used until there is some uniformity, some tradition of standards.

These anxieties were echoed by *Dr. Charles Youamini Tamini* (Upper Volta), who said that one cannot ignore the absence of an economic infrastructure in many of the developing countries when considering on-the-job training.

In connection with on-the-job training, *Dr. Jerome S. Bruner* (United States) cited the example of what industries did during World War II—men and women were given crash courses to train them for specific jobs in a specific context. If they showed any aptitude, they were then moved up to another specific job, until they had gone as far as they could.

16

SCIENCE AND TECHNOLOGY IN VOCATIONAL AND AGRICULTURAL SCHOOLS

By Emanuel Waril

National Board of Education, Sweden

The technology used for the provision of material and nonmaterial products—processes and services respectively—has developed in close interaction with the evolution of science. This collaboration under mutual stimulation will clearly grow in extent and intensity. Technology and science in combination with each other already have a powerful impact on our environment and on all our activities, especially on the bases and forms of all work. This impact will increase at an accelerated pace with the development of skills and knowledge in both areas.

A basic understanding of the principles of science with a general knowledge of its relevant facts is therefore of considerable consequence for everybody studying technology or applying it in work, *inter alia* students in vocational and agricultural schools. It is a prerequisite for an understanding of modern methods of work, of the design, construction, and operation of equipment used in work, of properties of materials, the biology of organisms, etc. Furthermore, an outline of science should give students a glimpse of an important sphere of human activity and thought and make it easier for them to understand the world around us, including some of the factors shaping society and its milieu.

Before science was more generally applied to practical ends technology was a multitude of well thought-out practices and the skills that go with them, tools and equipment formed by trial, error, and tradition, information about materials, plants, animals, and principles of design developed empirically with much ingenuity and dexterity. In this form technology is about as old as man's plight to meet his needs and satisfy his desires by the sweat of his brow. The motivation to exert thought and imagination instead of bodily strength in these efforts and to exploit for his own ends all means and possibilities in his power is obvious.

Technology, as developed at the beginning of the first industrial revolution, used principles and experiences well known for centuries; the spinning jenny and the first practical steam engines were designed, produced, and operated without the benefit of science. The present rapid development began, as mentioned above, when the application of science in technology proved to be profitable. This experience in its turn stimulated progress in science and supplied it with the means necessary for research. New discoveries in their turn opened new avenues to technology and started the now well-known process of interaction and integration.

Technology is not merely applied science, it applies *inter alia* science, esthetics, economy, etc. for its own purposes. It has its own history, which is an important aspect of the history of mankind, and its own aim: to "know how" to conceive and create new products and processes that have never existed or to realize old dreams for specific uses by man.

In technology's pattern of work a task begins with the definition of a definite goal, in contrast to science's open question. Prerequisites of a technical and nontechnical nature are established and suitable solutions sought. Each suggested possible solution is analyzed and tested, one of these selected for realization, involving a process of value judgment. Under different circumstances another solution may be chosen.

In science there is only one correct answer to a problem, independent of emotional or other human factors. Technology's method of work demands an understanding of purpose and feasibility; access to interdisciplinary knowledge from every known sphere and an understanding of one's own and others' experience; material resources necessary to reach the set goal; last but not least, creativity, scientific thinking, a sense of responsibility, and a will to achieve. As most work is performed together with others in a social environment, ability to cooperate is a necessary condition. It has been shown that these skills, abilities, and attitudes can be encouraged by performing suitable assignments in the described way under experienced guidance.

From the point of general culture, technology offers a living, actual, and therefore stimulating picture of human endeavors, successes, and failings. It explains many of the turns which history has taken, illuminates other fields with new concepts, and gives them increased vitality. By reflecting man in his everyday striving to reach self-set goals it gives a concrete picture of man's nature. Actual curriculums in vocational education as a rule fall short of the ambitions illustrated above.

Science and Technology in Curriculums

Science, as far as it is taken up as a discipline in vocational education, is presented as a body of knowledge, a set of definitions, rules and formulas. Its content is limited to sections which are applied in technology and is consequently not necessarily coherent. Laboratory work is concentrated on proving and determining already "proved" and presented theory, instead of as a probe of inquiry. In actual instruction tendencies may be observed to reduce science to a form fitted for examination purposes.

Science presented in this way must be apprehended by students as a sequence of absolute truths and not as approximate and often simplified theoretical models, which may or may not have temporary validity. The aim and meaning of science, the excitement of scientists' work, and the significance and universality of the scientific method cannot in this way be conceived by students. They will not be stimulated to think, draw conclusions, analyze, check critically, and take initiatives, nor will they be motivated to study. Reform projects in natural science like PSSC, Nuffield, Harvard, Chemstudy, Biological Science, etc. [see pp. 124-30] do not seem so far to have been introduced into vocational education.

The content of technology consists usually of instructions in work practices and skills covering foreseeable situations in work, descriptions of tools, instruments, machines, and other equipment, plants and animals, processes, etc., their properties, use, operation, care, design and construction, biology, etc., pertinent theory and items of science, cost calculation, etc. In recently developed curriculums practices and skills, equipment, theory and science are presented in a manner that simplifies coordination in instruction of related manual and theoretical items.

The exercise of initiative, planning, enquiry, drawing of conclusions, creativity, book skills, group work and other cooperation in work, etc. is hardly or not at all encouraged. This cooperation as well as interdisciplinary integration is of special importance to instruction in agricultural schools, e.g., in ecology.

The above description is necessarily sweeping, and there are notable exceptions to it. A more detailed relation would have to be very extensive, because no type of education varies as much as vocational education from country to country and even within countries in organization, content, aim, management, duration of courses, teacher training, collaboration with "users," status, etc.

Any conclusions from a comparison between the presentation of the two disciplines at the beginning of this paper and the above schematic description of actual syllabuses, for example a shift of syllabuses and teaching methods in one or another direction, must be drawn in relation to the general aim of vocational education and the special requirements of a specific occupation. A reform of the syllabuses and instruction of science and technology as has been indirectly advocated above would have to be justified by a shift in the desired outcome of the courses, i.e., a change of educational policy and/or the situation in work. These two possibilities are at present of considerable current interest.

Vocational education in a number of countries is at present seeking answers to some serious questions which concern the entire vocational sector. Among these are countries with more as well as less pronounced industrial structures. One important problem is to establish the aim of vocational education in contemporary, changing society and for "tomorrow's" jobs and to bring the actual outcome of education into conformity with the desired one as set out in a curriculum. Another problem is concerned with the recruitment to vocational education, the number, background, and profile of aptitudes of applicants to vocational and agricultural schools. Both problems contain a number of separate questions, and both are naturally interconnected.

Aims and Policies of Vocational Education

The aim of a course in vocational education is traditionally established on the basis of occupational requirements and instruction preparing students for life outside work and in some cases even for continued studies.

Occupational requirements are usually presented in the form of specific skills and items of knowledge, which are derived from job analyses, structured into subject-matter areas, and expressed in language relevant to educational craftsmen. The part of a curriculum arrived at in this manner should be periodically revised on the basis of assessments of skills and knowledge retained by adults in employment a few years after leaving school. The volume of the more general part of the course has to be considered with respect to its value to individuals and society, additional cost and extended study time. The degree of adaptation to momentary practices of the occupational requirements influences the longevity of the training.

The choice between an education dealing to a considerable extent with basic principles as against instruction mainly in actual work methods will be a compromise between high schooling—in costs in work combined with adaptability and low schooling—in costs at the expense of frequent retraining.

The development of a curriculum—the aim or desired outcome—therefore entails a number of far-reaching decisions of importance to students, employers, and the rest of society. Education in science and technology will be conducted in different ways depending on the principles of the solution chosen. The compromise, or balance, will depend on a number of occupational, educational, economic, and political factors.

A shift in educational policy and subsequently reforms of curriculums are in many countries slowed down by the unavoidable procedure of reaching new compromises to such a degree that certain branches of education, e.g., vocational education and education in science and technology in general, chronically lag behind developments. Developing countries which for the time being use educational systems from abroad are here at an extra disadvantage. The compromises reached are usually of no concern to them and they lack sufficient opportunities to correct mistakes and omissions committed in education by the process of schooling-in of school-leavers at efficiently run enterprises.

The above-mentioned "indoctrination" of *inter alia* school policy by concepts from past time which in their turn have been formed by still older traditions influences policy-makers and policy-followers. Sociologists, educators, and politicians, who may hold differing opinions in other matters, therefore advocate a break from the "hereditary environment" influencing mankind from generation to generation. It should be replaced by an attitude favoring analysis and reasoned judgment of a situation or problem, distinguishing between facts, beliefs, traditions, and predilections, and encouraging a penetration of arguments in order to develop the ability to reach a decision or opinion on rational grounds. In this way, valuable traditions would be preserved.

A development in this direction must start in school. It is well known that attitudes and modes of thinking can be strongly influenced by involved educators. One of the most efficient fields practically insuring objectivity is science and technology. Apart from its importance to the individual and society, this development would be of great importance in work. Technological development is often hampered by irrational reactions to changes and unsatisfactory control of technical innovations. These problems can be solved more easily by a rationally conducted discussion but will never be cleared up on an emotional atmosphere or by subjective "arguments."

A shift in the desired outcome of vocational education by improved instruction in science and the humanities has been under discussion for some time. This change should affect positively the purposefulness of vocational education toward the introduction of school-leavers into contemporary society and should further their possibilities for occupational and personal development in life. In many cases the motive is to make vocational education more attractive to successful students in primary school.

Lately a number of vocational schools have introduced new curriculums with instruction in science on general secondary school level and technology completed with engineering science, i.e. a combination between vocational and technicians' education. Examples are vocational schools in Israel, the Richmond (Calif.) plan of vocation-technical education, and Polytechnics in the United States. Most, but not all, curriculums are more a collection of subject-matter areas than a new structure of education. Suitable pedagogic and didactic methods will have to be found before this shift in aim leads to something like the desired outcome.

Instruction in directly "marketable" skills and items of knowledge has so far not been affected by known reform plans. The organization of work outside school has until now been accepted as a model for vocational education. There are many reasons for this. Vocational technology is based on job analyses. The historical background of vocational education, teachers' practical experience and, in most countries, industry's dominant influence over the organization and content of vocational education and "its" decisive importance as the customer of vocational schools, make this state of affairs seem natural. In many ways it is in fact natural to let employers and employed influence vocational education. But if this influence is too dominant it can perpetuate a work situation which should be reformed. This seems to be the case today.

Alienation and Engagement in Work and Education

Endeavors to improve efficiency in production and design have up to now resulted in a division of operations into smaller and smaller components. In this way unqualified "hands" could be used after a short introduction and the influence of "workers" could be reduced. Work procedures had to be prescribed in every detail and were often strictly steered by machines or the organization of work (the Taylor system). This part of the production process is completely separated from planning, design, control, development, and management.

Cooperation and control of the separate part-operations into production processes is entrusted to personnel with staff functions, from foreman on, and has led to a pyramidal organization in control and decision. Any matter taken up at the "lowest," i.e., shop-floor, level must be taken "higher up" for decision, at least to the nearest foreman. It has been found necessary to introduce strict rules and rigorous administrative controls, with fines and dismissals, combined with financial inducement in the form of profit-sharing and piece rates, in order to insure discipline and loyalty on the shop-floor level. The loyalty of staff personnel and experts is taken for granted. As is well known, this organization has been successful in terms of productivity and nobody really dares to question it, or has until now had other arguments than purely "emotional" ones.

Social and psychological researchers working in industry have for some time observed a connection between personnel turnover, absenteeism, and alienation on the part of both workers and clerical personnel. Symptoms were lack of interest in the job and the place of work, unwillingness to accept responsibility, lack of initiative in introducing improvements, etc. Interest is concentrated on take-home pay. In other cases, aggressiveness, irritation, resistance against changes were experienced. Workers either resigned or were "kicking."

Polls conducted in Norway and Sweden show that between 70 and 90 percent of workers interviewed had little interest in their work and considered that they were capable of performing more demanding jobs and could make decisions connected directly with operation as well as or better than "those higher up." The percentage of alienated workers increases with the introduction of more repetitive work and jobs operated by machines, and dissatisfaction is greater in large enterprises with a complicated administration than in small units with direct contacts between categories.

Further research showed that social relations at work follow a general pattern and that interest in the job depends mainly on several factors:

Physical safety expressed in terms of income, safety against hazards in work

Security from unemployment and from arbitrary treatment

Esteem, self-respect, estimation of the job as important

Participation in decision on work organization, operations, etc.

Proposed changes, depending on the conviction of advocates, are cooperative or state ownership, "participation" as known from a number of countries. None of these suggestions has so far had any really noticeable direct effect, although there have been side effects due to better contacts, improved communication, etc.

In Norway the Samarbeidsprosjektet LO/NAF, Employers and Workers Co-operative Project, together with experts from the Technical University and the Tavistock Institute of Human Relations in London, has been conducting at four enterprises experiments with changed forms of work organization. In principle, workers employed in one production unit formed a production team and were given much scope to organize the work of the unit in collaboration with foremen and technical experts. The implementation of the plan, even controls, was left to the group. The result has so far been unchanged or mostly improved productivity, less scrapping, and a real engagement in the job. Personal development of everybody engaged in the experiment could be observed. As this work has been going on since 1964 (planning from 1962), the results can be accepted for further developments.

In Sweden the associations of labor unions, employers, and clerical workers have formed a working group for a follow-up of the work done in Norway and for an introduction of similar experiments in Sweden. One representative of the employers' organization has suggested that a lower productivity paid for better relations at work, and improved satisfaction should be a good alternative to an improved standard of material living.

The situation in school resembles the situation in work in so many points that direct conclusions should be drawn for a change of educational process; *inter alia*, school is a social environment offering social relations of great importance for the pedagogical process. In theory, this has been suggested long ago. The change can be introduced more simply in technology—which should be an image of the work situation adapted to educational purposes. This would be an attempt to improve both students' engagement and educational result. Since education should participate in the development of society and the individual, vocational education should prepare students for a more active role in work and outside work. The content of technology should include more independent work on the part of the students, better theoretical instruction, and closer collaboration with science. Science must in this context be extended from the traditional natural sciences to social and human sciences.

To conclude this argument, vocational education must be given a new aim. Instruction in science and technology should be extended and redirected towards basic principles. This instruction must be integrated with practical work and the pedagogical process redesigned to make students more active. Much greater attention than hitherto must be paid to social relations in work.

Students enrolled in vocational school come in most cases from so-called lower social groups. In industrialized countries there is a close correlation between parents' educational background and occupation and the choice of occupational education of their children. Applicants to vocational education are in many cases less well adapted to traditional teaching in school, although only a few of these students have low learning capacity. Many of these scholastic failures are hampered by the difference in behavioral and cultural patterns from the middle-class teacher. Others combine low verbal receptivity with pronounced creativity. This combination almost invariably leads to conflicts with well-adapted low-creative teachers.

Vocational schools in most countries cannot hope to attract scholastically successful students and students from well-to-do homes until conditions on the labor market, in society, and in schools of higher education, including universities, have changed.

Therefore vocational schools have to employ educational methods adapted to students who otherwise do not succeed in university-influenced education. They have, in other words, to make a better job of it than general schools. This is a condition for a shift of vocational education towards more "intelligent" instruction in science and technology and a "must" before students can be active in their studies.

Results from an inquiry into the effects of technicians' training at Swedish Technical Colleges (upper secondary school level) conducted in the traditional "academic" way show that subject-matter remained fragmented in the students' minds in the same way as it was taught. Students found it easy to work according to routines acquired in school but were really helpless as soon as something in the pattern was changed. The ability of the students to make use of their knowledge, to work, was therefore limited before they were properly schooled-in at work by qualified persons.

Therefore, the educational process in vocational education must be redesigned for two reasons: to suit those who now enroll, and to provide a better education for the future. A new automechanics course has been developed in Sweden along these lines.

This development will take much time. So far not much is known about the learning process for subjects like science as well as technology, but what little is known seems to be quite unknown at vocational schools. When instruction in science and technology has been changed in accordance with the above proposals or similar suggestions, vocational schools should provide a better general cultural background and be a better recruiting ground for university studies than today's general schools.

DISCUSSION

Dr. Ehud Jungwirth (Israel) said that he was a teacher of both agriculture and biology; he had taught seventh-graders and he had taught at university level. When he started teaching, he followed the official syllabus and taught subjects separately. Then he decided that it was absurd to keep a plant artificially separate from its environment, so he began to integrate. Now his students ask: "Where does biology end and agriculture start?" He answers: "This is exactly where I wanted you to be, asking that question." He does not want them to know where pure science ends and applied science begins.

The relevance of science to agriculture, implicit in Dr. Jungwirth's remarks, was raised again by *Dr. Augustus Caine* (Liberia). What science, and how much science, should be taught to villagers to make their agriculture more productive? For example, how much biology is relevant? How much chemistry does a villager need to know if he wants to be more productive than his father? So, too, with a boy in developing country who wants to be an automobile mechanic—how much physics does he need to know?

Replying to the questions asked by Dr. Caine, Mr. Waril said that the best advice he can give him is to study actual curriculums in use, together with possible reformed curriculums suggested by various people, to analyze them, and to see what traditional influences, things taken over from the first developments of industry or the medieval ages, they contain. He should then cut out everything that is unnecessary and add what the students will need in 10 or 15 years' time. The result, taught by suitable teaching methods, will give his students something they can apply to agriculture and industry, something in which they can take pride.

17

HOW CAN THE COST OF TECHNICAL TRAINING IN DEVELOPING COUNTRIES BE REDUCED?

By John Vaizey

Professor of Economics,
Brunel University, and
Member, British National
Committee for Education
and Technology,
Great Britain

The subject of my paper is the problem of reducing costs of professional training in the developing countries. It is a well-known fact that the relative costs of training a professional in a developing country are higher than the costs of training in a developed country. This is in principle because the amount of opportunity cost which is implied in constant real costs is bound to be higher in a poor country than in a rich country. Thus, although the costs may be "reasonable" in a prosperous country, they are unduly high in a poor country, and take too great a proportion of disposable income. Further, because of the fact that the distribution of incomes in a poor country is usually much more unequal than in a developed country, the money costs of training are often higher in a developing nation than in a developed nation, because training costs include a high proportion of salaries. But real costs are also higher because the student wastage rates and other ancillary costs of professional training in a poor country are significantly higher. Therefore cost per year of training programs in opportunity cost, in money cost, and in real terms is higher in many developing nations than in developed nations, and cost per completed student is usually higher as well.

There are really three separate questions involved in the problem of reducing costs. The first concerns stepping up the efficiency of the training procedures, so that the costs per completed student fall. The second is the question of reducing expenditures by such measures as increasing the scale of the activity, which I shall call reducing the real costs. The third is the question of whether or not it will continue to be often cheaper to use overseas facilities for training, and at what point this break-even point occurs.

Reduction of Student Wastage

The first part of this paper concerns attempts to reduce student wastage rates. One may enumerate them as follows:
1.   Attempts at better selection of students.

2.   Attempts at eliminating economic causes of withdrawal by means of grants, scholarships, etc.
3.   More careful individual guidance of students during the course of their studies.
4.   Intensive attempts to improve the motivation of students.

The point is that all these are traditional quasi-psychological techniques (or crude economic techniques, as in the case of income maintenance) and it has been shown that, on the whole, these factors are not of sole importance in causing wastage. The major cause of wastage is rejection of a proportion of the students by the higher education institution, either because a way of establishing its own standard of excellence is to show that it has high failure rates (which is traditional in engineering, natural sciences, and medical faculties) or else because the receiving culture is hostile to many aspects of the culture from which the students come. Both of these attitudes can be changed. The refusal to increase pass rates is usually defended on grounds of maintaining high international academic standards, but differences in wastage rates between institutions have been shown to have little to do with the standards of the institutions concerned, and much to do with their own traditions of what is a "normal" or "acceptable" wastage rate. Therefore an urgent examination of these traditions is required before wastage rates can be got down.

The nature of the "receiving" culture of the institution may be hostile to women, hostile to poor people, hostile to people from different tribal backgrounds. It may well be that residential institutions are more difficult to adjust to than nonresidential institutions. It is exceptionally difficult to change the "receiving" culture, but the first step to doing so is recognition that differences exist.

As a second point, we now turn to improvement in the productivity of the institutions. This is dangerous language to use—but it is in essence the increase in the overall efficiency with which the resources of institutions are used. It applies to plant, to teachers, and to students' time.

In the developing countries, the degree of utilization of plant and equipment in many higher education institutions appears to be significantly less than in many developed countries, partly because of the difficulty of organizing and running institutions in countries where administrative skills are scarce, and partly because of over-grandiose building programs. There also appears to be a paradoxical combination of low overall utilization of teaching staff accompanied by very long hours of teaching on the part of some members of the staff, who are teaching by rote in inefficient and pedagogically old-fashioned ways.

Thus one of the major aims of developing policy should be to reduce the capital costs of scientific and technological education: first, by standardizing and reducing the cost of building capital installations; secondly, by careful administrative techniques designed to reduce wastage in the utilization of buildings and capital equipment; thirdly, by concentrating attention on evening out the work load of teachers over the year, so that their talents are more fully utilized, and at the same time giving them intensive training in modern pedagogic techniques.

The adaptation of curriculums to manifest social and economic requirements is an important step forward in economizing the costs of technological and scientific training. It is clear that at the moment many professional people, not only in the developing nation but throughout the world, are either mistrained or overtrained. They are mistrained because many of the curriculums are irrelevant to the jobs that people are likely to take up. In many countries, particularly in Latin America, there has been no significant updating of the curriculums to cope with new knowledge and new requirements. At the same time, the establishment of very high international standards of professional attainment, particularly in wealthy countries like the United States, has often had the economic and social effect of restricting entry to those skilled professions in the United States—medicine being the most notorious example. Yet most of the advanced skills acquired in this way are not necessary for many of the practitioners of these skills. In developing countries, where the problems are gross and where simple techniques to deal with the problems are essential, the more recondite specialization is often irrelevant and positively harmful.

Thus the problem of adaptation of curriculums and of skill requirements breaks itself down into three separate problems:

1. Techniques for updating the curriculums, and eliminating unnecessary material
2. Frequent evaluation of the jobs that people are being trained for, so that careful specification of training may be made
3. Recategorization of skills in order to make training easier.

An example of the third problem is that much of the work performed by doctors can, in fact, be performed by medical technologists or nurses, and by a careful adaptation of skill requirements it may be possible to step up the training of technicians more rapidly and more cheaply than to increase the number of doctors.

The pattern of manpower utilization in the developing countries is often such that very skilled professionals spend a great deal of their time doing low-grade semiprofessional work. It is very important to see the whole pattern of technological and scientific training, and to ensure that enough subprofessionals are trained to enable the professionals to make use of their skills.

All this points administratively in the direction of a continuous program of on-the-job training interspersed with short courses and evening work, and work at weekends and at summer workshops, in order to upgrade semiskilled people until they become top professionals. In other words, the typical American model of a student coming through the academic tracks from a high school, into college and then going on to four, six, or more years of graduate and post-doctoral studies is probably in many cases a misleading one for the developing countries. It would be far more appropriate to think of a large number of inadequately trained people, coping with larger-than-life problems, improving their skills as they go along, learning by experience, and needing a whole framework of advanced training and of professional progression.

This also (particularly in the case of advanced engineering skills) applies to the formal use of on-the-job training within industry and business, and in government establishments. The rigid division between educational institutions and other institutions has produced parallel systems of training which only meet at the end of the training process. All countries have made attempts to overcome this division, ranging from the Khrushchev reforms of the Soviet Union to the sandwich courses now so popular in the United Kingdom (see also p. 122). None of them have been wholly successful, but it is in the developing countries that the requirements are most acute, because it is there that the need to adapt and upgrade informal, on-the-job training and to integrate it with the often extremely remote, academic, and formal higher education system is most acute.

A further means of attempting to reduce the costs of training in technological and scientific institutions may well be the use of modern pedagogical techniques. These include the whole field of programmed learning, whether by texts or with machines, television and radio and correspondence courses, and computerized learning, either used singly or in packages. There is considerable evidence that most of these techniques are more effective than conventional techniques, but little evidence that many of them are cheaper per student than conventional techniques. What they can do is to provide means of teaching where skills do not exist, or alternatively they can supplement existing teaching with scarce resources. The likelihood is that as the techniques are developed the unit costs will fall dramatically, and if so the means of using programs developed specially for the developing countries will become more feasible than in the past.

Summarizing the argument so far, it can therefore be seen that the relatively high costs of training for technological and scientific pursuits in the developing countries are due first of all to the fact that as a developing country is poorer than a rich country, if absolute costs are the same for training a skilled person, then relatively the costs in the developing countries are higher. Therefore, to make costs more reasonable in principle, the costs of training in a developing country ought to be below those of an advanced country. This would require the developing country to be more radical in its approach to training techniques and purposes than a developed country is. It cannot afford cultural conservatism.

Secondly, the costs are relatively high because the people involved in the training are paid more than they would be paid if they were doing the training in a developed country. This arises quite largely from the more unequal income distribution of developing countries and from the necessity to hire foreign experts. The use of other nationals to train in a developing country at high salaries may well be inevitable in a number of instances, but it carries with it socioeconomic disadvantages of which the skewedness of the income distribution is but one example. It may well be, too, that other nationals are more prone to identify as universal excellence the standards and techniques that are applied in their own countries than to adopt a more pragmatic and experimental approach suitable to the developing nations.

Thirdly, we have seen that in an absolute sense the training programs in developing nations are less effective both because of higher student wastage and also because building and staff are used less effectively.

Thus there are, in principle, three separate approaches to this problem, all of which combine to make a strategy for reducing overall training costs in the developing nations. The first and major suggestion is that a complete reexamination of the ultimate objectives of skilled manpower, and a division of the categories of skills into much smaller components so that each skill can be much more specifically trained for, may well be fundamentally what is required in this field. If we could take a group of skills traditionally categorized into four or five in a developed nation, and break it up into forty or fifty in a developing nation, it may very well be possible to reduce the total overall costs of training that whole segment of highly qualified manpower, as well as ensuring that the true highly qualified professionals devote their skills almost entirely to those tasks for which they are uniquely qualified.

In addition, the central problem of the reevaluation and reorganization of the curriculum requires a major and radical attempt to eliminate material which is taught purely because it has become a traditional part of the training of highly skilled people. Already in the United States and in the United Kingdom radical reexaminations of the medical curriculum are under way. The demand for such a reevaluation in the developing countries is even greater. Thus, fundamentally, the major task which lies before those who would reduce the costs of training is a profound reevaluation of the purposes and nature of training.

Secondly, at the level of the performance of the individual institution, a pioneering job must be done in eliminating drop-outs. Drop-out rates at the moment are so high that the cost per completed student is astonishing. It must, however, be said that many of those who leave without the formal qualifications have nevertheless acquired some knowledge which is useful to them in their career, but this knowledge is not nearly as useful as it would be if they had stayed the course. Therefore, a requirement on all institutions that they should attack drop-out rates is essential. This will require both socioeconomic action, particularly in income maintenance and social welfare, and action on academic criteria of selection and on individual psychological evaluation. Above all, a more careful selection of students would be extremely beneficial. Thirdly, there is a need to increase the overall productivity of the resources devoted to high level training. This requires a reevaluation of the use of expensive buildings and equipment, much of which is far too complex and sophisticated for the purpose in hand, and a radical restructuring of the functions of the staff.

Making Training Programs More Efficient

One of the major causes of the high costs of training programs, particularly in poor and small countries, is that the scale of operation is necessarily very limited. It has therefore often been suggested that these programs should be regionalized and should be available over a much wider area, particularly in those parts of the world like Africa, where a number of small states are unable to support extensive training programs. There is little doubt that the evidence suggests that larger, more comprehensive programs of training yield considerable economies of scale, and that there are grounds for believing that unit costs would fall if the programs could be made larger. On the other hand, regionalization has some if not all the disadvantages associated with expatriation. It is often cheaper to send people overseas to undergo training than to install training programs at home, but by doing so you run the risk that the people who have gone overseas will not return but will stay in the country where they have trained. In addition, the side effects or secondary consequences of training programs in the country where they are given are so considerable and beneficial that the host country is bound to derive far greater benefit than the countries that send students to it. There are other difficulties too, connected with language, with living away from home, and with finding practical and on-the-job experience, which should be carefully gone into before this proposal is further developed.

In addition to the regional institutes, there are the traditional systems whereby people are trained abroad in the developed countries. The extent of this overseas training is difficult to measure, but has undoubtedly often been underestimated. It has further been the traditional mode by which skills have been disseminated throughout the world. One of the reasons why it is difficult to measure is that many students who go overseas to acquire training become immigrants in their host country. Thus one of the costs of expatriate training is undoubtedly the nonreturn of students. Secondly, there is considerable evidence that overseas students have higher failure rates and a greater degree of difficulty in their host country than native-born students do. This is almost inevitable, as the problem of cultural shock is a very difficult one that causes very many students' breakdowns. In addition, the education that students acquire in their host country is often not directed to their major needs, but is in fact directed mainly to the requirements of the host country. Thus the greater the problem of transmitting training from the host country to the developing country, the less appropriate is likely to be the training received overseas. Many host countries have, of course, developed special programs for people who are later to go back to work in the developing countries, but it is important to realize that these programs are more expensive than the programs for home-based students.

In all this, one of the major problems, of course, is that on-the-job training and sandwich-based courses are essential for most scientific and technological education. There is a great tendency to think of scientific and technological training in terms of educational institutions rather than in terms of the skills that can be acquired on the job, and the major task of the educational system is to try to take the skills straight into the places where the skills will be exercised.

The development of on-the-job and sandwich training is organizationally and administratively more complex than the organization of formal educational institutions. The aims of industry, business, and agriculture are predominantly economic, and training is inevitably a by-product of their main task. The organization of a training system, especially at the higher levels in the economically productive enterprises, requires considerable skill. This is particularly the case when, as so often happens, the education system is the responsibility of the ministry of education, on-the-job training is the responsibility of the ministry of labor, and the supervision of the enterprises is the responsibility of other government departments. It is for this reason that overall manpower planning has been advocated, and that the location of manpower planning has often been found in the central planning machinery of the developing nations. There is not space in this paper to develop this side of the question, but the point is being made here because inevitably the emphasis within the administrative structure is for education and training to be divorced from each other, whereas the necessity in economic development is for them to be linked together. It is in this context that a radical reevaluation of the skill requirements for economic development, and a breakdown of those skills into their component parts can have a very important part to play, because it will be seen that many of the skills can in fact be acquired through systematic on-the-job training.

It would be a mistake, however, to take the view that on-the-job training is necessarily cheaper than training in educational institutions. It is usually thought to be cheaper because many of the costs of on-the-job training have traditionally been absorbed into the overheads of the enterprises. Many of the points that have been made in this paper about the need to reduce the costs of education in traditional educational institutions apply with equal force to the need to reduce costs in on-the-job training situations. The necessity to cut drop-out rates, to insist on high levels of pedagogical skill and a careful program of study, is just as urgent in on-the-job training as in formal educational institutions.

The argument of this paper has been, then, that there are many ways in which the costs of training for high-level and medium-level skills can be reduced, but that the reduction of these costs in the developing countries requires a radical restructuring of the pattern of skill requirements and a radical overhaul of many of the traditional patterns of meeting skill requirements. It is suggested that, at the level of organization and administration, this task is a very complex one. Therefore, one of the major aims of aid to the developing countries in this sphere should undoubtedly be to improve the organizational and administrative capacity of those sections of the government dealing with these problems. It is only by our ensuring the strength of this side of a government machine, and giving it the analytical tools to analyze the situation, that a breakthrough in costs can be achieved.

DISCUSSION

In the absence of Professor Vaizey, the subject of money was introduced by *Chief Stephen O. Awokoya* (UNESCO). "You cannot begin to think about making expenditure reasonable if you haven't got a decent amount to start with—money is very necessary," he declared. "How do you get money?"

In Nigeria they have discovered that it is much easier and less painful to rely on raising indirect taxes rather than income tax.

Another way of getting revenue that is not sufficiently exploited is to set up machinery to canalize external aid. "There is a great deal of money floating around throughout the world, but many underdeveloped countries have not created the machinery to get it," declared Chief Awokoya. Nigeria has created a special bureau to channel external aid, and, during the first year of its existence, this bureau brought in nearly $40 million for education alone. What is more, a minimum of traveling to see foundations and agencies, and of begging, is involved; it is surprisingly simple.

On the expenditure side, money is needed for buildings; for equipment, for salaries, for bursaries, for fellowships, for research.

As to buildings, he warned the delegates against developing an edifice complex. Grandiose buildings are very nice as status symbols, but excellent work can be done in sheds. As for equipment, locally made goods are often cheaper than imported: Nigeria discovered this when it produced its own exercise books. Salaries have to be paid, but it is worth remembering that salaries to foreigners tend to be higher than local salaries: if they are perpetuated, a tendency develops for local salaries to rise after them. Efforts should be made to get rid of the overseas experts as soon as possible.

With regard to bursaries and scholarships, these cost much less in the countries of origin. Little money is being spent in developing countries on the research they need. A survey in Nigeria showed that much of the research is similar to what is being done in Harvard and Oxford, where it is being done better. The money should be diverted to research of a kind that can be better done in the country.

Mr. John L. Lewis (Great Britain) pointed out that good education costs money at the primary stage, even more at the secondary stage, and yet more at the university level. A certain amount of foreign aid in the form of funds or experts is available. Countries like Israel, Singapore, and Great Britain need as much scientific and technological manpower as they can get, and so they need to promote all three stages of education. But countries like India, Mauritius, and one or two of the African countries are already producing more university graduates and school-leavers with secondary education than their economies can absorb. In Mauritius, for example, 1,200 applicants with "0" level qualifications, with high grades, applied for a job as a messenger in a ministry. Such situations are economically wasteful and lead to a brain drain. So for countries like this money should be concentrated on the primary level.

Local manufacture of equipment is a very good idea, but Mr. Lewis did not believe that teachers should be encouraged to make their own equipment. In England they once took great pride in doing so. But it is a misuse of the teacher's time to turn him into a craftsman. On the other hand, it is a good idea to train assistants to make apparatus.

Trade schools should be encouraged to manufacture equipment and apparatus rather than useless articles. Urban schools should share laboratories:

he was sorry to see in Ashdod, Israel, an academic high school and a religious high school standing side by side, in identical buildings, both with laboratories which were inadequately equipped. They should have pooled their laboratories and equipment, thereby getting better apparatus.

Dr. Fernando Raul Romero (Peru) was perturbed by the amount of educational waste: an investigation in 12 African countries revealed that 100 million dollars was going down the drain annually. More data about financial problems have to be collected. On the other hand, the careful selection of students for universities, recommended by some people, should not be modeled on European standards; very often there is no alternative but to choose the tallest among dwarfs.

Saving money involved making the best possible use of human resources, declared *Professor David Samuel* (Israel). The first thing to be done in any country is to make an inventory of human resources.

Mr. Samuel Maxwell Adu-Ampoma (Ghana) warned against the glib use of formulas, such as saying that use of local materials would make a great difference. New science programs cost money, whatever is done, and there is no purpose in hoaxing people, although local material and improvization may help to make the impossible possible.

Dr. Sitali Mundia Silangwa (Zambia) said that his country had one engineer, three doctors, one agriculturalist, eight other scientists, and a total of scarcely 100 university graduates four years previously. They decided to set up their own university, and to increase their primary school enrollment threefold, their secondary school enrollment by 3½ times. It was very onerous and very expensive, but it paid off. The problem of skilled manpower to teach at the university and schools they solved by getting in foreign experts on a contract basis, usually for three years. It was very expensive, but they are being replaced by Zambia's own people. One of the short-term problems is orienting these external experts to face the problems of the country.

To get the best use of foreign advisers, *Dr. Gerald Holton* (United States) suggested that developing countries should draw them all from one center, which could learn from successes and failures. Generally, they should calculate that the first year of an expert would be lost, his second year would be better, his third year he would be able to give really good advice. One economy in the use of equipment may be to let students use it in rotation, so as to cut down the number of sets needed.

The problem of wastage was raised by *Mr. J. Barthes Wilson* (Sierra Leone). A country spent 20 percent of its income on education. The theory is that society will get back its investment through the individual contributing to it. But sometimes the person trained disappears down the brain drain by going abroad, sometimes he abandons teaching to enter commerce or to do administrative work. So the investment is lost.

18

HOW TO INTEREST OUT-OF-SCHOOL YOUTH IN SCIENCE AND TECHNOLOGY

By C. L. Godske

Geophysics Institute,
University of Bergen,
Norway

Let me acknowledge that I represent no authority on "out-of-school youth activity" in developing countries. However, more than 20 years' work with amateur science camps and expeditions has given me friendly contacts with and some experience about young people from many of the developed countries. Such experiences may be of some value even when trying to solve problems of more global nature.

I will first discuss four fundamental problems, briefly characterized by "why," "how," "when," and "where." Then I will present a brief report on my own youth work, and discuss how far my experiences may be important for scientific amateur work in developing countries.

The Problems of Extracurricular Science

Why Do We Need Out-of-School Amateur Science?

The answer may depend largely on the point of view selected. Let us first consider the point of view of the *professional scientist*. For two reasons he will recommend and support amateurs. On the one hand, he may be interested in using them as assistants for his special investigation, say a botanical study of an unknown region where a great amount of simple collection work is necessary. On the other hand the professional will look on amateur science as a source of inspiration for young people, leading to a better recruiting. In fact, the problem of recruiting is and will remain a very important one in all branches of science and technology. Consequently, it is useful to give young people personal motivation for education and further studies.

From the point of view of the general *educators*, the economic and cultural level of a nation is strongly correlated with the level of education. Supplements—for young and old—to school education will always be necessary, especially in countries where the schools still may be in a rudimentary stage. The general out-of-school education must especially provide knowledge that is useful for community life. Moreover, one must be aware of how rapidly this life changes, so that all knowledge soon becomes obsolete. "Experience" based on former generations must not be overestimated by the old when teaching the young. And experiences from one country must not be imported uncritically into others.

Finally let us consider what I will denote as the *Aristotelic* point of view. The founder of science has said (in modernized version): "There are two types of science, the useful and the non-useful, which stimulate leisure activity. The second type is, according to my opinion, the most important."

The Aristotelic point of view seems, of course, to be of special interest for developed communities with their increasing number of leisure hours. Perhaps it is of equal interest to developing countries, especially because of the by-products rendered by "pure" amateur science: *respect for facts* (which may or may not support the official authority), *a sense of criticism, the spirit of adventure, the joy of being a pioneer*. We hope, in a not too remote future, to give all people a higher standard of living. This is, however, only a means to a high standard of life—and only one of the means. Another, partly independent of the first, is the intensification of life experienced by active artistic and intellectual contact with nature.

How Shall We Promote Interest in Science and Technology Among Nonprofessionals?

The answer will in part depend on the answers given to the above "why" problem. If we adopt the professional scientist's view, we might emphasize amateur science as a means to professional education in science and technology. Then regular "open" courses on topics of practical importance given by schools, colleges, and universities will be in the foreground. The very regularity, and the pedantic systematics which may be a danger of such courses, will perhaps repulse persons with special, perhaps fairly limited interests. Let us not forget our future specialists, who represent a non-negligible mental capital, but try to reach them via scientific advisers and sponsors. The role of science museums, clubs, fairs, and exhibitions must then be emphasized.

Also the educator will, when promoting amateur science, have a special aim in view, say, the promotion of useful knowledge. From the Aristotelic viewpoint all branches in science may be equally valuable, when they give inspiration and recreation (in the literal sense of the word) and lead to understanding of the principles and methods of science. In fact, these principles and methods are to a large extent common to most sciences. Thus, nothing prevents our combining in science clubs, fairs, exhibitions, camps, and expeditions, studies of various aspects of nature: geology, botany, zoology.

What branches of science can now expect to have a popular appeal? As a first approximation we may distinguish between theoretical sciences, laboratory or experimental sciences, and field sciences. We cannot expect theoretical sciences, mostly based on a high level of mathematical knowledge, to have a wide popularity. Even scientists may look back to their school mathematics with far from friendly feelings. Laboratory sciences, on the contrary, may become very popular especially among boys, most of whom pass through a technical stage (which may lead to stolen cars and road accidents!). Some of the young rebels and criminals may need understanding, friendship, sympathy and guidance, especially when they have the impression that the community is dull and lifeless. Perhaps the philosophy of the historian Arnold Toynbee about "challenge and response" can be applied to our youth. Is the challenge today sufficient? Why not present the study of nature—especially in regions far from cities and tourists—as a challenge to the young! Their response may, in the long run, lead to a pioneer spirit especially useful for work in developing countries.

A general answer of "global" character cannot be given. We need knowledge about the economic and cultural level of a country before we successfully can try out the different combinations of lectures, science clubs, fairs and exhibitions, science camps, and expeditions. Such experiments should be made on a national as well as an international scale. The ministries of education of the countries involved must take active part in the work—but organizations like the I.C.C. (International Coordinating Committee for the presentation of science and the development of out-of school scientific activities), the Council of Europe, and UNESCO may also play an important role. Last, but not least, all cooperations between institutions must also be cooperations between individuals.

When Should Out-of-School Amateur Science Work be Taken Up in a Developing Country?

This "when" has a double meaning. On the one hand it may refer to the stage of development reached by the country in question, on the other hand it may refer to the age of the young people involved. Before any kind of out-of-school education is possible, the common man must have asked, again and again, the question "why." Without curiosity, no science. Moreover, schools, elementary schools, must not be satisfied with giving facts, but must also give stimulation (how many schools in our developed countries have been more interested in the letter that kills than in the spirit that keeps alive?). In this connection I want to stress a point, to me a very important one. Together with the problems of school curriculums we have—even in countries considering themselves highly civilized—that of sex discrimination. I have read that some developing countries are not very eager to educate girls—the boys have an absolute priority. If a priority should be given (I do not think it should) I would give it to the young women, the future mothers, the home-makers of the next generation.

At what age can a girl or boy give a positive response to the challenges of science? A child lives in an expanding world, the frontier between the known and the unknown continually receding. The scientist's world is of the same type, so that the similarity between child and scientist is striking. But in addition to the thirst for adventure, which children have, the scientist also has the systematic methodology, the time continuity in work, and the sense of criticism. As soon as a child is ripe enough to adopt these ideas, he is also ripe enough to enter into the workshop of field sciences. The "critical age" may vary with general conditions of life. I would not dare to draw definite conclusions, although, for my own amateur science work I have coined the phrase "young people from 17 to 70."

Where Can Amateur Scientific Activity be Promoted?

Here we may also divide the question into two: "In what countries?" and "in what regions of a selected country?"

Promotion of laboratory sciences by experimental teaching is most practically achieved in larger cities, preferably those that have universities and/or technical colleges. Instructors may then easily be obtained, instruments and laboratories may be rented or given (an instrument obsolete in modern science may be first class for an amateur laboratory), and money may be given by big industrial firms.

The tendency towards urbanization, however, is one of the dangers of our time. Big cities are not good for children and young people. Field studies naturally bring them away from smoke, dust, noise, to the hidden worlds of the littoral zones along the sea shores, to the wild bird life in the deep forests, to the pure air up in the mountains where those plants and animals that are able to survive in the rough climatic challenges present interesting fields of studies. Of course, camps and expeditions need much planning. In tropical regions climatic conditions and problems of snakes and malady-carrying insects arise. On the other hand especially in the unexplored parts of the world, far from great cities and tourist hotels, there are unique possibilities for research and recreation. Here young people may renew their contact with the earth and gain life, joy, and inspiration. Moreover, camps and expeditions offer—much more than laboratories and lectures do—opportunities for international living if young people from different nations are brought together.

Amateur Science Camps in Norway

We started in 1945 under the motto "Research and Recreation" in the Hardangerfjord, south of Bergen. Each year we have had at least one major camp. Moreover, expeditions all over Norway were arranged, four of them bringing my young friends and myself far north of the Polar circle. Each year we had a Scandinavian camp (people from Sweden, Denmark and Norway understand each other fairly well after two days' contact). Some international camps, intended more for general contact than study of nature, were arranged. However, the most interesting camps were those that comprised both "Research and Recreation" and "International Living." They were both planned in cooperation with I.C.C. and the Council of Europe, which also gave a considerable number of travel grants.

Let me briefly state some of the characteristic features of my arrangements. Since 1953 we have had boys and girls together in all courses. I do not believe in sex discrimination and sex segregation and have found the girls at least as enthusiastic and cooperative as the boys. Moreover, when girls participate, the cooking problem gives no difficulty. Only the first years we had professional cooks; it is not to be recommended. Now veterans from earlier camps take the jobs of host and hostess, helped by female house assistants and male "house slaves." We always have a high percentage of veterans, who keep the traditions alive and help me with the administration. My own job is an easy one in good summers. But often we have bad weather and must keep mostly indoors. Then lectures about different topics (music with illustrations, art, literature, diverse branches of sciences) must be improvised.

Let me emphasize that we practically always include in our program studies of Norwegian rural culture—for example, the registration of old fishermens' huts on our Arctic Camp last year. These studies, just like field work in nature, give introduction to and experience in general scientific methods. Moreover, they lead to contact with the population, especially to contact between generations, and open the eyes of our young, Norwegian or non-Norwegian, to an old—but to them new—type of life. I believe that investigations of culture will be an even more important supplement to scientific study in camps in developing countries where so many old traditions are rapidly dying out and will have disappeared already in the next generation.

The following topics have been studied in my summer camps: geology, botany, ornithology, entomology (butterflies, dragonflies and bumblebees in particular), marine zoology (especially on expeditions of some weeks' duration), local culture, and archæology. An old farmhouse, found on one of our expeditions, has been bought and erected on a fine plain up in the hills, as the first house in our museum of West-Norwegian rural culture.

Let me finally mention the last important event in my youth work. After 20 years of backing, the Bergen Rotary Club has now presented the Kleppe camp farm to the "Research and Recreation" Society, founded by the cooperation of the several hundred "veterans" from earlier camps. Amateur science activity is our main objective. The Scandinavian camps and expeditions will be continued and extended. We will also continue our tradition of international camps, as far as our economy allows. As the chairman of the new society I want to emphasize that if we in any way can assist in the planning and arrangement of out-of-school amateur science in developing countries, we will gladly do so.

19

SCIENCE AND TECHNOLOGY AS MOTIVATION AND AS CONTENT IN ADULT EDUCATION COURSES

By Michael K. Sozi

Director, Center for Continuing Education, Makerere University College, Uganda

In many·developing countries there is so much concentration on youth education that the complete neglect if not exclusion of any treatment of adult education is taken for granted. If one looks at development plans of these nations one will discover progressive schemes for youth with only casual references being made to adult education, and this limited, perhaps, to the spread of literacy among rural communities. Recently the Conference of the Adult Education Association of East and Central Africa noted this attitude in their deliberations and urged that it should be corrected.

However, the picture may not be as dark as I have painted it in certain areas. For example, one important educationalist, politician, and statesman, President Julius K. Nyerere of Tanzania, in an address to Parliament on May 12, 1964, said "First, we must educate adults. Our children will not have an impact on our economic development for five, ten or even twenty years. The attitudes of the adult, on the other hand, have an impact now." This statement displays a great deal of thought and foresight. It focuses attention on the fact that adults with maturity of outlook and variegated experiences in life can be mobilized through relevant programs in education into a sizable force which can be used to accelerate development. On the other hand, a child entering school may not be absorbed practically into the economy until at least some ten years or so from the time he starts his education. It is therefore of the utmost importance that developing countries reexamine their educational programs and try to include the adult element among the strongest efforts that are being made to build the nations. One of the important considerations of developing states is that of manpower, and with accelerated programs in adult education this problem may be solved much faster than it would otherwise have been.

The field of adult education covers a wide range—from literacy classes to evening humanities courses for scientists, from better-housekeeping classes to field days for farmers—and includes correspondence courses, study vacations, folk high schools, community development centers, and many other such institutions.

Developing countries are changing; the processes of industrialization or intensification of the agricultural economy are just starting. What was completed through long processes in the Western world over many years will have to be completed within a much shorter period. Therefore, the programs for retraining in the field of science and technology have to be intensified, so that both adults and youngsters can benefit from the scientific and technological changes that affect daily activities. If we have to produce the increasing quantities of technically advanced goods and services required by the affluent society, we must retrain the people that are on the jobs. Otherwise the old and obsolete methods will not take us very far.

The two terms in the title of this paper, "motivation" and "content," are complementary; that is to say, they go together. Motivation may determine content in the sense that people should be taught what they want to learn, and this may be determined by what they think will benefit them if they learn it. Content may also sharpen the student's motivation in the sense that those who arrange curriculums and syllabuses include what is likely to be of benefit to the students materially, perhaps educationally in general, culturally, and morally.

What do the two terms "science" and "technology" cover in this context? These two terms are synonymous in the field of applied sciences as related to agriculture, health nutrition, etc. For instance, an adult is in this sense more interested in knowing the use of a drug or a fertilizer or the irrigation process rather than the chemistry of it. It would seem immaterial if he is asked to irrigate his crops with H_2O rather than water. It is the use, the function, and the experience that become relevant. The second concept appears when science and technology become separated in courses for adults leading to specialized training. Very often one can bring in pure science and applied science, one can provide courses for adults in biology or chemistry and one can also provide for them the technical aspects such as engineering and electronics. The third concept is the revisionary role: the courses for adults include the latest developments in the field of science and technology, and there is a need for people to be aware of these new developments if they have to keep their knowledge and experiences up to date.

Scientific and technological discoveries have moved in various ways to the developing nations. It is true, of course, that some countries are in this respect more advanced than others; but the basics are the same in each nation and the issue becomes just a matter of degree. Computers and other machines are already used in developing countries. Therefore, the need for a reeducation of this type is also an important factor in the education of adults in developing countries. Here, courses for, say, technicians working in business and industry, would certainly be very relevant. These can be day or evening classes, and certainly both employer and employee will seize this opportunity to advance themselves and improve the efficiency of the system as well as to generate some material advancement for themselves.

The other factor is that of providing science and technology courses to those adults that require them for formal studies. It is a well-established fact that during the colonial era in developing countries the education system was very competitive, and it is still competitive to a certain degree during the post-independence period. Many adults in Uganda, for example, were left out of the education system at various stages not because they did not possess the necessary skills and abilities to continue with their education but because of the economics and politics of the colonial situation, which were such that they could not be accommodated in the structure. For example no rational and adequate explanation can be given as to why only one doctor qualified at Makerere College Medical School in 1953 to serve East and a great part of Central Africa. No reason can be given why engineering education was almost discouraged and neglected for a long time in East Africa; no one can say there were no people with brains to undergo this kind of training. If the demand is to be met some of these people have got to be given courses, possibly through the nonconventional media—radio, television, and correspondence—to carry on with this training. But even with the arrival of independence and the expansion of education in developing countries there is a limit as to what can be done without upsetting the whole economy. There will continue to be adults of this type who will benefit from courses that can be provided in the fields of science and technology. People will be motivated to come to them out of a desire to improve their education and employment opportunities and the country will be able to accelerate the manpower supply in such fields requiring expert scientific and technical personnel.

But it is the last group of society that I want to concentrate on. This is science and technology in society as a whole. The 1964 International Conference on the organization of research and training in Africa recommended among other things that each African country should "implant science in the soil and culture of the country through all media; educational mass media and extension services." Too often scientific or technical assistance to the developing countries is delivered by a simple transfer of knowledge, with results that are neither deep nor lasting. There is little weight given to the understanding and appreciation of basic structures, and there is little chance given to enable people to assimilate properly or to achieve intellectual and social prerequisites for technological progress.

I believe also that educational reforms should not be confined to the urban areas alone. Rural communities have a claim to benefit a great deal from the scientific and technological changes that are going on. These are the people that may have benefited least from progress, and programs can be arranged which will help to improve their output in terms of cash, and of expectations from life. In such areas courses in nutrition and hygiene are bound to have the most lasting consequence. Quite often it may not be lack of means but ignorance that prevents people from having a balanced diet; quite often they spend a lot of money buying expensive foods which are nutritionally useless, whereas simple foods are available but ignored. Quite often it is conservatism and ignorance joined. Patrick Van Renburg has rightly observed that the conservatism of a peasant is rooted in his prescientific culture and he may thus tend to resist scientific practices. I know of a certain area where fruit is regarded as merely for children and the adults are not supposed to eat fruit; that is ignorance. I know there is a certain society which regards pawpaw or papaya as food for the fox; avocado pears, which are a luxury in certain western countries but are in great abundance in some tropical countries, are thrown away, despised. What is needed here is elementary courses in the field of good and nutritive food to help improve the lives of the people. This is going to help in the eradication of other evils as well, for when we talk of the evils of developing countries we are talking of disease and quite often a lot of disease is brought by ignorance, bad feeding, and other bad habits.

I can here give no better example than that from my homeland, where a nutritional unit mainly for children, supported by the Ministries of Education and Health and the Department of Paediatrics at Makerere University College Medical School, has helped through an adult education program to spread practical knowledge to the general mass of ordinary people by instructions and advice as to the best way of looking after the health of the children, by advising as to how good food can be grown by everybody on the soil, and how to make the best use of this food. Parents and teachers visit this unit and it is quite clear that the practical knowledge obtained is invaluable. This practical approach to science and technology is what the mass of the people in developing countries need. This is where they need adult education courses and not to study journeys to the moon.

DISCUSSION

All too little attention is being paid to the adults in the developing countries, Mr. Sozi stressed when he presented his paper. A small projects center to develop materials for teaching adults has been set up by UNESCO in Nigeria, but there are hardly any major programs. Yet adults teach their children; the home is an important factor in education.

What becomes of people who study only until the end of primary school? 60,000 out of 70,000 pupils in Uganda fall into this category. Does this mean that their education should stop abruptly when they leave elementary school?

Agreeing on the urgent need for adult education, *Mr. Godfrey Eugene Lardner* (UNECA) pointed out that the bulk of the actual physical production in Africa is carried out by illiterate or semi-illiterate persons. The tasks of the working population in Africa are to sustain existing levels of output and consumption, to effect a modest improvement in the standard of living, to provide an increment of real resources for investment in future development. The productivity of the workers is one of the keys to the whole development process; this makes adult education of critical importance.

In the towns, productivity depends on the workers on the factory floor and on those who supervise them. Both obviously need to continue their education. So, for that matter, do people on higher levels of management and technology, those who have already obtained their degrees—they too need to continue their education.

In the rural communities, the problem is very complex. There has been discussion about motivation: how are we to determine motivations for people living in rural societies in Africa? They need some sort of social technology, social as well as economic studies. How teach a farmer the value of irrigation? What are the techniques of persuasion to accept and to want change? Clearly, adult education is all-important.

Dr. Kosonike Thomas (Sierra Leone) discussed adult education as a means of reducing superstition. In regard to the biological sciences, it is not so difficult to get the farmer to learn something that will enable him to get better crops or greater yields. But the problem is more acute with regard to the physical sciences. How can you persuade a man not to pray for rain when your own forecasts are so unreliable?

To teach science, we should use the same techniques in Africa as the new leaders of Christianity use; we have to use terms that the Africans understand. It is necessary to "use magic to beat magic"—that is, to use the magic of the physical sciences against the magic of superstition. It is necessary to teach electricity by experimenting in magical terms. This will arouse the adult student's interest.

Dr. Fernando Raul Romero (Peru) said that there is a tendency in Peru to place great emphasis on university degrees; an adult who has not completed his elementary education, needs to continue his formal studies if he seeks advancement. So they tried an experiment with approximately 30,000 workers in the manufacturing industry. They grouped social sciences, physics, and chemistry in courses, and set up an admissions examination based on the applicant's actual knowledge rather than on an official listing of years of study. The results obtained by this method have been very satisfactory: 90 percent of the workers who took the courses subsequently registered in public night schools, where they now are continuing their formal education.

Referring back to Mr. Lardner's comment on teaching peasants the value of irrigation, *Mr. Michael Cahn* (Israel) described Israel's experience with Arab farmers on the West Bank. For years they had been getting 80 kilograms of wheat per quarter-dunam. Some Israeli agronomists, together with Arab research workers who had previously worked for the Jordan government, started experimental patches in which better strains of wheat, irrigation, and mechanization were used. The farmers saw the green belt and got the message. They were now getting 400 kilograms per quarter-acre. Adults can be best taught by showing them, not by preaching at them.

Replying to the discussion, *Mr. Sozi* said that one impression he got was that educators should move away from traditional separations into public schools, grammar schools, technical schools, and agricultural schools; what is needed is a combined curriculum, so that one part of education will supplement another. This principle applies to the education of youth and adults. It is essential to do something about semiliterate and completely illiterate people now, for the sake of their children as well as for themselves.

PART V

SCIENTISTS AND TEACHERS

20 TRAINING OF SCIENTISTS AND TECHNOLOGISTS IN DEVELOPING COUNTRIES

By Kosonike Thomas

*Professor of Engineering and
Dean, Faculty of Pure and
Applied Science,
Fourah Bay College,
Sierra Leone*

After a long period of scientific and technological isolation, the newer nations of the world have had to face the development of their territories and their peoples with a background totally unrelated to the requirements of the task before them. The education and training of their people in the pre-independence period were geared to producing a class of people whose future was mainly to be in the colonial administrative service. The training of scientists was never given any serious consideration and technology did not seem to have any relevance to colonial objectives. Indeed, the colonial territories existed purely as a storehouse from which raw materials needed for the functioning of European technology were obtainable. The means of collecting and exporting these raw materials were devised by European talent and operated by European skills. Office equipment and other materials required in connection with these processes all came from Europe, even food in many instances, and sometimes even water. The whole character of life in these countries was one of dependence upon Europe for everything except local food-stuffs.

The developing countries thus emerged from colonial rule in the middle of the twentieth century with this tradition of dependence. The present effort being made in many of these countries to break this tradition is obviously too feeble for the magnitude of the problems facing them. Far too many conflicting needs shroud the development picture, and forthright decisions and well-meaning programs lose out to political gimmicks and prestigious schemes. Science and technology still have to be given their rightful place in development programs. It is quite understandable that for a brief period following independence new nations will want to give priority to the training of nationals to replace colonial administrators. Nevertheless, these countries ought not to wait too long before giving attention to the intricate business of training scientists and technologists.

Present Trends and Training Methods

Almost every country in Africa has now embarked on some form of training which, it is hoped, will lead to technological development. After a few years of experience in training nationals locally, the subject has been open to a great international debate. Already a large amount of experimentation goes on to discover the best methods, the standard required, and the coverage necessary to satisfy national conditions. The question of training has become so complex that it is now difficult to generalize on the matter. While some countries aspire to producing for their own markets what they once imported from the developed countries, others because of the limitation of their resources are forced to accept that the uses to which their scientists and technologists will be put cannot be as sophisticated as they would wish them to be. Nevertheless, for some years to come, the needs of developing states cannot be significantly different, and one could be excused for making broad generalizations at this time.

In most countries today, the science training program was hurriedly devised to meet urgent demands, without a proper assessment of the type of manpower required. The training of science teachers, technicians, and craftsmen has been in a similar state of neglect; and our countries have consistently overlooked the fact that the proportions of trained personnel needed in these various areas ought to be adjusted to obtain the maximum benefit from each individual. As it is at present, and here I refer particularly to the experiences of my country, too much emphasis is placed on sheer numbers. Planners want to know how many teachers will be needed by 1975, for example, how many scientists or technologists or technicians or doctors will be needed by a given date or other, and so on. This "number theory" has led to the creation of overtraining in certain fields—for example, in the field of technology, where because of the shortage of skilled technicians the technologists being presently produced find themselves in a situation in which they are compelled to perform the duties of technicians and foremen in addition to their own duties. Quite apart from this, the theory has caused contradictions between need and the satisfactory deployment of personnel. Science teachers become career diplomats; engineers become sales managers in oil companies, and physicists become bankers. Confronted with evidence of this kind, governments are bound to be confused, and are bound to ask whether or not developing countries can use highly educated scientists and technologists, and whether or not they ought to invest money training them.

The problems of training are more fundamental than this. Lapses in developing and programming of a training scheme are bound to lead to failure and to subsequent frustration everywhere. The debates going on in African universities today, although relating primarily to curriculum modifications and research orientation, were sparked by the outward signs of pessimism which such a frustration has created in policy-making bodies of governments. These debates have led to some critical examination of the present courses which constitute university training.

Many of the undergraduate courses in the pure and applied sciences in English-speaking Africa, for example, are carbon copies of British university courses, unadulterated in the interest of "establishing standards." Such courses normally assume good school-leaving material, an industrialized community, and a strong labor force of skilled technicians and craftsmen. The teaching methods are also borrowed, since the instructors have themselves been trained outside Africa, and they insist that the methods by which they were taught, if good for them, must be good also for their brethren. They tend to dismiss the fact that their training had taken place under far more sophisticated conditions. Instruction in the sciences therefore consists of wading through treatises on such topics as molecular spectroscopy, quantum theory, thermodynamics, control systems, etc., as though students were being prepared for services in a technologically advanced society. The scope of the subjects taught is hardly related to the present level of practical activity. Perhaps the greatest weakness in the present methods is that they do not encourage students to relate certain topics in their courses to others, even in the same area of knowledge. It must also be admitted that not enough attention is being paid to the teaching of fundamental principles. In instances where fundamentals are taught it is discovered that very little is gained, because those lecturers who attempt to teach them lack the necessary teaching aids suitable for students living in a rural African environment.

The policy determining postgraduate research and training is no less perplexing than that for undergraduate training. Research and postgraduate work are being pursued mostly in fields of international interest rather than in those emphasizing local problems.

Scholars in Africa seem to be torn between their personal ambition to achieve international acclaim for work in the frontiers of modern scientific knowledge, and their moral obligation to their country to concentrate on tackling local topics connected with national development. Of course, various considerations influence which line of research scholars follow. Not least of these considerations is the flexibility of movement from a local university to another overseas without loss of status. Attitudes towards "local research" need drastic change. In the pursuit of research at the national level the challenges of some local scientific problems can be as formidable as those with international prestige. The rewards of achievement, in human terms, can be greater and even the chances of international acclaim are many times better. It must nevertheless be emphasized that there is hardly any reason why curriculum changes and research orientation cannot take place so that courses and research studies will have direct relevance to the country's development, while at the same time maintaining a high standard of scholarship.

Needs of Developing States

The main objective of education ought to be service to society. No matter what grade of manpower is being produced, the first requirement for a useful participation in his country's development is a man's conscious devotion to his duties and his behavior as a responsible member of his society. Quite a few of the products of our present training system seriously lack these qualities. Students enjoy a unique status in society during their training period, and they exploit this privilege to the full. The impression is created that the state owes them an education, rather than that the state merely gives them an opportunity to get an education.

What is needed, therefore, in the broad field of higher education is a training which will develop in students some drive and incentive, some feeling of indebtedness to society, some respect for, and appreciation toward the institution that gave them their training and an understanding of their responsibility to society to use their knowledge.

At the present stage of our development it will be unrealistic to train equally for all fields of science and technology. Knowledge is required more urgently in some areas than in others, while in a good many more, it is valueless at this time. Certain important fields in which developing countries need trained personnel are easily identifiable. It seems hardly necessary to emphasize the importance of transport and communication to a developing nation. The improvement of many aspects of our life will depend enormously on the rate at which facilities in these fields are developed.

Public Health and Rural Area Development

There has never been doubt that as far as the practice of medicine is concerned the curative and preventive aspects are complementary if not inseparable. In the developing countries of Africa preventive medicine has lagged behind curative medicine, and its continued neglect may ultimately affect our capacity to provide a healthy and adequate manpower pool upon which our future industrial development will depend.

Public health schemes embracing sanitation, drainage, water supply, and housing form an especial need. Such schemes should not be confined to the cities and towns. The rural areas must be developed to encourage their inhabitants to live and work there. The rush to the cities has created serious unemployment and health problems in recent years. A great improvement in a rural district could follow the adequate supply of treated water to the area. This service would normally need the complementary service of drainage. Both these services will not only reduce health hazards but will make life more comfortable for the country dweller, who would then want to stay home and work on his farm and contribute to the total agricultural effort of the country.

Mining and Agriculture

Almost everywhere in Africa, mining and agriculture play an important role in the economy. In these two fields of activity our nations need scientific and technological personnel of the highest standing to participate fully in the only two really big units of productive enterprise which Africa can boast of. Geologists, mining engineers, soil scientists, agriculturists, and agricultural engineers will be required.

In the mining industries, where in most countries, financing, management, and operations are still under foreign control, it seems odd that neither the industries nor the governments concerned have felt any urge to accelerate training for responsible senior positions in these industries.

The mining business is no small affair. Taking examples from West Africa alone, we find that iron ore is mined in Liberia and Sierra Leone, bauxite in Sierra Leone and Ghana, rutile and diamonds on Sierra Leone, gold in Ghana and coal, tin, and crude oil in Nigeria. There are still more countries elsewhere in Africa with more important mining industries on a much bigger scale than those already mentioned. Quite apart from those being presently mined, vast known resources of valuable ores remain untapped and still more resources remain undiscovered. In such a vital field, vital in the sense that for some years to come our greatest foreign earnings will have to come from this industry, the training of nationals for work in mining must be given a high priority in development programs.

Agriculture, on the other hand, has had a certain amount of attention, and there are some encouraging signs of planning. Nevertheless, a reassessment of training programs is necessary periodically, to ensure that the desired quantity and quality of manpower is being produced. The present difficulty in agriculture is providing the right incentives for increased productivity. Agriculture, however, cannot leap beyond the subsistence level to the much richer goals of world export markets by the use of incentives alone. Mechanization must be introduced into farming in a big way as well, and agricultural engineers will be required for this. If mechanization is to succeed and progress, planning in this field must ensure output of agricultural engineers in gradually increasing numbers.

Water Resources and Power Generation

The resources in nature have not really been properly explored, and mankind has tapped to date only an infinitesimal fraction of these. The possibilities of the future are enormous, and although predictions are difficult at all times it seems clear now that the course which power generation will follow has been charted out already.

Scientists are now looking forward to the production of power through the control of energy from thermonuclear reactions; they are now planning to tap the limitless solar energy at present dissipated in the atmosphere and also to make use of the underground heat in the earth. In Africa we are merely starters, who must go slowly along this course. Here we have a predominance of large and fast-flowing rivers. The cheapest method, therefore, of producing adequate and reliable power for the industries we must have, and for the many homes we badly need, will be through hydroelectric schemes. Already big hydro-schemes have been planned. The Volta River Project in Ghana has gone into operation. The Kainji dam project in Nigeria is under construction, and Zambia and other countries are in the process of planning their own projects. Apart from the technical personnel needed during construction, there will be needed skilled mechanical and electrical engineers to maintain and run the hydro-stations once they have gone into service. It will be wrong to think that only large hydroelectric plants are worth having in a developing country. Where the immediate demand may not warrant the expense of a big plant and a country feels she must plan for this over a period of time, well-trained engineers in rural districts could plan and execute small projects for their area. Where access to districts is difficult or impossible by road or rail, a hydro-plant, if not cheaper than an engine generator, may prove the only means of obtaining electricity. During the long vacation months of 1968, students from the Department of Engineering at Fourah Bay College worked with students from the Imperial College of London on a survey for one such scheme for the township of Yifin in the northeastern part of Sierra Leone. Here the only source of supply is from a 15-kVA generator run only at night and supplying the mission compound. Intermittent supply of fuel has made the system unsatisfactory. It is intended to supplement this supply from a proposed hydro-plant, so that distribution can be extended and electricity made available for 24 hours a day.

The lessons from this survey are, first, that unless districts are fortunate enough to have rivers with high heads, only turbines of the Francis and Kaplan types, which are quite expensive pieces of equipment, would work efficiently and therefore the scheme would prove costly, even prohibitive in certain circumstances. Secondly, if small schemes are going to be in demand, a cheaper type of turbine which would work efficiently for low heads of 10-20 feet will have to be designed and developed by research teams in institutions in Africa. Africa can then make use of design engineers in the mechanical and electrical fields even on this small scale.

The mention of design skill introduces a much argued issue in technological education, namely that of training design engineers as opposed to training maintenance engineers. It is true that both are needed and that the duties of both in Africa can be considered complementary—the design engineer specializing mostly in the design of machine parts for the maintenance of imported machinery but giving attention occasionally to designing simple, even manually operated machines for use in small-scale local craft or food industries.

Training for the Future

Taking Sierra Leone as an example of a typical Middle African country, we find that in the educational structure (nursery school, primary school, secondary school, and university) the weakest link has been the secondary school. Although there is selective entrance into the secondary schools (only 50 percent of those passing the common entrance examination can have places in the secondary schools), the quality of the output from the science streams of these schools has been disappointing. Of the 72 secondary schools in existence, 45 offer science subjects up to fifth form but only four offer them up to sixth form. More revealing than this is that the number of science teachers graduating from the universities and teacher training colleges is dismally low. In 1968 only about 10 percent of the graduates from the university had specialized in the sciences. We thus see a vicious circle of a mediocre science school-leaver produced by a poorly staffed school science department, training for a degree which he can just barely pass to take up science teaching in a secondary school. To break this circle we must first adapt our university teaching methods so that the school background can be strengthened. It may even be necessary to restructure our courses so that much of what had been learned at school may be repeated. This may mean a lengthening of the present course by one year, but the future dividends should warrant this additional expense. Since it is so obvious that for a few years to come, the greatest demand for our graduate scientists will be in the field of science teaching in secondary schools, it is imperative that emphasis should be placed on fundamental principles and on exercises which stimulate students' brains and make them capable of appreciating and investigating problems on their own. University instruction should become less descriptive and dogmatic and more experimental and free for the development of new ideas—ideas connected with practice and with life. Only by this means can we hope to equip young men for the task for training children between the ages of 11 and 18 to understand and apply scientific principles in problem-solving and to enjoy the thrills of creative thinking.

The training of technologists must follow lines similar to those outlined for scientists. Most of the weaknesses brought from school will, unfortunately, have to be remedied at the university, until our secondary schools have been strengthened. The special needs of pupils intending to pursue a university degree in engineering, must be considered seriously when reorganizing the schools. The lack of a technical background at entry to university must be corrected by introducing technical subjects in secondary schools and making a period (3-12 months) spent in industry after leaving school compulsory for admission into an engineering degree course.

The universities must strive to meet the challenges of the times, never hesitating to change methods or modify courses to suit the changing society. Conventional courses which have to relevance to our development at this time must be replaced by new ones. For example, there is a case for training analytical chemists for industry; for combining, for the time being, the present courses in electrical and mechanical engineering; for introducing into the engineering curriculum subjects like transportation, hydrology and hydraulic machinery, public health engineering, and plant design and maintenance, and for instituting courses in mining and agricultural engineering.

One of the most important tasks of our universities will be to keep abreast of the times, constantly analyzing new scientific material in order to ascertain when certain types of materials should or should not be brought into the curriculum. We have seen in recent years the massive strides made in the field of automation. Man has used electronic techniques to effect automation not only in production in the engineering and chemical fields, but also in the analysis of mathematical data by means of the computer. Automatic processes will soon become the rule rather than the exception. It seems, therefore, that it will be wrong not to teach the principles of automation as a regular part of all scientific training. Soon, Africa will be compelled to use these methods, even for the most basic industrial activity. The electronic computer has arrived, and no one whose aim it is to work in any field of science or technology should be unaware of its possibilities or ignorant of its practical use. Training in the use of computers should become an essential part of scientific and technological training for the future. Students must also be given the opportunity to learn foreign languages, so that in the future there will be a more intimate association among scientists from different countries.

At our present stage of development it will be a folly to rely on orthodox processes in training our peoples. The university must extend its services to those talented people, young and old, who for some reason or other cannot undertake full-time university courses. Finally, there is the challenge for the university to associate itself with scientific study and research at all levels, from village improvement to primary school research and then to secondary school and research institutions. There is no doubt that it will take time to develop all the important links in the chain of activities proposed. Nevertheless, in view of what is known about world trends in science, we cannot but reluctantly admit that we must either quicken our pace of development or sadly miss the influence of the great cultural evolution which must follow modern scientific achievements of the future.

DISCUSSION

Dr. Thomas stressed the difficulty of convincing teachers that what had been good enough for them is not necessarily good enough for their children. Their teaching methods have to be compatible with the way of life, social structure, and background of the countries in which they live. Courses on relativity and photo-elasticity are of little use of peasants in rural villages.

Mr. Yao Paul Akoto (Ivory Coast) said that, speaking as a teacher himself, he wonders whether the teacher can be expected to do very much more than just teach—that is to say, think up a method of teaching and adopt an attitude of curiosity followed by sustained reflection before his pupils, each one of whom he had to know psychologically. Perhaps the experts are being a little patronizing; a real teaching reform has to involve the teachers who are actually teaching on the job.

There are two kinds of scientists and technologists, according to *Mr. Jorge Alberto Sabato* (Argentina)—there are those who use their science and technology to take care of the health, production, administration, education, transportation and so on in a country, and there are those who use their knowledge to produce more knowledge. Dr. Thomas concentrated on the need of developing lands for the first group, but there is also a need for the second type, although their functions are purely scholastic.

They are important because they make it possible to evaluate human resources and natural resources. For example, oil was discovered in Argentina in 1910, but it had sulfur in it, and a scientist was needed to decide whether it was worth developing. Such experts can advise the politicians who have to

make decisions, for instance, about which new technology to introduce. Should they take solar energy, conventional energy, nuclear energy? In what industry should they invest, chemical or petro-chemical or iron? Many countries undertake steel industries that are out of date before the initial contracts are signed. The switch from an agricultural economy to an industrial one requires similar expert advice.

Such producers of knowledge, as compared to the "professional staff" type of scientists and technologists of whom Dr. Thomas spoke, have to be "the best brains" so as to give the best advice.

Mr. Peter Inocent Mwombela (Tanzania) said that the basic problem is the teacher's attitude: does he think, "I am teaching mathematics" or "I am teaching pupils"? If the teacher really thinks in terms of the pupil, he will not go far wrong. *Mr. William Farquhar Conton* (Sierra Leone) said that he agrees with Dr. Thomas' list of priorities, except that he would like to add to it medicine and veterinary medicine. In the primary schools, the biological sciences should be emphasized for two reasons: firstly, there is a rich natural laboratory around every primary school in Africa, just waiting to be explored and requiring no more equipment than a lens; secondly, the pupil will find that his problems in biology can be more easily solved, with the guidance of a teacher, than problems in the physical sciences.

The universities in Africa should set up technician training in agriculture and technology, so as to upgrade the status of technicians, urged *Mr. Meir Avigad* (Israel).

Defending the teaching of physical science as well as biological in schools, *Dr. Herbert D. Thier* (United States) said that it can be taught outside the classroom just as easily. For instance, there are a lot of principles involved in hanging a rope—or a vine, if there is no rope—from a tree. Best of all, and most fun for teacher and student, is to teach both types of sciences together, without separating them.

Replying to the discussion, Dr. Thomas noted sadly that a research worker dealing with local problems earns far less prestige, even at home, than he would get if he went abroad and tackled some non-local topic. This makes it difficult to keep at home the kind of scientists Dr. Sabato mentioned.

21 SCIENCE EDUCATION CENTERS IN DEVELOPING COUNTRIES

By Dolores F. Hernandez

Director, Science Education Center, University of the Philippines, Philippines

Science education centers are the avenues through which many countries are introducing new curriculums, new programs for teacher education, and other innovations in science education. These centers have become vehicles for educational reform in the teaching of school sciences and mathematics. Attempts to improve science education in developing countries have focused mainly on the elementary and secondary school levels, and on the retraining of teachers at this levels. In this chapter, the discussions of science education will be limited to these levels which are within the experience of the Science Education Center of the University of the Philippines.

The Philippine Center

Before World War II most books used in the Philippine educational system were foreign in origin. A few, particularly at the lower levels of the educational ladder, were published locally, but even these tended to be superficial adaptations of foreign books. The organizers of the center felt that an independent unit within the university could contribute greatly to the improvement of science instruction by developing instructional materials in line with currently accepted major objectives of science teaching and viewed against the perspective of the national economic levels, the national goals, the needs of the country, and the conditions of its schools.

It was decided to develop student texts and teacher's guides in the sciences and mathematics for use in elementary and secondary schools. Some teaching aids and equipment necessary for the courses and not commercially available are also being developed. The involvement of the center in this type of activity has been limited to development of prototypes.

The adaptation of science teaching to national and local needs can best be achieved by developing for each science and mathematics course specific lessons and laboratory exercises that can be used in the large majority of the country's schools. Thus, although the science and mathematics curriculum materials developed abroad were used as models, and in many cases their rationales and objectives adapted, the choice of specific topics and the supplies and equipment for the laboratory exercises in each course were kept as simple as possible, and except for some basic equipment, were constructed out of local materials. Also, rather than seeking a new scheme that would change science teaching radically in the country, the Science Education Center has developed and is developing courses in the sciences and mathematics that fit into the present general pattern of the sequence of courses currently followed in most schools.

The sequence of science courses in most Philippine schools is elementary science for grades 1 to 6; at the secondary school level it is general science 1, general science 2, high school biology or chemistry in the third year, and physics in the fourth year. For mathematics, the sequence generally is arithmetic, grades 1 to 6; arithmetic in the first year of high school; algebra in the second year; second course in algebra for one semester, applied arithmetic for one semester, and plane geometry in the third year; trigonometry or solid geometry in the fourth year. Mathematics in the fourth year is optional.

In formulating general guidelines for the development of curricular materials by the center, the organizers examined the national goals and development plans of the country and selected those ideas for which there is general acceptance. They are as follows:

1. To make science education more responsive to the needs of the country.
2. To use science and technology effectively in the achievement of national goals.
3. To produce scientifically literate citizens.
4. To stimulate the choice of scientific and allied careers by those with the corresponding aptitudes and thus increase the number of scientists, technologists, and technicians.
5. To communicate the excitement and aspiration of scientific endeavors and to increase the powers of innovation and invention through an understanding of the methods of science.
6. To emphasize imaginative inquiry and promote skills for independent learning rather than dogmatic assertion and memorization of facts.

It should be noted in the above statement of major goals that one of the less tangible objectives of science teaching is recognized—objective number 6 above. This objective has been variously styled the methods of science, scientific or rational inquiry, or the processes of science.

The production of suitable curricular materials is only one aspect of the larger problem of improving science education. The materials have to be disseminated, teachers must be trained in their use, and administrators oriented so that adequate administrative support can be given the new programs. Quite obviously all these and other concomitant problems cannot be dealt with single-handedly by one small unit such as the Science Education Center. To enable the center to function beyond the milieu of the university two committees were established, an advisory committee and a steering committee. The members of the advisory committee include representatives of the Department of Education (public, private, and vocational bureaus), the major associations of private colleges and universities, top administrators of the University of the Philippines, and the National Science Development Board. Although the members of this committee are not necessarily scientists or science educators, this would be desirable, since one of their functions is to serve as a final review committee of the work done by the center. A more significant role of this committee, however, is assisting in the dissemination of the new materials and ideas relating to improved science education programs. The steering committee is a smaller committee consisting of individuals whose units are more directly involved in the project, i.e., the Dean of the College of Arts and Sciences, the Dean of the College of Education, the assistant director of the Bureau of Public Schools, an administrator of the University of the Philippines, and the director of the Science Education Center. This committee meets more frequently than the advisory committee, reviews more of the materials, and helps the director administer the projects.

Direct responsibility for developing the materials rests mainly on the working committees, of which there is one for each of the subject areas: biology, physics, chemistry, mathematics, and general and elementary science. At least two members of each working committee work full-time at the center; the rest are part-time writers, reviewers, and consultants. The membership of this group includes both subject specialists and practising teachers.

The chairman of a working committee, with the advice of colleagues in the center, decides who should be consultants, reviewers, and writers. Most working committees work as a team. After overall objectives and the content for a course have been agreed on and a tentative outline developed, objectives for each chapter are decided on. Finally, individual group members are assigned to their chapters. As the individual writers develop their chapters, they are encouraged to consult with specialists. The entire committee or a subgroup of the committee meets to discuss whether a manuscript is acceptable and to suggest revisions. The manuscript is then revised by the original writer or, if the revisions are slight, by some full-time staff member of the center. The manuscript is then submitted to the steering committee and/or advisory committee. It may be referred to a specialist upon suggestion of the committees. During the process of development, research assistants try out laboratory exercises or particular lessons and give results of their observations to the writer and the chairman concerned. This is the general pattern of development of most of the center's materials.

Some of the writers in each working committee are secondary or elementary school teachers. Many of them became experimental teachers; that is, they try out experimental editions of the courses. However, since there were not enough of them, it soon became clear that the staff of the center needed to train teachers to use the new materials. Each summer since 1967, therefore, the SEC has held six-week teacher-training courses on the materials which were completed in time for the opening of classes in July. The summer institutes are specially designed programs intended to develop in teachers the various skills they need to cope successfully with the new materials and with new methods of teaching. For this reason, the institute for a particular subject area is taught by the chairmain of the working committee assisted by one or more staff members of the SEC. The general pattern of activities followed for each subject area included class sessions on: (a) aims and objectives of the new materials, using SEC materials and those of other projects as models; (b) writing instructional objectives, stated in behavioral terms; (c) study, discussion, and demonstrations of processes of sciences of methods of science using specific lessons from the new materials; (d) study and discussion of concepts basic to the course; (e) performing selected laboratory exercises; (f) when pertinent, constructing a few simple teaching aids; (g) teaching sample or micro classes; (h) discussion of evaluation techniques and construction of sample test items.

An evaluation committee which borrows staff from the College of Education takes charge of evaluating the materials during the two-year try-out period for each book.

Just before the first experimental editions were ready for try-out in the schools, an evaluation program was drawn up with the assistance of an international expert on evaluation. Essentially, the program includes securing feedback from teachers on each chapter of the text and each laboratory exercise, testing achievement of the students two or three times a year, pre- and post-testing students using process-oriented tests, meeting monthly with the teachers, and meeting twice a year with the administrators. All tests used in the evaluation program are prepared by the working committees with the assistance of the evaluation committee. Each set of materials for a course is tried out for two years. The materials are then revised on the basis of the data accumulated over this two-year period, after which the books are released for general use. The books for high-school physics, high-school chemistry, and high-school mathematics 1 and 2 are among the first materials available to the general public in 1970. These books have undergone a 5-year period of development, tryout, revision, and commercial publication. The evaluation committee members handle the sessions on evaluation and testing during the summer institutes and will do the same for the graduate programs.

The art and production staff takes charge of the illustrations and duplication of experimental editions of the books, as well as achievement tests and the various forms used in the center's evaluation program.

Even before personnel were selected for the center, a collection of materials on curriculum development, samples of the new project materials from countries that had spearheaded the movement, and a few pamphlets and books that attempted to explain the rationale of the new projects had been gathered. These served as orientation materials for the center's staff and writers. The collection has grown into a reference library and is now open to a limited number of public and private school teachers and graduate students of the university.

It is pertinent at this point to state that orientation to new developments in the substance of science and the means by which this substance is conveyed to school children is not confined to secondary sources. The Science Education Center has a faculty development program which allows members of the staff to take short trips abroad to observe various curriculum development projects, or to study for advanced degrees in their fields of specialization in science education.

It was earlier pointed out that curriculum development and teacher education are inextricably related. Once the materials are available, large numbers of teachers must be trained in their use. As a start, the SEC began cooperating with the National Science Development Board and the Department of Education on training teachers through summer institutes and other short-term programs. However, despite such massive efforts it was soon recognized that not all the teachers could be trained in summer institutes. Several decades would be needed for this, and besides, a six-week period seemed too short a time to effect changes in teacher attitudes and behaviors. The individual easily absorbs the content of the new materials, but the methods of science and the spirit of inquiry which such materials should develop tends to be lost in the process. Thus we have teachers using new materials in the old way, that is, with neither the methods nor the spirit.

Very recently, therefore, various Philippine educational and funding agencies that had previously been engaged in science education improvement programs came together to plan and carry out a coordinated program for the education of teachers in the science and mathematics and for the development of regional science teaching centers. This program includes a specially designed graduate program for the faculties of teacher training institutions. The institution of each teacher participant will, upon completion of the eighteen-month course, receive equipment, teaching aids, and books. The teacher participants will be selected from those institutions that give promise of becoming a regional science teaching center for science and mathematics teachers in a particular local region. The staff of the SEC will assist the returned participants in conducting their first summer institutes. Thus, the institutions whose staff are selected to participate in the program are committed to a science education improvement program for their regions, which they are expected to effect through in-service programs for teachers. The institutions will also undertake reforms of their undergraduate courses. This in brief is the plan for coordinated efforts at improving science education, with the Science Education Center and the College of Education of the university providing the leadership in the degree programs for teachers. The responsibility of disseminating ideas and new materials rests on several institutions, among them the National Science Development Board, the coordinating body for this program, and the Department of Education. The final outcome of the program will be the establishment of about 10 science teaching centers strategically located all over the country. These centers will be primarily engaged in retraining teachers of their respective regions, and in providing within their own institutions a strong undergraduate program for pre-service education of teachers.

A nation-wide reform in science education will, it is hoped, be effected through the coordinated effort of several educational as well as funding agencies. It is within the degree programs that teacher educators will learn the importance of changing teacher attitudes, so that they may in turn convey to their students not only the substance of science but the methods of rational inquiry that characterize science itself. Certainly the participants will be with the program long enough to acquire a clear understanding of the spirit of science and the best methods of imparting to their students this less tangible but vitally important objective of science teaching. This is the most important task faced by those involved in planning and executing the degree programs.

The Science Education Center itself now has other functions. While still maintaining its independence as a unit, with a separate budget and direct administrative responsibility to the university president's office, it now serves as the science teaching department of the College of Education. Science education courses, programs, and advising of graduate students on their theses have thus become the responsibility of the SEC staff.

The Science Education Center also serves in a limited way as a materials resource center, although physical space is limited. It maintains an up-to-date library on science teaching, with science books to serve as reference for curriculum developers and materials produced by curriculum development projects of various countries. It also has a collection of various types of teaching aids, including films. It is available to teachers and they have made much use of it, especially during teacher conferences.

Another function of the center is that of research. At present its research activities are confined to evaluative studies of its course improvement projects, a survey of the country's teacher education programs in the sciences and mathematics, and guiding the research of graduate students on the master's level. More work of this nature is planned once the pressure of work on development of materials lessens, including studies on how Filipino children learn science concepts and cultural factors that affect such learning.

It becomes apparent that the functions just discussed are all closely related. A new curriculum in science needs trained teachers, and research studies add to knowledge about the effectiveness of programs and the ways children learn, as well as providing data that help improve existing programs. The center also plans to use wherever possible the studies done by other units such as the National Coordinating Center for the Study of Filipino Children and Youth. As for the question of which of these functions is most essential for a developing country like the Philippines, curriculum development and teacher training are believed to be of primary importance. The production of new materials may be viewed as the basic function of the center because it is around such materials that the retraining programs for teachers are built.

Although the center has from its inception been committed to the idea that science teaching should involve both the methodology of science and its substance, the former has been difficult to achieve and transmit. One of the earliest problems faced by the organizers of the center was orientation of the staff toward this objective of science teaching. It was eventually accomplished by making available literature on this aspect of science teaching, and through the use of sample lessons produced by some curriculum development projects. A series of short-term consultants, specialists in the different subject areas experienced in curriculum development projects, were invited to assist the working committees in the development of new materials. Through actual involvement in curriculum development the staff gained a clear perspective of what it means to teach science as inquiry and how students can be taught rational inquiry.

It is doubtful whether this purpose has been successfully met in summer institutes. Most science teachers have heard about it and accept it as a major objective of science teaching, but teaching toward this objective is not so easily achieved. Providing the teachers with materials developed with an eye to realizing this goal is a great help, but unless there are teachers who understand it and are able to convey it, very little can be accomplished in this direction. A number of summer institutes and short-term programs have been held in this country, but the quality of these institutes leaves much to be desired. It is hoped that a long-term program which will train teacher educators in depth on new developments in both substance and methodology in their fields of specialization will produce better qualified teachers, who will in turn conduct retraining courses for high-school and elementary-school teachers.

The use of behavioral objectives has helped teachers see how the methodology of science may be taught and measured. These have been used in the center's courses and are gaining wide acceptance outside the center, but in the hands of inexperienced teachers it is often the format rather than the spirit that is caught.

A problem of a different type is the administrative support needed by the experimental teachers working with new materials. These teachers need freedom to give their own examinations instead of having their classes take the departmental examinations given by their schools. Because of their involvement in the evaluation program, they need reduced teaching loads as well. Adequate space and equipment are also needed to enable them to do a good job of trying out the materials, and they need ready funds to purchase the many small items that are needed for most laboratory exercises. Securing administrative backing for experimental programs has been the responsibility of the SEC administration and the chairman of each working committee. The key persons involved here are the principals and supervisors. Their support is sought even before the experimental teachers are selected.

To prepare the way for acceptance and support of new programs on a wider scale it also becomes necessary to promote some understanding and acquaintance among administrators outside the group already involved with the experimental schools. The Science Education Center has assisted in conducting regional seminars with this objective in mind. In these regional seminars, which are funded by the National Science Development Board, the administrators listen to, see teaching demonstrations of, and discuss the new curriculums and new approaches in teaching.

Establishing Science Teaching Centers

The need for establishing a science teaching center may be gleaned from various sources. Indications of such a need may be found in a country's schoolrooms—in the content of the courses, in the way sciences and mathematics are taught, in the type of learning activities for the children, in the type of books the children use, and in the methods the teachers employ. Do these reflect new developments in both the content and the methods of teaching science, or do they rely heavily on classroom recitation with almost no student participation except verbalization and memorization work? Other sources of such indications are the teacher education programs: do these provide the students with the necessary skills and knowledge they need to be able to teach the new materials? The skills the prospective teacher would need include such things as a broader subject-matter background in the sciences, updated science courses, knowledge of the works of psychologists and scientists whose thinking has influenced science education today, a working knowledge of research methodology, observational skills for observing, recording, and interpreting pupil behavior, ability to analyze teaching behavior, and skills in testing and evaluating student performance, including the appraisal of student achievement in the direction of acquiring the methods of science and the scientific attitudes.

Once it is determined that a science teaching center is needed, the next problem is to determine the implementing body. Local or national science education needs may be met by one or more units already existing and operating. The nucleus of such a body in terms of personnel, resouces, and units already in operation may be found in existing departments of a university, a department or ministry of education, or some other educational or scientific organization or agency. The question resolves itself into this: can the existing resources operate to fulfill the various jobs that a science education center might undertake? Do they have enough flexibility to allow a flow of specialists, teachers, and other workers on short-term assignments to do particular jobs? Basically the need is for a unit that will facilitate education reform—one that will not be bogged down by details of administration.

The location of a science teaching center in a university has many advantages. A center that undertakes curriculum development needs the services of various specialists in the subject matter, in teaching, and in psychology. The university more than any other unit would have such people available and they are more likely to be cognizant of developments in their field of specializations. Such a center would more easily be able to use the services of specialists under various administrative arrangements—a procedure rather difficult to achieve if other agencies external to the university were involved. The role of young research assistants should be mentioned at this point. Much of the lower-level work of a center can be done by a corps of graduate students majoring in science or mathematics education. A university setting makes it possible to recruit such a group. Moreover, instruction and research are the normal functions of a university. A science teaching center that undertakes these functions would profit from a university setting, and likewise, the university is enriched by the presence of a center which facilitates the introduction of innovations in education.

The plan for establishing a science teaching center should take into account first of all the overall plans for education that are part of the national development goals of the country. Even if only one aspect of science education is selected as a function of a center—e.g., the teaching function—the plan should still consider the other components of science education because these aspects are interdependent. For example, a center that limits its activities to retraining of teachers needs to concern itself as well with new developments in science education cirriculums at the lower levels of education, because these provide the core around which to build a retraining program.

The plan for a center should specify its objectives over a period of time and should indicate which objectives have priority during particular periods of the center's development. It should also consider measures that will give some assurance of the center's viability, and the precautions that need to be taken to avoid anticipated problems. In setting up the organizational structure of a science teaching center the following are some of the points that need to be considered:

1. Selection and appointment of a full-time project director and an international expert experienced in the various activities of a science teaching center
2. Creation of a committee or committees to assist the director in policy-making; to help keep lines of communication open with various government units, private and public schools, colleges and universities, and professional organizations and associations; to facilitate coordination; to help settle problems; and in general to assist in keeping the center operational
3. Assignment of a full-time staff with at least one senior person in each science subject area in which the center is working
4. Assignment of working groups for each subject area and/or course to be developed, including specialists and practicing teachers from both schools and universities
5. Designation of schools for try-out and dissemination of the new materials produced by the center
6. Designation of short-term consultants in various subject areas to serve as critics of the materials produced by the center
7. Appointment of an evaluation committee to assist the center's staff in preparation of tests and to take major responsibility for the center's evaluation program
8. Designation of an art and production staff to take charge of the physical aspects of textbook production
9. Provision of laboratories for teaching and preliminary testing of laboratory exercises and a shop for constructing simple equipment
10. Building up a library. It goes almost without saying that a good reference library is essential to curriculum development and related activities, particularly where the number of scientists and educators who are knowledgeable about the new developments in their fields of specialization is limited. Thus, it is essential to have a collection of books and journals that deal with the philosophy and psychology of science teaching as well as materials on recent developments in the content of the sciences, instructional procedures, and the psychology of children and

learning. Perhaps the most important part of such a library is a collection of materials developed by various curriculum development projects to be used as samples or models of how the new ideas about teaching the sciences and mathematics take concrete form in lessons that can be used in the classroom.

It is very likely that in a developing country there will not be enough people available who are knowledgeable in all the varied aspects of the work they will become involved in and who are aware of the new approaches in teaching, particularly that aspect of science teaching that deals with the methods of science and the teaching of science as inquiry. An orientation period will therefore be necessary, and for this purpose a science education library will be of great value.

To keep the staff abreast of developments in science education and in their fields of specialization, it is important for a center to have a faculty or personnel development plan. This should enable the staff to go abroad or take time off locally for study and observation trips, fellowships, and special training programs. The fellowships should enable the staff to earn master's or doctoral degrees in science education with specializations in a science subject area.

The composition of the staff is also important. It should include subject specialists interested in applying the knowledge of their disciplines to the problems of education, experienced educators and teachers, and psychologists or educational psychologists.

Many problems can be avoided by enlisting the support of administrators and those in a position to facilitate educational reform. Such problems as the examination system (either national or at the school system level), the schedules and teaching load of the try-out teachers, the need for laboratory space and equipment, and scheduling and administration of the center's tests in the schools can become particularly difficult when new materials are to be tried out in actual classrooms. It is important, then, that school administrators be familiar with the center's programs and that they be continuously apprised of developments.

Similar problems will have to be faced when programs are ready for dissemination on the national level. One way of minimizing these difficulties is through orientation and discussion sessions with school and college administrators. A series of such conferences on a regional basis would be helpful.

To be truly and fully effective, however, the improvement of science education cannot be confined to the retraining of teachers. The basic undergraduate and graduate education of future teachers must be brought into the picture. This—the long-range development of science teachers with modern progressive attitudes toward their profession—is the real challenge to the science teaching centers.

22

SCIENCE EDUCATION IN THE GENERAL TEACHERS' COLLEGE

By Joseph Elstgeest

*Head, Department of
Science Education,
Morogoro Teachers' College,
Tanzania*

In the beginning of 1968 there was a rat plague in our neighbourhood, I happened to walk through some of the fields surrounding a small village. The rain had been good, and the people had planted maize, millet, and rice. The men working in the fields, friendly as ever, stopped and stood to chat and to exchange the news of the day. But the news was not too good: "The rats come at night, after we have planted, and they dig up the seeds and eat them!"

"That is really bad! What are you doing about it?"

"What can we do about it? Nothing. They come and they go during the night. We plant again, and they come once more. It is a bad year for us."

"But is there nobody who has some idea?"

"Nobody."

Although some of the men suggested that perhaps the agriculture officer in town could do something about it . . . would he be a wonderdoctor?

They thought that the idea of keeping cats was a pretty good idea, "But who is going to give them to us?"

So they went on with their work. If the rats eat their seeds again, they would plant again in the same way, and hope for the best; until either the rats or the seeds are finished. The rats would probably win. . . .

This is a small, but typical example from rural Tanzania. It does illustrate the magnitude of the problem this country is faced with: the problem of development beyond the level of pure subsistence, beyond the struggle for pure survival.

The big problem is not the rats that eat the seeds, the big problem lies much deeper: here is a situation which baffles the people, which defeats them; against which they have no weapon, no resource. They feel defeated, and consequently they are defeated. It is a basic lack of self-confidence.

If we believe that all human beings are equal, that every citizen is an integral part of the nation with the right to take an equal part in the government of his nation, then we must provide an education of equal efficiency to every citizen.

If there is an undeniable need for "intelligent hard workers," progressive minded, and confident in their own ability to improve their life, then there is an undeniable need to revolutionize primary education, and to step up the opportunities for primary education, so as to make it benefit one hundred percent of the children, and not only a tiny handful of so-called lucky ones.

Then it is essential that all citizens be educated to make intelligent decisions, based on an understanding of their environment, carried out by a constantly inquiring mind, and reinforced by the ability to identify and solve problems arising from the needs within this environment. The ability of independent thinking—and reaching conclusions only on the strength of reliable evidence—will then help the people to share their intellectual resources in communal planning where decisions are made. These decisions will depend on evidence presented, interpretations shared, and the amount of understanding acquired. This may make national self-reliance productive to the largest extent possible, so as to get nearer to true—including economic—independence.

Science Education for Progress

This necessitates a complete re-thinking of the educational approach. The modern trend in science education, especially at the lower levels, attaches less importance to memorized factual knowledge. It has become widely accepted that factual knowledge which is not fed into an inquiring mind is dead, sterile, and unproductive.

It is obvious enough that the fields of ex-primary school leavers yield no more than the fields of those who never covered an agriculture syllabus; neither are their cattle any fatter. No amount of lessons, books, and visiting experts on health education have left behind a trail of cleaner villages.

A little conversation may clarify the point:

Health educator:	"What should you do with the drinking water in the village?
Ex-primary boy:	"Drinking water should be filtered and boiled."
H. ed.:	"Why?"
Boy:	"Because it is unsafe to drink unpurified water. It carries the germs of sickness."
H. ed.:	"Good. Do you filter and boil your drinking water at home?"
Boy:	"No."
H. ed.:	"But . . . don't you get sick?"
Boy:	"No."

Many more examples could be cited here, but that is not the purpose of this paper. The fact is that we have made syllabuses, and revised syllabuses, often in the comfort of an office, and never seriously considered their effect. The fact is that we have always given answers to the children, and never real problems. When we did ask the children questions, it was with the intention that they regurgitate the answers we had given them previously. The fact is that we have never taught the children to ask questions, and we have never given them the chance to rely on themselves to find the solutions.

We gave them answers, and kept the confidence to ourselves.
We gave them memory, and kept the thinking to ourselves.
We gave them marks, and kept the understanding to ourselves.
This must change.

The aspect of education which we conveniently call "science education" must aim at educating the children towards a logical approach to identifying and solving problems. In Tanzania we call this: "Elimu ya Kufikiri," which could be translated as "Education toward clear thinking."

Environmental Learning

By confronting the children with their environment, and by providing them with materials to manipulate, taken from their environment, the children are encouraged to solve problems that they can handle.

The children are thus always placed in a problem situation, and not told any answers. The answers are hidden in the real things they are allowed to handle, be it water, a crawling insect, or growing plants. They are encouraged to explore. They have to do it themselves, to puzzle themselves, to experiment themselves, to make mistakes themselves, and to reconsider their conclusions themselves in the light of fresh evidence that they have uncovered themselves. Later in life they will have to face many problems, also by themselves.

The value of these experiences lies in the trying, and not in the final result, or "answer." No matter how many answers they do uncover, they will always end up with a new problem. Slowly they may become conscious of the fact that we are ever surrounded by problems, but we can face them with confidence, since we have learned to do something about them, by ourselves.

This special way of thinking in which we try to educate our children—the logic of cause and effect—stimulates the inquiring mind. It goes together with training in basic skills and techniques, so that the children increasingly acquire the ability to satisfy their inquiring minds and transform them into the confidence of understanding, away from fatalism ("We plant again and they come once more.") and away from defeatism ("What can we do about it? Nothing!").

This does not imply a new way of teaching science facts. This is not a new and ingenious practical approach facilitating the digestion of the three classes of levers, or the internal structure of the dogfish. This is not even a new discovery method in which the children must themselves discover what we think they should discover. It is a change from teaching about science to educating through science: this is a revolution, a new philosophy of education. It is a change from teaching curriculums to teaching children.

The goal for an effective science education then is to assist the children in developing certain skills and abilities:
The ability to observe accurately
The ability to recognize and understand relationships
The ability to measure
The ability to make and use abstractions

The ability to manipulate numbers, and to compute
The ability to design meaningful experimentation.
The ability to gather and organize evidence
The ability to evaluate evidence
The ability to communicate understandably
The ability to use and increase one's own resourcefulness and creativity.

The materials we use to make this education a reality are quite irrelevant. We can use anything that is available around the school, as long as it is real. Everywhere there are plenty of stones, insects, plants, seeds, soils, string, fibers, bamboo, paper, sticks, water, cloth, or whatever we come across when we look around. School budgets, although usually very meager, sometimes allow us to purchase useful little things. But no particular piece of apparatus is ever essential. The children can learn to solve their own problems through such a variety of alternatively available objects that lack of apparatus is never an excuse for bad education.

The "subject matter" or "content matter" is equally irrelevant. Whatever goes together with the available local materials, whatever fits into the situation of the school, whatever catches the interest of the children, whatever lends itself well to an education in thinking, inquiry, investigation, and problem solving, whatever, in other words, serves the basic purpose of science education, is suitable and welcome.

The little boy who planted a seed in a tin, and spat on it daily to see whether it would grow this way, may be quite ignorant about magnesium-type fertilizers, but when his plant did germinate, grew stuntily, and then died he had established a relationship between a living plant and an outside influence. "It died because of the poison in saliva," he reported in his book. Who would regard this as a "wrong" answer?

Those who still worry about a syllabus can be told that the syallabus is: "the children and their interesting environment." A teacher started a topic named "Measuring Time." It started off with a candle under a jar, and the children were asked to shut their eyes and guess how long it would take for the candle to go out. Instead they started to wonder what really burned: the wax or the wick. "Measuring Time" was completely forgotten, and this class spent three weeks experimenting with wax and wicks and other fuels. Wax (dripped off the candles from a nearby church) and the hollow stalks of pawpaw leaves provided the materials to make their own candles, in which they put wicks of cloth, sisal, match sticks, green and dry grass, and cottonwool.

The scientist might have been amused at the crude ways in which they conducted their experiments; the syllabus-eater might have approved because they did discover that it was the wick with the melted wax that burned; the linguist would have been interested in the argument that evolved around the term "burning" (the children in this class call anything with a flame "burning," while "smoldering" has nothing to do with it); and the teacher was reassured by his busily working class. I was delighted at the totally uninhibited way these children went about their activities, free of the fear for the "wrong" answer, and continuously learning.

This revolution, we hope, may help to bring about the desired change in education benefiting all, and serve an effective system of "Education for Progress."

Teachers

However, it is the teachers who will have to bring about this change.

There is no lack of curriculum development schemes in the world. Curriculum development centers pour out new materials. Curriculum development panels reject and accept new materials. Curriculum development publishers circle keenly around, gladly assisting in the spread of new teaching aids. But the implementation of any new program will either fail or succeed with the teachers. There is a much greater need to change teachers than to change curriculums.

And here the difficulties accumulate.

There are the thousands of serving teachers, often rusted in a routine, and handicapped by the disease called "syllabusitis." Too often, especially in the past colonial systems, teachers were just told what to tell their children. They happily or unhappily swung about with the tides of changing syllabuses, and were never asked for their opinion, nor for their judgment. Even the enlightened teacher who dared to experiment was told by the inspector: "This is all very nice, and the children like it, but what about the examination?"

Most teachers acquired the attitude of playing it safe, and pleasing the inspectorates by "keeping the standards." What these standards really were was none of their business.

Next, there are the young students in the teachers' colleges. They are the product of the very system they will have to change. In many cases they have taken up teaching as a last resort. The need for teachers in an expanding school system is often so great that the training time is reduced to a minimum, the required qualifications are reduced to a minimum, and the rigorousness of the selection is reduced to a minimum.

They have come through a system of rote learning, and don't share the dissatisfaction with the existing system. After all, so they reason, this system was good enough to produce us. Therefore it cannot be all that bad. But they forget to ask themselves about the 90 percent that were left behind: What good did it do to them?

Our students have come through a system of rote learning in order to be successful in the exams. It is difficult for them to change their attitude. Their conservatism, together with a certain degree of intellectual inertia ("If you learn what you are told to learn, you'll be busy enough!") catches them in a vicious circle. They rote learn the most modern principles of education, but teach the way they were taught.

This vicious circle must be broken. No place is better to accomplish this than the teachers' college.

Science Training in the Teachers' College

The teachers' college must keep ahead of the changing patterns in educational thinking, and gear its program toward the future. The main task of the college is not to provide the trainees with a bag of teaching tricks, commonly called "methods," nor with so-called "higher academic background knowledge" as if it were a glorified secondary school, but to train them in, and help them to accept, a complete change of attitude toward their profession, toward children, toward the society in and for which they work, and thus toward education.

In the field of new science education the acquisition of a new attitude is a slow process, sometimes painful, sometimes rough, but always interesting to watch, and rewarding in the end. It is essential to introduce the students to a number of activities based on the ordinary local environment, to get them involved in some basic experiences of problem-solving activities of the type we envisage for the children they will teach. This often necessitates some shock treatment, and a little brain washing. It usually meets with some resistance.

When encouraged to investigate the amount of animal life present in various soil samples, some of my students objected: "We Africans are not interested in these small creatures." At another time the students worked with momentum bars made of a wooden stand and a strip of pegboard. These things are remarkably sensitive and rather accurate. The students, all being able to recall the law of momentum, had the greatest difficulty with the simplest problems to be solved with the help of these pegboard balances. This was painful, and they violently objected to working with these home-made balances, saying: "We are used to proper analytical laboratory balances."

Yet it is absolutely necessary that they go through this stage. It mainly serves to initiate the students into the true nature of scientific and mathematical processes, to develop and reinforce scientific and mathematical concepts, and to illustrate how this is transferred to a primary school situation.

The initial resistance wears off soon enough when the surprises come, when they find satisfaction, and thus gain in confidence. When I introduced a group of students to the use of a simple bead microscope that they could make themselves, they sneered that these things were no good. Of course, they have their limitations, but are surprisingly useful, giving a magnification of about sixty power. But three weeks later five of these boys worked four hours with me designing and improving a microscope made of used soap packets. They got so excited that they invited everybody passing by to come and have a look at the hairs on a fly wing through this waterdrop contraption, of which they were very proud.

Inseparably connected with all the activities done by the students, constant reference is made to children in the schools, the environment in which they live, and the basic goals and principles of an effective science education.

This is often done in discussions that arise from the activities, from difficulties encountered, and from successes scored. But whenever possible children are brought in. A small group of students may work with a small group of children. They may try out a new idea, introduce a new piece of local apparatus, or conduct an activity they have talked about and experimented with. The value of these micro-teaching situations lies in the opportunity to watch real children and their response to the problem-solving situations created for them, and at the same time to help the students recognize the merits or demerits of the materials used.

Once the students gain in confidence, they are encouraged to open up new areas of study. Going out from any environment, there is never a lack of interesting areas of scientific investigation. Some areas may place a greater emphasis on scientific abilities, whereas others may have a greater mathematical bias. In all cases there is every reason to encourage the students to follow their own interest to wherever it leads them. Open-endedness is an essential characteristic of this kind of approach. The awareness that personal interest is the main indicator of the direction of study is an important part of their training.

This has led students to investigate carefully the life history of an easily available insect: the ant lion. They traced it from the larva through the adult to the eggs. The fact that they failed to produce a second generation may have been disappointing, but was in no way discouraging. It became a challenge.

In order to study food preference in corn weevils, other students constructed an ingenious eight-way cross-passage out of a cork and eight straws leading to eight tubes with different food sources. They were very surprised to find the corn weevils ignoring the varied food supply, and boring into the cork. Again this was not regarded as a failure, but rather as a challenge leading to a whole series of further investigations.

Two students taking up the challenge of making a pendulum swing in a perfect figure of eight spent two solid weeks trying and trying again, slowly collecting clues, and finally succeeding.

To my mind there is no better way of training teachers than by actually involving them in exploring and trying out new ideas, experimenting with new materials, and considering and evaluating the pedagogical possibilities of these new materials. The complete absence of pressure by predetermined academic standards makes the students free, flexible, and confident. This may help them to become less dependent on written source-materials once they start teaching. They become more alert in discovering where the children's interests lie, and so avoid a situation of so-called "rote discovery" by the children.

Teaching practice, where they are in full charge of a class of real children, gives them the opportunity to convince themselves of whatever they think of this approach, or to convert themselves to whatever we think of it. To many this is a real revelation. The children are never a problem; they take to new science with glee and enthusiasm as soon as they realise that the strait jacket of "academic" instruction is taken off.

Naturally not every student teacher is equally successful, and some manage to make quite a mess of things. But we do have fine examples of classes bursting with activity, and teachers exclaiming that the children "know more than I do," because they are so keen in observing and finding out, and are allowed time to do so. They really benefit from these enjoyably noisy classes where children are learning, instead of being taught. The children are the best teacher trainers, and this is the most convincing part of the students' course.

"It is they, the teachers now at work and now going through the training colleges, who are shaping what Tanzania will become much more than we who pass laws, make rules, and make speeches." These words of President Nyerere, spoken at Morogoro Teachers' College, emphasize the fact that teacher education is a task of great complexity, and should be carried out more on the basis of a firm commitment, than from a prescribed syllabus or scheme of work.

The task of a teacher-training instructor reaches far beyond the boundaries of the teachers' college campus. By his very existence he is directly concerned with educational development. The object of this development work is not a program nor a curriculum, but people: in this case teachers, and through them children, and through the children the communities in which they live, and through these communities the nation.

Behind every student in the colleges we see masses of children growing up to be productive citizens of what they hope to be a prosperous nation. This prosperity will depend on them. If the schools are to be the centers of education in the villages, then the teachers' colleges should be the centers of continuous development, and a rich source of assistance to all teachers. This implies that college tutors, apart from forming teachers with the right attitudes, must be continuously engaged in real primary-school situations. This is essential in order to make development work meaningful. The college tutor can only offer valuable guidance if he is personally involved in the trial and evaluation of new materials, or the reevaluation of "old" materials in the light of a new environment.

Then the teachers' colleges may fulfill the task they deserve: to help establish the relationship that exists between science as a way of learning and as a way to self-confidence and self-reliance, and its impact on progress in a developing society.

The task of the teachers' college in science education can now be summarized as follows:

> To provide the students with basic experiences concerning their environment, so as to stimulate an inquiring mind—better late than never. Through their own experience they must discover the richness of doing science, and forget about learning science facts for the sake of learning science facts.
>
> To make the students aware of the value of science education as a progressive way of learning, as a way of thinking, and as a way toward self-confidence.
>
> To make the students proficient and competent in the processes and abilities through which we want to educate our children—the basic skills and abilities for an effective science education.

To stimulate in the students a degree of resourcefulness and creativity and understanding with regard to handling materials and children.

To make the students aware of the special nature of children, their relation to their environment, and the way they learn, so that the students learn to identify problem-solving situations suitable for the children in their charge.

To help them see and realize the need of their society as a whole for progress through the efforts of "intelligent hard workers" who have become conscious and confident of their ability to assist in solving the many problems of progress.

Building a teacher-training program which fulfills all these worthy aims is not an easy task. So much depends on the quality of the students, on the flexibility of responsible authorities, on the immediate environment, on the existing school system, and on the commitment of the tutors in charge of science education.

But I believe that life in a developing society is more than tending crops and raising cattle, and that a sound and good science education aids more than the doubtful ability to answer questions on a competitive exam and to get a job with a bicycle.

I believe in teachers who have learned to challenge their children with problems that appeal to them, and who give them confidence by allowing them to find their way out of these problems. These teachers have learned to use the environment as a source of wisdom, and their children learn to benefit from this source of wisdom.

I believe that children who have uncovered some of the secrets of living things by themselves, who have experienced some of the physical laws, be it by spinning, bouncing, dropping, or swinging things, who have recognized relationships and enjoyed their own ability to do much more with maintained and constantly renewed interest are better prepared to face the many problems of obtaining a livelihood and taking part in building the society in which they live and on which they depend than children who have been forced to swallow indigestible formulas and foreign facts laid down in syllabuses of factual knowledge and knowledgable facts.

I believe that if we change the teachers, and work together with them, then there is no longer any need for "curriculum development" as a separate entity. The teachers will change the curriculum. As for science education in the teachers' college, we must recognise priorities. We don't train teachers for their own sake, but for the sake of the children they will educate.

I believe that an educator with a real scientific mind can achieve more than a teacher blessed with advanced science courses, but forgetting about the education. That is why I prefer to see the teacher-training students involved directly in the educational process by which we attempt to create in the children the ability to learn from their own environment by their own intellectual powers. If the students need an "adult" challenge, then this is their adult challenge, more than ripple tanks and periodic charts, more than relativity and quantum mechanics.

As President Nyerere puts it: "In some nations people try to reach the moon; we try to reach the villages."

DISCUSSION

Rev. Elstgeest said that the principle his college is applying in Tanzania is to get the teacher to understand he is not teaching a syllabus, he is teaching children, and his equipment is the soil, the seeds, the plants, the whole universe about him, his textbook is the world in which he lives. Their present aim is to form a cadre of teachers before starting to implement the new program on a universal scale. This is to avoid a failure and frustration through launching it prematurely. Training a teacher in this way was very difficult, because they had come from a system, had learned by rote how they were going to teach. Yet they welcomed the change because they belonged to the lucky few who had been selected for further education.

The Teachers' College was 40 years old, and the village school it used for training purposes was 80 years old. In the beginning of the reform movement, the children were very resistant, they felt insecure because they suspected they were not being given the right answers from the teacher's head. They had to get down on their hands and knees in soil, instead of reading a book. But later they did get involved and enthusiastic, and so did the teachers.

Teachers must bear in mind that 90 percent of the pupils finishing primary school in Africa will return to a village with a subsistence agricultural economy, a rough sort of house, a few implements, a stream. The aim of education should be to help them to adapt to this life, and to improve it, not to make them frustrated and discontented, seekers of the bright lights of the cities.

Dr. Augustus Caine (Liberia) wondered whether any system would induce young people to remain in the villages, because historically there has always been a drift from village to city. Does the new system of science teaching in Tanzania really make a young man or young woman stay at home?

The move from pilot project to the whole country is a major problem everywhere, said *Dr. Fletcher G. Watson* (United States). In the United States he found that people on a pilot project are very able and enthusiastic, but then a program has to be dispersed among a large number of teachers in a large area.

Another question bothered *Mr. D. G. Chisman* (Great Britain): what becomes of a young teacher from Father Elstgeest's college when he finds himself at a school, probably a large school, where the headmaster and the senior members of the staff are not sympathetic to the new ideas? Will he lose his enthusiasm? How do they maintain contact with such a teacher? Furthermore, are they not losing a lot of teachers to other professions, as is happening in other countries?

Dr. Ademola Banjo (UNECA) doubted whether it is really possible to let the students wander in whatever direction happens to excite their interest, as

198 Science and Education in Developing States

seems to be implied by Father Elstgeest. This is simply not practicable; there has to be some selection. Finally, one has to come to what can only be called some sort of effective curriculum, a selection of topics instead of undirected curiosity. Otherwise, how will any progress be made in science? A second question is, how does he select his teachers for special training; what are the criteria? Do they have to be graduates?

In his reply, Father Elstgeest said that his program has only been under way for three years, so he cannot provide complete answers. All he could say at this stage, in response to Dr. Caine's query about persuading young people not to leave the villages, is that formal education had certainly failed to keep them at home. Perhaps the new system will succeed.

With regard to helping young teachers against unsympathetic headmasters and staff, he hopes that his program will give his graduates sufficient support; it is backed officially by the ministry of education. As for teacher drop-outs, they have suffered from this in the past, but the position is now much better, the teachers are government employees and sign five-year contracts.

The criteria for selecting candidates for the college are enthusiasm and dedication, not necessarily degrees. As for a formal curriculum, the real question is what one is after, what kind of children one hopes to produce.

23

HOW TO DEAL WITH THE BRAIN DRAIN

By Théo J. M. Lefèvre

Minister in Charge of
Science Policies and
Programming,
Belgium

Recent economic analysis has led to the definition of three bottlenecks that hamper development:
1. Lack of human resources, or of skilled labor
2. Inadequate formation of capital
3. Inefficiency of the international division of labor, in such measure as it results from obstacles placed in the path of commercial exchanges.

These three bottlenecks form part of a theory of stages of growth set forth in an interesting study by Chenery and Strout.[1] The authors conclude that the developing countries come up mainly against one of the three bottlenecks, according to the stage of growth that they have reached. It appears that the existence of human capital and skilled labor constitutes in underdeveloped countries an essential precondition of the capacity for favorable absorption of foreign financial or economic assistance.

Human capital plays a considerable role in development. The primary, immediate objective recommended in the study is a better-balanced distribution of know-how and aptitudes in the organizational line, and in technical and vocational training, in order to enhance the favorable effects on world-wide development as a whole. Scientific research and development constitute, with other things, the essential elements of human capital that contribute to divergent development between the poor and the rich countries.

The gap between the developed and the underdeveloped world is further accentuated by the importance assumed by the systematic application of science in the growth process of industrialized countries, where scientific research and technological development are increasingly regarded as the very basis of industrial innovation (invention of new products and processes) which, in the present conditions of international competition, has become decisive.

Scientific discoveries thus enable the most highly developed countries to achieve further economic progress; and economic progress, in turn, by creating new wealth, allows more resources to be diverted to science. The process is therefore a cumulative one.

---

[1] H. B. Chenery and A. M. Strout, "Foreign Assistance and Economic Development," *American Economic Review* (Sept., 1966).

Information presently available indicates that the resources relating to science are concentrated in those countries whose level of economic development is highest, in other words, in a belt consisting of North America, West and East Europe, and Japan. This belt contains 30 percent of the world's population, 75 percent of its revenue, 80 percent of its higher science and technical teachers, and 95 percent of its researchers.

In this developed zone, it is the industrial sector that absorbs the major part (60 percent, on average) of national resources earmarked for research and development.

These resources applied to industrial research are concentrated in the newest fields of industrial activity, which offer the most favorable prospects of expansion: the mechanical, chemical, and electronic industries (93 percent in the United States, 80 percent in the industrialized parts of Europe).

This, obviously, is the background against which the brain-drain problem must be envisaged.

The Brain Drain: Causes and Effects

The brain drain is a symptom, and at the same time an aggravating factor of the gap between the stages of development. Nor does it exclusively affect the developing countries; some European countries also have a "brain drain" problem, involving migration to a more highly developed society:·the United States.

It is particularly serious, however, in the Third World, where an estimated 25 to 30 percent of young researchers leave their country of origin soon after completing their education.

Causes

The causes of the brain drain fall into a number of different categories:

More or less specific, identifiable causes of imbalance between the demand and the supply of particular skills in the developing countries; we refer to persons wrongly oriented in training and too highly specialized for the requirements of the underdeveloped countries.

Motives of personal advancement: those who wish to emigrate are attracted by prospects of better pay, of better careers, of a more favorable atmosphere for work.

Cultural motives: skilled personnel whose education has given them an opportunity to widen their horizon become by that very fact exogenous elements in an autochthonous society, unassimilated enclaves at odds with an uncongenial sociological environment; they have difficulty in communicating with the majority of their fellow-citizens and are hamstrung by the lack of scientific and intellectual traditions.

Obstacles of a structural and institutional nature: the brain drain is also largely due to the instability of political and economic structures and to lack of adaptation of educational and scientific systems.

The brain drain seems to involve mainly those with a higher scientific and technical education: holders of degrees in science, engineering, medicine. On the other hand, those whose education is more in the arts and social-science fields—literature, political science, economics—seem to find it easier to integrate, often, admittedly, because of the bureaucratization process which is apparent in the new countries.

Effects

Obviously the emigration of the scientifically trained mind makes it even harder to catch up. It impoverishes the country of origin, since the latter cannot benefit from the talents of those whom it has educated at heavy expense—a particularly tragic waste of resources.

As an instance of this, and allowing for marked differences from one subject to another in the present-day costs of training a university graduate, average annual public expenditure in Belgium per head of student was running at Fr. Belg. 101,000 in 1969.

This wastage of resources in the developing countries is sometimes twofold: an initial loss through training being provided at the expense of the underdeveloped countries, and thereafter the lack of well-being caused by the exodus of skilled personnel.

Actually, the considerable efforts made by the underdeveloped countries in the higher education field coincide with a demand for highly qualified personnel in the industrialized countries which increases faster than the supply. This situation creates a powerful attraction phenomenon, and a young Indian, Ugandan, or Argentinian graduate will evidently need a good deal of civic consciousness and even willingness to make sacrifices to resist it.

The brain drain thus accentuates the concentration of highly qualified manpower resources in the most highly developed part of the world. Consequently, it strengthens the dominant position of certain countries still further and creates situations of tension.

The brain drain can no longer be regarded as a normal phenomenon of scientific migration, as apparent from its extent, its effects, and its artificiality: it is further intensified by systematic prospecting on the part of foreign organizations and particularly of industrial firms, which organize veritable "brain-hunts." There has even been talk of a "pathological" form of intellectual migration, that has existed throughout history.

Recent research has shown that, in 1967, 20,000 qualified personnel (university graduates and hospital nurses) moved from the poor countries to the industrialized countries. In 1966, emigration to the United States of highly qualified personnel from the developing countries totaled some 6,000 persons, half of whom were qualified engineers and experts in the exact and natural sciences.

What Steps Can Be Taken?

My own impression is that any steps or statutory measures that might be taken, whether by the countries of origin or the countries of destination, any international plans that might be devised to solve this specific problem of the brain drain, would be likely to be basically inadequate unless they form part of a world-wide policy designed to enable the young nations to enter into a new stage of development through rational use of their natural resources.

There have been suggestions to restrict the immigration of highly qualified personnel into, say, the United States, to encourage emigrants to return to their own countries through appropriate financial measures, and to debar holders of foreign scholarships studying in American universities from accepting employment in the United States in the first two years after graduating.

In England several proposals have been put forward that a university graduate who leaves his own country for another industrialized country should refund to the government an amount equal to the cost of training, e.g., some Fr. Belg. 720,000 for the holder of a university degree. It has been increasingly suggested that scholarship contracts contain a clause specifying that a student from a developing country undertake to return to his native country for good. Many private organizations that provide aid to developing countries already insert this clause.

But can one be sure that these trained men will *integrate in their native society* and adequately apply their talents there, while *serving the interests of their country*? Can one be sure that a chemist or physicist who has left an underdeveloped country would have been efficiently utilized if he had stayed in his own country? One may doubt it.

If not, it would be even more tragic for young nations to pay a high price for recovering specialists who would be of no use to them: the waste of resources would be double.

The real problem therefore may lie in the *lack of adaptation* of underdeveloped societies and their governing structures. In those societies, the production of highly qualified personnel is obviously out of step with the level of socioeconomic development.

In this respect, financial considerations (the wish to earn more) do not seem the only determinant factors in the brain drain; they seem less important than cultural factors and the better prospects of social and personal betterment.

The main problem is that those who emigrate want to escape from an inhospitable and in some respects even hostile environment. A final solution of this problem therefore calls for a deep-going change of social organization in the underdeveloped countries.

Steps to be Taken by the Underdeveloped Countries

The problem is a twofold one, that of concentrating the resources at the disposal of the new nations, and turning such resources to the best possible account. This calls for organization and political purpose.

The primary requirement is that the underdeveloped countries *train manpower able to fill* those *countries' concrete needs*, and that they develop *specific* solutions for the physical obstacles of any kind that stand in the way.

Is it not significant that, of the 600,000 qualified persons with university-grade training in Latin America, only 3 percent are employed in the agricultural sector, though the latter accounts for 46 percent of the active population in that part of the globe? Yet some 60 percent of all university graduates have studied literature, law, or the arts.

In India, qualified persons with a higher education fall into the following categories, according to their degree: 90 percent have studied law, the arts and commerce, 4.9 percent technical subjects and technology, 3.4 percent medicine, 1.2 percent agriculture and 1.7 percent other technical subjects.

Still more serious is the fact that among the few persons with scientific training in such countries, many prefer to engage in fundamental research rather than research applied to solving the specific problems of their country. Winning a Nobel Prize in nuclear physics may be a source of prestige for a country, but it may also be a costly luxury if nuclear energy is not an economic proposition for that country.

Reverting to India, where per capita gross national product is only $86 a year, the laboratory system specializes essentially in nuclear physics, the utilization of solar energy, and road construction, although researches in soil utilization and potentialities in the food production line are a matter of compelling urgency.

The real tragedy is that all too often the highly qualified personnel of Asia, Africa, or Latin America—mainly because of a traditional education system copied from that of the developed countries—are better able to solve the problems of an industrial society than those of an underdeveloped society.

It is therefore necessary to *create appropriate motivations* for young people who embark on a higher education. It is the responsibility of the universities in these countries to concentrate their research and training facilities in the fields of science in which discoveries may provide solutions for the nation's problems. It is the responsibility of the economic planners to provide employment for university graduates. This applies particularly to countries that have few resources to devote to the training of their intellectuals and of the auxiliary personnel destined to assist them.

Those going abroad for purposes of study should be briefed on the problems and priorities of development in their own country, informed of their prospects of employment when they return and encouraged to orient their studies abroad toward solutions of the problems of their own country.

The education system of a country can actually produce a surplus of certain types of qualification in relation to what that country's economy can absorb, while turning out too few skills of the type necessary for development. This inevitably leads to a brain drain.

It is essential for the underdeveloped countries to realize that science does not produce solutions automatically; one should not want to engage in research at all costs, in any field, in the hope that some applicable discovery will eventually emerge. Research is a necessary condition of progress, or rather a catalyst of the different factors of progress, but it is not the only condition. Training scientists and building laboratories is not enough; their activities must also serve the common interest, not merely satisfy the curiosity of a few initiates. Research, then, should *lead to useful things*; and in order to do so it should be backed up by a whole range of activities designed to utilize its results at the economic and social level. If research is ultimately to help increase the national income and improve the foreign trade balance, it should be directed toward certain well-defined needs and integrated in the whole range of operations that add up to the economic development process, with a view to achieving definite general development objectives.

Another essential need for a country passing through the first stages of industrial development is to concentrate its efforts on transplanting the principles of foreign science and technology and *adapting them to its own local conditions* and its own problems.

The underdeveloped countries could in fact have access to a sizable "stock" of technological know-how perfected in the industrial countries, which with the necessary local adjustments could be used to solve those countries' specific problems.

This would require the establishment of a nucleus of scientific personnel not primarily concerned with making original discoveries but with keeping abreast of achievements abroad and also of probable future developments in science and technology. As we shall see later, this objective would also require that the industrialized countries make their know-how more readily accessible.

The most recent researches in manpower show that the number of technicians of all kinds that are needed in the poorer countries far exceeds requirements in university graduates. In Iran, for example, the number of physicians is seven times greater than the number of qualified nurses. In 1965 Colombia had an enrollment of only 1,150 in its higher technical schools, as against 23,000 in the universities. The reasons are obvious. The technical schools do not have the prestige of the universities and therefore do not attract the best students nor the most competent teachers. The pay and status of technical personnel are well below those of university graduates, and the universities generally have enough room for secondary-school graduates. Thus the main weakness of higher agricultural education is the students' refusal to enroll.

By raising the pay levels and prestige of these technicians, more young people could be attracted to take an interest in tasks that are vitally necessary for their own well-being and economic development.

Finally, if a research effort is to be meaningful, the manpower and financial resources made available for it should exceed a certain minimum. This holds good at the level of specific research projects and at that of the overall national effort.

International Science Projects

The answer for the poorer countries is to pool their resources and undertake cooperative projects. It would seem desirable for underdeveloped countries belonging to regions where the problems do not differ much from one country to another to pool their efforts to solve them and to set up joint organizations in which young scientists could find a more appropriate environment, more and better equipment, and more favorable material conditions than they can hope for in their own countries.

European governments allocate on average between 10 and 15 percent of their science budgets for international scientific cooperation. Since the resources which the young nations can devote to science lie generally much farther below the threshold of effectiveness than European allocations, one might ask whether the underdeveloped countries would not do well to appropriate a larger proportion of their science budgets for joint scientific programs than the European countries do.

That being said, one should get a clear grasp of the *conditions* in which international cooperation in the field of science can be *really effective*. In this respect, it would be well to study the mistakes made by the European countries in international scientific cooperation, so as to avoid them.

European experience shows that the essential condition for the success of such cooperation is that the participating countries should not merely confine themselves to the joint pursuit of a certain number of scientific projects, but from the beginning set targets for their efforts—economic development targets, so that all the participants can derive material benefits from their pooled efforts.

In other words, scientific cooperation should be integrated within a larger, continuous framework of cooperation, bearing on *all stages of development* from the laboratory to industrial production and commercial exploitation of the product, within a well-defined program and with specific objectives.

For whereas all countries can easily enough reach agreement on a joint research effort, the difficulties arise when it comes to exploiting results and sharing benefits. At the latter stage, selfish and nationalistic considerations tend to gain the upper hand, and each partner is tempted to develop the results of the joint scientific effort on his own, within the limits of his own means. The difficulties presently experienced by Euratom and ELDO are striking instances of the foregoing.

Steps to be Taken by the Industrialized Countries

Although UNCTAD at its inaugural session recommended to the industrialized countries that they earmark at least 1 percent of their gross national product for aid to the poorer countries, one finds that this figure has not risen since 1960; on the contrary, aid granted by the member countries of the EEC to the developing countries, expressed in percentages of their GNP, showed a drop (0.75 percent in 1967 as against 0.89 percent in 1960).

Moreover, two fundamental errors on the part of the industrialized countries should be set forth here:

An all-too-frequent mistake made by industrialized countries in extending their more or less generous aid to underdeveloped countries has been to assume that the methods applicable to a society on the threshold of the first stage of industrialization are the same as those that apply in an already industrialized society.

Too often the technical aid lavished on a new nation has failed to bear full fruit because it had not been properly adapted to the country's specific problems and to the real aspirations of the population. *Such aid has often remained an exogenous element*, unintegrated in the national development process.

The same applies to industrial cooperation. Setting up factories has too often resulted in the establishment of a foreign industrial superstructure which, through lower production costs, served the needs of the investing rather than those of the receiving country.

It would no doubt have been more profitable if the industrailized countries had given freer access to their techniques and know-how and encouraged its adaptation by the underdeveloped countries tehmselves under appropriate agreements, according to their own requirements and with on-spot utilization of the imagination and creativity of the receiving country's own scientific and technical personnel.

It follows that the creation of *appropriate and adequate research centers* should be promoted in the developing countries. Lacking well-trained technicians, the developing countries cannot afford to undertake fundamental research on a large scale in many fields; such research would be uneconomic. Moreover, they can acquire up-to-date technological know-how from better developed countries.

Nevertheless, in certain sectors such as agriculture local research is of capital importance. Agricultural production depends on the climate, on the soil, on geographical facts, and on the system of land tenure. In each country these various factors have their own special character, and in order to increase yields quickly it is not enough to borrow seed material and techniques evolved elsewhere.

In other fields too, research is a function of the special requirements of each region: we refer to geological and ecological research, or to land utilization. There are also interesting research prospects through the application of industrial techniques to locally exploited raw materials and agricultural produce, ensuring better on-spot utilization.

Much work of capital importance for the well-being of the developing countries could be done more efficiently in some cases through *cooperative research on the regional scale*, and technical assistance could play a primary role in setting up appropriate research centers of this kind.

Although in principle such research programs should be developed with priority in the developing countries, it should be pointed out that in some former colonial powers there are research centers created essentially for studying the problems of overseas countries. Enabling these institutes to pursue their tasks and detach their experts to developing countries is an extremely useful form of technical assistance.

The second shortcoming lies in the fact that the most highly industrialized countries have failed to find an adequate solution for the production of the highly qualified personnel they need in order to keep up their rapid pace of development.

The United States does not turn out enough graduates, and resorts to the whole world in order to make up the shortage. Several European countries actually make up for their own brain drain to the United States by importing specialists from the underdeveloped countries.

This organizational fault, therefore, has direct repercussions in the new nations and creates an intolerable situation which can only be remedied through deep-going reform of the higher education system in the developed countries and a fairer immigration system.

Conclusions

The problem of the brain drain cannot be solved independently of the overall problem of the young nations' access to a more advanced stage of development, which in turn calls for tackling the social, economic, and political stresses of all kinds that hold back development.

Certain steps can of course be taken to slow down the escape of talent: for instance, stricter immigration regulations in the countries that import "gray matter" or steps making it more attractive for specialists to return to their country of origin.

One should nevertheless not hope for too much. Really effective solutions will have to be on a more ample scale and spread over a much longer term. They consist, on the part of the developing countries, in gearing the training of their highly qualified personnel to the solution of such countries' own problems, (this applies to the contents of training as well as to the number of trainees); and on the part of the developed countries, in giving aid more in terms of freer access to the information and know-how they have gained through their power and wealth (for adapting foreign experience to their own problems is the best way in which underdeveloped countries can make use of their own scientific experts in the first industrialization stage).

Only in such conditions can world solidarity effectively cure the brain drain. Such solidarity cannot be expressed in the form of hand-outs, which cannot solve the underdevelopment problem. On the contrary, it should be organized with well-defined objectives and be based on political realities, however unpalatable they may be; that is the only realistic approach to the problem.

DISCUSSION

Dr. Marcelo Alonso (OAS) reduced the problem of the brain drain to three basic elements—the production of human resources, their utilization, and their conservation. The educational system is responsible for the production end. Utilization takes place either in the scientific infrastructure or in the industrial productive sector of a country. If production exceeds utilization, there will of necessity be a brain drain: if it is too low, there will be what might be called a "brain strain." If production and utilization are equated, there should be neither drain nor strain.

But Dr. Alonso is opposed to this attempt at equalization, because it will introduce a limiting factor to development; it is better to produce more human resources than are needed according to forecasts. This brings up the question of conservation. In his opinion, it is impossible to stop the brain drain if a country cannot utilize its trained personnel. One partial solution is to use regional projects, to direct brains into large, neighboring countries with which the small country is engaged in a regional scheme. Basically, it is impossible to stop brains draining to where they are needed most. This happens inside a country too; for example, there has been a brain drain to California at the expense of other areas of the United States. Apart from regional planning, the only hope is national development, but there can be no easy formula to stop the brain drain.

Mr. Hanoch Smith (Israel) agreed with Dr. Alonso that it is impossible to stop the brain drain if a country is still too undeveloped to utilize all its brains. There are demographic and educational pressures making it essential to expand education; the demands for widespread education are very healthy. But it is not such a tragedy if a man from one of the developing countries becomes dean of a faculty at Harvard University; there is no reason to hound him, or bewail the money spent on educating him. On the contrary, a country should be very proud of him. Soon, the possibilities of utilizing people at home will increase, and the brain drain will flow back again.

But *Mr. Jorge Alberto Sabato* (Argentina) pointed out that a serious brain drain can exist even when a country is already industrialized, like Argentina. One of the factors leading to this form of migration is political instability. Secondly, a lot depends on the status of scientific personnel; in Argentina they feel that their status is lower than that of scientists in the United States or Soviet Russia.

The brain drain is a necessary evil, but it can be abated by international solidarity, thought *Mr. Yaya Bagayogo* (Mali). The cost invested in every scientist includes the amount spent on him in primary school, secondary school, and university. The country *receiving* him should refund the amount involved to his country of origin, at the same time providing precise data and technicians able to do the work the scientist is expected to do and does not want to do. There will be an element of natural justice if agreements embodying these principles are drawn up between the developed and developing countries.

Mr. William Farquhar Conton (Sierra Leone) said that Sierra Leone has found that the answer to the brain drain is to create its own university. People are attracted, not by higher salaries, but by teaching and research facilities. If these are available at home, even though salaries are not as high, the graduates stay in Sierra Leone. If every nation cannot establish its own university immediately, nations in a given region can cooperate to form regional universities.

PART VI

NEW METHODS FOR NEW NEEDS

24

ADVANCED-GENERATION
TECHNOLOGIES IN
FIRST-GENERATION
EDUCATION—AN
INTERDISCIPLINARY CRISIS

By Seth Spaulding

*Director, Department of
School and Higher Education,
UNESCO (Paris)*

Curriculum Research and Development

It makes great sense to begin with the curriculum when one is interested in educational improvement. After all, the curriculum is the stuff of education. It is what we teach, what the students "get," what we examine for, and what we give certificates and diplomas for when the students complete it.

But precisely what is the curriculum, where does it come from, how can we be sure of its relevance, and what kind of continuous progress is necessary to be sure it is continuously relevant in the future?

In order to answer these questions, the curriculum must be defined in terms of how and what we want the students to know, do, think, and feel when they are no longer captives of the school. As we try to define the objectives of the curriculum, we must keep in mind what kinds of information, skills, thoughts, and feelings the children bring with them when they come to school, what kinds of things are happening to them outside of school, where they are likely to go and what they are likely to do when they finish school.

One of the reasons for current student unrest throughout the world is the fact that curriculum reform has not been continuous and the curriculum has not been entirely relevant, either to what the student brings to it, or to what the student expects from it. The student in today's secondary school and university is a very different kind of person from the student of a generation or two ago. The information explosion has affected the younger generation. The secondary-school student has probably learned more out of school than he has in school and the university student often feels much closer to the problems of his nation than does the professor who lectures to him. Yet, the curriculum has changed little to reflect the changing nature of the students and of the society in which education exists.

Similarly, we know that in many countries only one out of every ten students entering primary school will finish, yet we have a linear curriculum which assumes that the purpose of primary school is to prepare the student for secondary school. What can be done, instead, that will be useful to children no matter how few years they attend?

In the same vein, how do we define what should be done in technical education? How is technically based education related to general education? If technology is changing at such an accelerated pace, does it make sense to have several kinds and levels of technical schools, or should many technicians be trained on the job in industries and organizations that know what they need?

What about traditional subject matter areas? Are these structured so as to teach the behaviors we think are necessary for survival in the next generation? What do we teach students to know, do, think, and feel about population problems, about the role of the family in the future development of their country, about what each of us can do about pollution problems, transportation congestion, peace, and war?

In essence, are we asking the right questions when we build a curriculum? Do we have the right institutions and the right people involved when we make curriculum decisions? The students beating on and rocking the foundations of our institutions may be right—we may not have.

The New Curriculum Approaches

Academicians in the physical sciences, as indeed those in all academic disciplines, have become in recent years interested and involved in the curriculum problems of the elementary and especially the secondary schools. The new curriculum approaches in biology, physics, and mathematics were the forerunners of new curriculum approaches in other subject areas, including foreign languages, history, and social studies.

The strength of most of these new curriculum approaches is that they attempt to define the processes at work in each discipline and attempt to develop ways of teaching these processes. The assumption is that students will then think like scientists, historians, or what have you, and they will thus be able to keep up with the accelerated pace of change. We have little experience, as yet, in watching what happens to students who have come through these new curricular programs to find out if, indeed, they have learned to think like academicians and if, in fact, this does them any good if they do. Certainly, we have no answer to the question as to whether a student should think like a biologist or physicist, as opposed to a philosopher, or a demographer, or a historian, or a psychologist, or an anthropologist.

Presumably, one of the basic needs in most countries is for more entrepreneurs, more organizers and doers and ground-shakers, better administrators of government, more achievement-oriented businessmen. How many scientists do you know who are any of these things? Perhaps people are better if they know something of the processes of science, but what are the other things they need to know, do, think, and feel in order to become agents of development in their countries, and how can the schools teach these things (or how can we create the environment so that students can learn them)?

Institutionalizing the Curriculum Development Process

One of the basic needs in most countries is a substantial investment in new kinds of action-oriented curriculum research and development institutions to continuously seek answers to these kinds of questions. These institutions must first deal with the establishment of broad curriculum goals. Inputs into this goal-setting process must come from the community (what do parents and the public want in the way of education for their children?), the government (what are the political and economic goals of the future within the context of which the children will live when they leave school?), and from the various institutions that must interact with the educational system (what are the needs of industry, agriculture, government, etc., for certain kinds of manpower; what other institutions offer educational services or affect students, etc.?).

Once the broad goals are clear, the technology of curriculum-building can begin. Inputs here must be provided by subject-matter specialists (what is the nature of the content in each area and what are the thinking processes involved?), pedagogues and psychologists (what are the best ways of "mediating" whatever it is you have decided must be taught?), sociologists, anthropologists, and economists (what is going to be the effect on the society and the economy of what you are trying to do in the curriculum?), school administrators (how can you create and manage a school that does all of this well?), teachers (is it feasible to do this in a classroom or some other environment that takes the place of what we now know as a classroom?) and teaching materials specialists (how do you package all of this in the form of materials and display devices that can be used by the students and the teacher, in the teaching-learning environment you have defined, to achieve the goals agreed upon at the beginning of the process?).

This kind of curriculum-building process would begin to make use of the technology available to us. It would represent a scientific approach to the applied art of teaching. It would make possible a systems approach to curriculum planning (or at least a "systematic" approach), whereby various goals as seen by different sectors of society are considered and a matrix of goals agreed upon. Once these broad goals were set, behavioral goals would be suggested in very concrete terms. Alternate teaching strategies and materials would be tried in schools and universities until these strategies and materials were found to be effective and efficient. Collaborating teacher-training programs would adapt their programs to train the kinds of teachers needed to manage the new educational approaches. New kinds of school financing and school facilities would be developed to make possible the new strategies and approaches.

All of this would require specialist talents not usually found in ministries of education in large numbers. It would require a commitment on the part of government to invest monies where heretofore they had not been spent. It would require interdisciplinary collaboration among disciplinarians who must work together in the designing of a total school curriculum, taking into consideration as complementary not only each of the subject-matter areas in the curriculum but also the total school environment.

Technological Devices in Education

A true technology of education includes the entire process of the setting of goals, the continuous renewal of curriculums as described above, the trying out of alternate strategies and materials, the evaluation of the system as a whole and the resetting of goals as new information on the effect of the system is acquired. However, educational technology is often identified with the various devices and processes that make possible the recording, storage, manipulation, retrieval, transmission, and display of data, information, and printed and photographic material with an efficiency and speed unheard of even ten years ago. If these capabilities are considered as part of a broad curriculum research and development design, they have tremendous potential in education.

Technological devices and materials useful in the instructional process range from those that help the teacher develop and present his material more effectively in a more or less traditional classroom to those that completely alter what goes on in the classroom, including what the teacher is expected or required to do. A number of technological devices can be useful in both instruction itself and in the management of administrative data that is necessary in modern mass education. The computer, for example, can be used to make new kinds of administrative strategies possible (by, for instance, making complicated individual tests of students and the flexible scheduling of classes feasible) and, at the same time, can be used in the instructional process itself in the more efficient manipulation of instructional materials (computer-assisted instruction).

The unsophisticated enthusiast often believes that new educational technologies will quickly and cheaply resolve the current problems of education. These enthusiasts usually underestimate the complexities of education and the immense problems inherent in changing the way we go about education so as to permit the new technologies to contribute effectively.

The Audio-Visual Aid

It seems reasonable to assume that it is good to have devices that help the teacher do better whatever it is he traditionally does. It is in this vein that the so-called audio-visual movement has run its course over the past two or so generations.

Many of us have visited schools which have been proud of all their audio-visual equipment. We are shown storerooms full of tape recorders, slide and filmstrip projectors, 16-mm. movie projectors, overhead projectors, record players, and the like. Often, much of the equipment is very dusty and much of it may be out of service because it needs minor repairs. If the equipment is heavily used, it is usually by the few teachers who take an interest in it, or because of a selfless teacher who has become the "audio-visual coordinator" and who acts as a missionary among the other teachers.

These "first-generation" educational technologies have suffered (and continue to suffer) from ineffective utilization because they are usually not conceived of as part of an entirely new strategy of instruction which requires new kinds of administrative support, new kinds of curriculum materials ("software") suitable for presentation via the devices ("hardware") and new ways of managing the materials so that they are easily available to the teacher. For instance, there may be a 16-mm. film library available to the school, but it is usually a complicated process for a teacher to locate an appropriate film in the catalog, order it for preview, then show it in the classroom. Add to this borrowing the cumbersome projector, setting it up in a classroom that is usually not designed for projection, taking it all down again, and you have the full picture of the reason why most classroom teachers are not excited about the use of films.

If we were really serious about the use of one medium, such as the 16-mm. film, in an educational system, problems such as the above could be resolved through overall systematic planning of needed services. These would range from the prior selection, by curriculum planners, of existing films for use at certain points in the curriculum to the development of new films where existing films do not do the desired job. Administrative problems that impede the use of the films could be resolved through the provision of new services (perhaps a film library in each school), the permanent installation of projectors in each classroom, prefocused and ready to use.

On the other hand, there may be alternate strategies for improving the teaching process which would be more efficient, more suited to the flexibility we want in the classroom and easier to adapt as the curriculum changes. For instance, why bother with 16-mm. at all, now that we have 8-mm. cartridge-loaded projectors available? With these, it is conceivable that each classroom could have, say, in science, a shelf of film cartridges, each showing one of the essential demonstrations of the course. Students and teachers alike could take the cartridge whenever they wish, insert it into a rear screen projector the size of a television set, and review a selected demonstration. If the teacher has creative abilities, he could make his own cartridge films as well, but it is likely that a prepared set of film cartridges would be part of a curriculum package developed by a curriculum research and development center such as that described earlier.

The overhead projector has similar potential. This was originally used as a kind of substitute blackboard, and very effectively at that. The teacher can look at the students while writing on the transparency with a grease pencil, and whatever he is writing is projected on the screen over his shoulder. But recently, curriculum planners have been making available complete sets of prepared transparencies. The transparencies are a packaged teaching methodology and they provide the skeleton for anything from one teaching unit to a complete course. If the transparencies are used in the right order and as per instructions, even the most pedestrian teacher can make a good classroom presentation. A good teacher, of course, goes far beyond the basic suggested presentation of the set of transparencies and becomes, with their assistance, an excellent teacher.

In essence, these second- and third-generation teaching devices and materials are making approaches possible that go far beyond the first-generation teaching aids. They increasingly depend on more and more sophisticated packaged "software" which is provided the teacher and which can come only from curriculum research and development efforts. They similarly depend more and more on global planning of what goes on in the classroom and a rebudgeting of how monies will be spent in the instructional process.

Mass-Instruction Technologies—Efficient and/or Effective?

Strangely enough, at one end of our educational spectrum some experts are stressing the need to adapt instruction to individual differences, while at the other end some are advocating systems of mass instruction that involve thousands of students simultaneously watching the same instructional sequence via a television screen. Certainly, the pied piper of television and radio often hypnotizes the unwary into believing that these mass media can somehow suddenly educate all our children painlessly and cheaply.

We not only have television stations that have a range of forty or fifty miles but we have satellites that will make it possible to transmit educational programs to an entire continent or to several continents at the same time. Hot and heavy controversies are underway in many countries as to whether or not the way to resolve their educational problems is through direct broadcast satellite (a system whereby slightly modified television sets can receive directly from a satellite) or through ground-based satellite systems (stations on the ground which depend on satellites for interconnection).

The ability to bring a wealth of outside experiences into the classroom at the flick of a switch excites the imagination. But the definition of what this should be, its planning, production, broadcast, and use in schools, must be part of the overall curriculum research and development process already described. In many cases, it might be more appropriate to provide libraries of 8-mm. cartridge films than to produce an instructional television course. In other cases, a set of transparencies to help the teacher, plus sets of workbooks for students, may be more effective than a television course. Certainly, the concept of televison "lessons" substituting for broad ranges of activities in the school is to be discouraged.

The Elements of Successful Broadcast Instruction

Of course, one might decide that at certain stages in the development of an educational system it may be useful to present a core of sequential instruction via television or radio because of the lack of highly trained and experienced teachers. If alternate strategies of improving what goes on in the classroom have been carefully examined and discarded as being less appropriate, television is certainly worth a try. In such circumstances, the technical problems of getting the material broadcast are important. But, as demonstrated in Samoa, Colombia, Niger, El Salvador, and elsewhere, transmission problems are much less important than (1) the planning of what needs to be broadcast, (2) specification of how it will be used in the classroom, (3) development of the materials that will be needed by teachers and students along with the broadcast, (4) development of feedback and evaluation devices to find out what is happening in the classroom, (5) establishment of a system for interaction with the teachers so that they know what to do and feel a part of the system, and (6) constant revision of the entire strategy as the teachers, students, and the context of the educational system change.

It is unlikely that such a system would save money in the sense that many more students can be enrolled at less per capita cost. The cost of education per enrolled student would probably rise, but the cost of the successful student might drop. Additional quality bought for the additional investment might be worth it in achieving fewer drop-outs, less wastage, and greater efficiency.

As with any other educational strategy, there must be a full financial and conceptual commitment if such a system is attempted. An instructional television scheme operated on a shoestring is doomed to failure.

Out-of-school uses of television or radio require the same sort of planning. Although experience has shown the drawing power of television, its effectiveness as an educational medium depends largely on the infrastructure at the receiving end to encourage continuous, sequential viewing and interaction on the part of the audience. Thus, the occasional program on agriculture probably has little identifiable immediate effect, but "farm forums," which are organized around reception centers, may be more effective. Similarly, attempts to teach literacy via radio and television have been discouraging, except when broadcasting is used within a system to encourage adults to meet in groups to watch the programs as a part of a literacy class which includes more than television viewing or radio listening.

Broadcasting has also been used successfully as a supplement to correspondence courses. Again, the broadcast program is rarely sufficient in itself to provide the core of instruction, in large part because of its inherent limitations (it cannot, for instance, be reread and studied at leisure). But, in conjunction with sets of self-study materials and a system for sending assignments to a central location for assessment and help, broadcasting can offer a significant contribution. The cost of the broadcasts in such a system may be the least of the investment necessary. The preparation of the self-study materials and the supervision of the correspondence activities will probably be much more costly and will require much more administrative infrastructure than the broadcast portion.

Broadcasting within Broader Educational Strategies

Current attempts to promote broadcasting, and especially satellite broadcasting, because of its possible benefit to education are often misleading.

Broadcast satellite systems are probably a good investment for many countries because of the advantages they would provide in telecommunications in general, but to imply that any educational problems would, in themselves, be resolved by satellite broadcasting is simply naive.

On the other hand, the technology of broadcasting has much to offer within the complex structure of formal and informal education. Educators must learn how to use the medium, however, and learn how to integrate broadcasting into an overall educational strategy. This will often mean changing the way we do things in a traditional classroom, if a broadcasting-oriented system is decided upon. It will also mean that broadcasters will have to collaborate with learning psychologists and educators in developing new styles of instructional broadcasts. There is much too much of carry-over from show-business in most educational television. Good instruction is not a "show." Nor is it the "talking face" of a teacher.

Other than broadcast uses of television and video-tape equipment may, in the long run, be more significant in instruction. For instance, closed-circuit television systems within a school would provide much more flexibility in displaying instructional sequences when the teachers in that school want them, rather than when they are broadcast by some central authority.

Similarly, portable video-tape equipment is increasingly used in the training of teachers. Student teachers, for the first time in history, can record their teaching performance on video-tape and then see themselves teaching. If this is done within an analytical scheme that helps them judge their performance, it can be very effective.

Programmed Instruction

At the other end of the spectrum from broadcast instruction we have those interested in programmed instruction. In a sense, these are the educational technologists who are interested in doing micro-analyses of the teaching-learning process so as to be able to construct a series of self-instructional materials which will, most of the time, teach what you want to teach. Behaviors to be taught are clearly defined, teaching steps are developed and tried out until they seem to work with most students, and with each step there is some sort of active involvement on the part of the student, often a response to a question or the filling in of a blank space. The instructional material informs the student if his response is correct or not, thus presumably providing reinforcement. The two basic approaches have been the "linear," in which it is assumed that all students should move in a linear fashion through all frames (each at his own speed), and the "branching," which assumes that a student who can move fast will be branched to fast material and one who learns more slowly will be branched to remedial material.

The early applications of programmed instruction were limited both in conception and in format. Psychologists who were new to the teaching-learning field would break the simplest concept into dozens of steps in an instructional program which would then be very cumbersome and time-consuming to use. The same concept could often be taught much more simply by a well-written, pretested and revised paragraph requiring a few seconds to read.

Similarly, extravagant claims were made to the effect that anything that can be defined can be taught by paper-and-pencil-type programmed instruction materials. Anything that can be taught by a well-written book can be taught by a well-written program, I suppose. But there is much that cannot be taught through reading alone, whether the words are strung together in a programmed instruction format or a traditional book format.

Early technical arguments as to whether linear programming or branching programming is best have given way to broader considerations as to where programmed materials fit in the total curriculum process, and to attempts to conceive and try out broader new strategies of instruction that go beyond paper-and-pencil programs. It is not likely that entire courses of study in paper-and-pencil programmed instruction form will ever become very popular. They are simply too bulky for easy use, too costly to produce and distribute. It is more likely that programmed instruction units will be increasingly used as parts of more sophisticated curriculum packages, perhaps as integral parts of new kinds of textbooks or perhaps as units cross-referenced with the textbook so that students can pick the programmed instruction unit off the shelf if they have trouble with the more succinct presentation in the text.

Individualized Instruction

In the long run, programmed instruction's most notable contribution to educational practice will probably have been the popularization of the notion that you can and should try out and revise instructional material to be sure of precisely what it does to typical students before you distribute it widely. On the other hand, many early programmed instruction enthusiasts have become interested in the more complex problems of something called "individualized instruction." As most often used, this refers to attempts to establish behavioral goals within the curriculum of a school and to establish procedures whereby the progress of each student is continually charted and whereby what he does and what he studies day to day and even hour to hour is determined by his individual progress toward these goals. Only a few examples exist of the experimental application of such an approach (one of these is the Individually Prescribed Instruction Project at the Baldwin-Whitehall School System near Pittsburgh, Pennsylvania).

In order to make possible fully individualized instruction, there must be constant, day-to-day, even hour-to-hour assessment of how well each student in the entire school is doing, so that he can be appropriately guided (or guide himself) to the next appropriate learning experience. This assessment must be built into the learning materials he is using. This would be possible on a mass scale only if such materials were computer-based and if the computer were automatically informed in some way of everything every child did. In this way, both teacher and student could have a full record of the learning accomplished at any point in time.

Many of the learning sequences would be stored in a computer-managed program and brought forth on a display console as demanded by the teacher or the student, or as the computer analysis of the student's cumulative history so suggested. In the ultimate, most of the learning activities available in the school could be scheduled by the computer program. For example, when five or six students out of the entire school find themselves studying a similar controversial point in history, the computer program would direct these five or six students (and no others) to enter into a round-table discussion of the matter. At the same time, the computer would select a room that is free, might suggest the questions to be discussed (displayed on a display console resembling a TV screen), and would direct the students to return to inform the computer of the results of the discussion so that this could be entered (again automatically) into each student's cumulative record. It might also, of course, automatically notify a teacher it knows to be free that hour that the discussion is to take· place, and the teacher would inform the computer that he would attend or that he wanted this to be a discussion not disturbed by a teacher.

So far, attempts to individualize instruction are much more limited, but inspired by the long-term view that something like the above may be possible. Such an approach in the ultimate would require the systematic analysis of all available learning experiences in a school curriculum and decisions as to how youngsters should be guided through these experiences, according to the interests and abilities they demonstrate day by day and week by week. It would require the development of a fantastic amount of new curriculum material and student assessment procedures in such a form that they can be managed by a computer-based system. It would require very sophisticated computer programming, even to the extent of providing fourth-generation computers with the ability to *create* new instructional sequences as the need arises.

Our present notions of children in a lock-step curriculum, grouped in classrooms managed by one teacher, would have to be radically modified with such a new approach. Our present notions of what a teacher must know and do to be a good teacher would require drastic alteration.

Innovation and Reform in Developing Areas

It is often suggested that developing countries cannot afford to invest in curriculum research and development centers and in educational technologies. I take the contrary position: they cannot afford not to. Although wealthy countries can, to a degree, sustain inefficient educational systems because they can afford it, the poorer countries cannot tolerate such waste.

The need is clear for new kinds of product-oriented curriculum research and development institutions at the heart of educational systems in developing countries. New approaches to education cannot emerge spontaneously in this age of technology. There must be a structuring whereby those with the various interdisciplinary skills and interests and resources can work together, with the necessary financial support and authority to change the way education is conducted. As we have come to accept educational planning as an institutional entity in most countries, we must come to accept research and development institutions which are constantly developing, trying out, revising, and improving the curriculum, methods, materials, strategies, and technologies of education.

There must be more than a patchwork approach to curriculum innovation and reform in each country. The introduction of remarkable new curriculum materials in one science area, for instance, will do little good if the rest of the curriculum is archaic, if the rest of the program uses inadequate methods, and if the school environment and teaching resources as a whole are impoverished.

Initial and continuing investment in systematic approaches to education that involve educational technologies is generally high. Most such technologies, however, permit the unlimited distribution of the fruits of this investment to the point where per capita student cost is very low. The production cost of a good textbook or of a good instructional television series or of a complete set of single-concept 8-mm. cartridge films for an entire course, or a set of programmed instruction materials, for instance, is substantial, as is the cost of gearing up the school system to use these materials effectively. But with thousands of students using the textbook or viewing the television series or using the cartridge films or programmed instruction materials, the percentage of the national educational budget would likely be very low.

Even computers can be used more extensively in education in developing countries. There are few countries where computers are not already being used by several government ministries and by various businesses such as banks. Very often these computers could be used by the educational authorities, at the very least to improve the administration of education. The better handling of student flow data, student records, teacher and employee records, and the like could be done on time given by or rented from those who now have computers. Many ministries of education, of course, already have their own computers and, in these cases, experiments could proceed with computer-assisted instruction with on-line terminals in schools. Similarly, most universities now have computers, many of these underused, which could be helpful in university administration and in new instructional approaches.

The first step by any country wishing to establish an appropriate agency for educational development and change may be to do a survey of all the patchwork pieces that already exist. Many countries already have pilot curriculum research and development centers in science or other curriculum areas. Many have some sort of educational or instructional broadcasting. Many have some interesting, innovative work going on in teacher-education institutions. Many have film production centers and audio-visual service agencies. Many have educational publishers and teaching materials companies which would collaborate fully in packaging and in helping distribute the fruits of innovative new approaches, if they are invited to collaborate.

A new kind of educational research and development institution articulating all of the above would have to have a doctrine and mission that would take it beyond the sum of its parts. To learn how to create and manage such institutions is one of the major jobs ahead in all countries. For the major task ahead is to learn how to institutionalize for appropriate innovation and change in education.

The time is right and the technology is with us. In another decade it may be too late.

SCIENCE EDUCATION IN WEST GERMANY

By Franz Karl Mutschellers
President
Association for the Advancement of Mathematics and Science Teaching
West Germany

[A Supplementary Address]

I am a teacher, and I come from a country that is underdeveloped when it comes to science teaching. This sounds very curious, but it is really true. In recent years we have revolted against our curriculum in mathematics, in chemistry, and I am quite sure that in a few year's time, our whole school organization will have been rearranged from the bottom to the top.

I don't dare to tell you anything or to give you advice about changing your curriculums I prefer to tell you something of our shortcomings and of the mistakes that we have made. When it comes to vocational training, our viewpoint is just the opposite of that described earlier by Mr. Avigad. In our primary schools, we have no vocational studies or training at all, if you don't call teaching applied science or the beginnings of applied science technical education.

In our primary schools we have science teaching, as we have in all stages of education. By science teaching I mean the teaching of biology, chemistry, and physics. We German science teachers fought our government for about ten years, because the ministries we have in West Germany canceled some of these subjects, so that not every pupil had to learn biology and chemistry and physics—they had a choice. Even now, our ministries of education are not persuaded that they made a very big mistake, but the position is now changed, and every German girl and boy will have to learn physics, chemistry, and biology. Why?

We are much more concerned with the nonscientists than with the scientists, because we are convinced that in our times our pupils will live their lives and have to understand the problems, and perhaps to solve them in an age of science. Even though the majority of them will not have to solve the problems but just to comprehend them, they will have to understand the basic principles of science. So we are now going in for all sciences for all pupils.

We come now to the question of vocational and nonvocational education. Our situation was different from that of Israel. We have not been able to induce the pupils of our working class to enter secondary education. We have tried and tried, but only a small proportion of them go to secondary schools. So we had to change our attitudes. I don't want to go more deeply into it but we had to make real propaganda, and we have now succeeded in getting some of our young people to go to secondary academic school—more than half, about 70 percent—and only about 26 percent go on in the second stage of our primary school, which really means a secondary school.

Of course we do not have enough boys and girls going in for a scientific career or a vocational and technological career. Why not? Because they don't know enough about the facts and about the circumstances of their future professions.

You really have to have the background, the statistics and facts. Now we have a statistical department, and I think it will be useful today for the men planning our education, but it is not useful for the orientation of our people, because the parents don't have any access to these facts it collects; the children don't use the information. I would say that if you have statistics, make them available to the parents and to the teachers, who are also involved in pupils' orientation, so they can use them, since orientation is based after all on statistics.

I am quite sure that the principles of subjects should be known to every teacher, but only the principles. His main task then is to teach science and therefore he has to study mainly science. He will never specialize in psychology or philosophy, and perhaps he will do more harm than good if he tries to orient his students through applying his knowledge of psychology and social sciences, apart from its taking him quite a lot of time.

So I say, let us set up orientation centers. I have seen one in Belgium, and I am quite sure that, if you send psychologists to these orientation centers, they—together with the teacher—could orient our people much better than we do it today.

Important for orientation is the teacher, by his teaching. A good teacher is an orientation too, and a bad teacher is a pest and is the end of the orientation. My opinion is that a good science teacher is the best orientation.

I am quite sure that if I were to ask all teachers present why they became teachers, in many cases they would reply: "Because I had a good teacher, and this example induced me to become a teacher myself."

We succeeded in bringing together industry, university teachers, and high-school teachers. You can always find top men who are interested in problems of teachers: of course you find them in industry—first line industry—which is interested in good science teaching and good vocational teaching, and there are university teachers who are interested in science teaching too because they get the output of science teaching.

If you bring them together and show them the problems, you can do quite a lot for science teaching in our high schools. I will give you an example. In Western Germany every school is entitled to write to one of the nearby chemistry factories and to ask for any materials they want. This is distributed absolutely free.

Industry in Germany is giving lots and lots of money—millions of marks—so as to get better teachers, better teaching, and more teachers. Everybody who buys a Volkswagen pays quite a lot of money to better the German shortage of science teachers. It is not widely known that the Volkswagen Foundation gives 75 million marks to induce more people to become science teachers. I am quite convinced that the real problem in science teaching is the problem of getting more and better teachers, and if you have them, you will get boys and girls going in for science, applied science, and technology.

DISCUSSION

Dr. Gerald Holton (United States) discussed the use of new gadgets in science education. These are very expensive, so, before buying, the people of the developing countries have to be clear what they can accomplish by using them. A good film on television brings the outside world into the classroom. Gadgets, frankly, make it more fun to be in a classroom, both for teachers and students. They create an ambiance, a mood of an actual science situation; a scientist is not just a man of books, as a teacher may seem to be.

The interdisciplinary approach recommended by Dr. Spaulding appealed to *Dr. Pradisth Cheosakul* (Thailand) but he fears that it is not always easy to get. In his university in Thailand, the faculty of education wanted to teach only education, and the faculty of science wanted to teach only science: it was very hard to get them together. Then UNESCO came with a proposal that Thailand should have a regional chemistry teaching project, and people got enthusiastic. As a result, again with UNESCO's help, they have added mathematics and other fields of science to the project.

Dr. Spaulding's doubts about staking too much on television were shared by *Dr. Isaias Raw* (Brazil). In some countries they are thinking of using a satellite to get programs, without considering how long a satellite operates, and that it costs more than anything else they are using, including teachers. The important thing is to get people with ideas, new ideas—they are more important than gadgets, software, budgets, secretaries, everything else.

25 THE LANGUAGE OF INSTRUCTION AND THE FORMATION OF SCIENTIFIC CONCEPTS

By Peter Strevens

Director, Language Centre,
University of Essex,
Great Britain

This paper is about an amorphous problem: in one sense it is about certain kinds of difficulty that are encountered by students in developing states when they come to learn about science but have to use a foreign language to do so. In another sense it is about the organization of education in such countries, and about ways in which the drop-out rate may be minimized and the success rate maximized. The themes which link these two aspects of the problem are those of concept-formation and language learning. We do not know a great deal, with certainty, about either of these processes, but by analyzing with some care the nature of the problem and applying to it some recent ideas a fruitful line of experiment may present itself.

Without being too precise in specifying what is meant, it is generally agreed that the education of scientists and technologists entails the understanding of a great many concepts and the ability to read, listen, talk, and write about them. When the learning of science is carried on in a foreign language, is the extent and nature of concept-formation different from that required of the student who learns science entirely in his mother tongue? The answer to this question may suggest changes in the strategies employed for learning and teaching science in the developing states.

The question hangs on the meaning of "scientific concepts," and here we find multiple ambiguity. The term is used both loosely and with apparent precision, though the precision evaporates upon closer inspection. The various usages of the term (other than the purely conversational) relate to five distinct ideas: first, to certain linguistic skills common to all advanced academic or scholastic study; second, to certain characteristics of the habits of thought of the individual scientist; third, to a number of concepts prerequisite to science but not unique to it; fourth, to one special prerequisite, that of practical numeracy; and fifth, to those concepts which are unique and proper to science, or which if they are not unique to it are at least inseparable from it. We shall look in turn at each of these uses of the term "scientific concepts."

English, French, and all the languages commonly used for advanced scientific study possess a group of words and expressions which I shall call the *grammatico-logical operators*. Presumably all languages possess some roughly equivalent list of items. They are essential for expressing any kind of complex, abstract, and especially recursively abstract ideas, whether scientific or not. In English the set of grammatico-logical operators includes at least the following:

although	once (something has occurred)
as a result of	only (e.g., only if . . .)
as if	suppose . . . then . . .
as long as	since (something has occurred)
because	therefore
for the purpose of	unless
if, if . . . then . . .	until
in order to	whenever
	etc. etc.

These items are vital not only to an understanding of science but equally to complex logical thought and verbalization in any field of discourse. Mastery of these items is normally confined to those whose education reaches the higher secondary level, and it may be determined by intelligence.

A second set of ideas that are frequently spoken of as "scientific concepts" comprises a certain objectivity of outlook on the universe, on the part of the individual, together with an ability to generalize from observation and to perceive and describe relationships and influences. It is customary to regard a preference for an objective, descriptive, rational outlook, or alternatively for a subjective impressionistic, nonrational outlook, as if these attitudes were inherent to the individual personality. I find this difficult to believe. Knowing of no evidence to the contrary, my intuition suggests that such preferences are learned behavior. If that is so, these attitudes may not be determined by intelligence and may be open to acquisition by all individuals, although it may well be that there is a developmental age at which they are more easily learned than at any subsequent time.

The third group of notions for which the label "scientific concepts" is sometimes used includes being able to generalize from observations, to talk abstractly about the generalizations, and to discern and describe relationships, influences, and patterns. These abilities seem to relate to aspects of intelligence in the individual, as well as to a fairly late stage of mental development.

The fourth type of idea of "scientific concepts" is practical numeracy: the ability to carry out a certain amount of mental arithmetic, to visualize in graphs and diagrams, to take for granted the use of statistical statements—above all a willingness to describe by quantifying. These abilities, like all the preceding ones, are essential for learning science. But they also form part of the general education of most young people whose education reaches the upper secondary level, whether or not they later specialize in science.

All four of these sets of ideas are necessary for the learner of science if he is to progress very far; they also form part of the education of specialists in other branches of learning. I shall refer to the four preceding sets of ideas as the "generalizing concepts," in contrast to those unique or essential to science, which I shall refer to as the "scientific concepts." Because they are prerequisites for the education of the scientist, the generalizing concepts cannot be ignored. They must be seen to constitute a learning problem of a conceptualizing kind for *all* advanced learners. When the learning is in a foreign language the same question arises as for science: is the task of concept-formation different, compared with learning in the mother tongue?

Within the concepts unique and proper to science it is possible to recognize large numbers of sets of concepts corresponding to different branches of science, different stages of general scientific discourse, different specializations. For example, some conceptual processes involved in learning science are:

classifying	abstraction-making	predicting
measuring	hypothesis-making	extrapolating
inferring	testing	quantifying
observing	replicating	differentiating

Mathematical learning involves:

greater	include	sequence
less	exclude	simultaneous
subtract	increase	zero
add	decrease	infinite

And theoretical generalization requires such terms as validation, evidence, axiom, corollary, model, relevance, and so on.

Every human being learns to form a great many concepts, and to verbalize some of them. Every language expresses the concepts habitually used in the society it belongs to. In each case there is a wide range of variation. Taking the individual first, there is a great deal of variation between the degrees of recursive abstraction which can be effectively handled, whether receptively or productively, by different individuals. (We are considering here not just the subset of concepts embodied in and manipulated by such operators as *unless, although, whenever*, etc. but concepts in general, very many of which are not verbalized.) One of the functions of education is (or ought to be) to steer each individual to the limits of his capacity in developing concepts; one of the tasks within science education is to ensure that the complexity of the concepts being presented at each stage is not beyond the capacity of the individuals concerned.

As far as languages are concerned, it is necessary to distinguish what *is* from what *could be*. Very many languages do not at the present time incorporate equivalents of the verbalizations of scientific concepts which exist in English, French, Russian, and the other languages in which scientific study is customarily pursued. But we should avoid falling into the error of arrogance and feeling that these languages are therefore in some sense defective, inferior, or primitive. A language reflects the culture of a particular society. If that society includes science within its culture, the language will contain all the necessary concepts and devices for talking and writing about science. If a society with no previous history of scientific interest begins to acquire such an interest, its language—*any* language—can and will develop internal grammatical and semantic rules for doing so. (Hebrew is an example of an language in which this process has taken place in modern times.) Unfortunately the task of developing scientific concepts *ab initio* in a language takes a good many years and can only rarely be engineered as a deliberate policy. Such development does not constitute a practical solution to the shorter-term problems of science education.

Languages vary, then, in the extent to which they give expression to both generalizing and scientific concepts. In saying this we are categorizing the mother tongues of potential scientists who may thus have been brought up speaking a language which carries either all, or many, or few of the total range of concepts relevant to education in science. What difference does this make to the education of the individual? The answer depends not only on the extent to which generalizing and scientific concepts are present in his mother tongue, but perhaps even more upon his age and the extent of his education in his mother tongue before beginning to learn science.

The young child who begins to learn science in an educational system where English or French (for example) is the medium of instruction from the beginning of schooling will be relatively little affected, compared with the adult, already literate in his mother tongue and thoroughly imbued with the culture of his own society, whose encounter with science comes after the completion of adolescence. In the case of the young child, his learning of concepts and his grasp of the more complex devices of his language are still largely before him. The fact that they may include generalizing and scientific concepts which otherwise he might not have met at all, and even the fact that he may face a language-learning task that he might not otherwise have had to surmount—these considerations are counterbalanced by two others: first, that his learning load is not X followed by Y, as in the case of the adult, but rather an amalgam of X and Y; and second, that the learning comes at an earlier period in his personal development, when concept-formation seems to be at its most plastic and insouciant. The adult, on the other hand, faces a learning load which is truly an addition, and he does so at a different and perhaps less favorable stage of personal development.

In the past two or three years, a group of specialists working in the area where the disciplines of psychology and linguistics overlap have proposed ideas concerning the acquisition by the child of his mother tongue. Some of the ideas are of interest in the context of this present discussion. Broadly, it is held that the normal child passes through a series of phases of brain development; these in turn produce states of readiness for different kinds of mental organization of the stimuli preceived from the child's surroundings. The well-known successive stages of undifferentiated cries, babbling, word- and sentence-formation, etc. are thus seen as occurring similarly in *all* children and as being the result of physiological and organizational changes in the brain.

The stages of the process during which the child begins to understand language and to produce acceptable utterances is described in terms of a growing *competence* to produce language rather than in terms of the child's actual *performance* at a given moment. The child is seen to observe, remember, and recall utterances, but he is not limited in what he can understand and say by the precise utterances he has already encountered: he understands unfamiliar utterances by their adherence to *rules* for generating sentences, rules that he is gradually working out and operating for himself; and he speaks sentences which in many cases he has never heard before by applying the rules that he has so far mastered. The mastery of the rules, it seems, also proceeds through a series of stages common to all children, with the result that what are usually called "childish errors" may be better described as the products of the normal sequence of rule-acquisition. By the age of four or five years, it is held, the child has largely mastered the basic sentence-construction rules of his mother tongue.

This model of language-acquisition (which is associated with the names of Chomsky, Miller, and others) has two main points of interest for our argument. First, the acquisition of language entails the acquisition of a very large number of concepts: number, singularity, duality, gender, animateness, tense, presuppositions of various kinds, even causality and subordination, and a great many more. The set of inherent concepts within language we will label the "language-borne concepts." If the Chomsky model adequately represents what happens in acquiring the mother tongue, it also represents (though in a manner not clearly defined) the acquisition of some concepts, notably the language-borne ones. They, too, may be built up into a framework of mental *competence*, in the sense of potentiality for exploitation, in which the limiting parameters are the stages of brain development on the one hand and the child's particular, personal experience of the universe on the other. Secondly, it is conceivable that normal development permits the growth of a certain basic stock of concepts and of conceptualizing competence common to all normal children regardless of individual differences of intelligence.

However, illuminating as this model of language acquisition may be, there is no doubt that normal children do develop further in language achievement and ability after the age of four or five, and that individual differences are clearly visible in the extent and nature of their subsequent development. We usually refer to this in terms of "creative ability" or of "stylistic awareness," criteria that are based on the literary norms of our society. But there exists also a second and nonliterary type of linguistic achievement which I believe can be expressed as the ability to handle with accuracy and precision the grammatico-logical operators of the language. Not all children manage this. Those who fall short also underachieve in relation to the complexity of many of the other generalizing concepts; achievement in this domain seems to correlate with intelligence above the normal.

We need to remember that the notions of a model of language acquisition have been developed in relation to the mother tongue. Much less attention has been given to the mental processes of acquiring a subsequent language. Some of the concepts embodied within language (for example those which underline language universals) will be common to mother tongue and foreign language alike; others in the foreign language will be unfamiliar. A "conceptual distance" between the two languages could be expressed in relation to three factors: degrees of linguistic cognateness; degrees of equivalence and similarity of writing system (whether they both run from left to right, horizontal or vertical, Roman, Cyrillic, etc.); and degrees of semantic and cultural similarity. The smaller the conceptual distance, presumably the smaller the learning task, other things being equal.

What is clear, from generations of experience, is that concepts *can* be learned in a foreign language. As the foreign language is learned, the language-borne concepts are themselves learned; as competence in the foreign language advances, if the opportunity presents itself and if the individual has the ability, the generalizing concepts may also be learned; similarly, under appropriate conditions the concepts of science may be learned, as well.

If one looks at the fairly rare but not unknown case (until now perhaps the "target" case) of a learner successfully learning advanced science in and through a foreign language, at least the following overlapping stages can be distinguished: first, the acquisition of a minimum basic competence in the foreign language (to roughly that point well-known to teachers but difficult to specify where a learner ceases to be a "beginner" and starts to become "advanced"); second, the acquisition of control in the foreign language of the generalizing concepts and particularly of the grammatico-logical operators; third, assimilation of the concepts of science; and fourth, simultaneously with all the other three stages, the learning of scientific vocabulary. (The learning of science in a foreign language is emphatically not a matter of vocabulary. If the events of the science syllabus are understood, and if the concepts embodied in them are grasped, the vocabulary items become no burden either for learner or teacher.)

It is not at all certain how far the *learning* of science and its concepts in a foreign language is made more effective by the manner of its *teaching*. What is almost universally the case is that foreign languages are taught with aims unrelated to science, and even where the foreign language is used in the teaching of science this is done with little professional acknowledgment of the special conceptual tasks facing the foreign learner. "First he learns English (or French, etc.); then he is taught science as an English learner is taught."

The underlying educational policy is to teach the foreign language to all the members of a certain portion of the population, and to select from among them, after they have been learning English for a given period of years, a further subset who will then be taught science. But the aims of teaching English to a major group of learners have almost always been defined in terms of general culture: these terms are in practice largely literary. Even where lip-service is paid to the need for a foreign language as a tool, as a means of communication, or as a force of cohesion, analysis of the English syllabus nearly always reveals that it is leading up to the study of Shakespeare, Wordsworth, or Dickens, and that its concepts are the subjective, aesthetic ones of literary studies. In many cases, too, the bias of the syllabus and teacher alike is openly *anti*-scientific, rejecting detailed observation in favor of the subjective response.

It is not my purpose to criticize these attitudes for their own sake. But if we look at the education of scientists we discover that *before* they start to learn science a great number of overseas learners are first taught a foreign language according to syllabuses that are in some sense opposed to the attitudes of science. What is worse, in most countries the general effectiveness of the teaching of a foreign language, although it may be better than it was fifty years ago, is by no means high or even encouraging. The results of this are reflected at least partly in the shortfall in the education of scientists, engineers, technologists, and fitters.

It can be argued that a high proportion of the teaching and learning effort in the foreign language which students of science undergo before they embark on science is wasted. Much of it is wasted because it is irrelevant to the needs of the scientists; some is wasted because it is ineffectively learned and taught.

Bringing together the various considerations raised in this paper so far, it is possible to suggest that a measurable and possibly a major increase in the effectiveness of science education might be achieved if the priorities were reversed, so that the foreign language was taught for science and through science in the first instance, with special attention paid to the deliberate inclusion of the generalizing concepts in the language course, as well as the special concepts of science. Those who fall by the wayside would be selected for the continuation along general cultural and literary lines. Under this strategy *all* learners would have the opportunity to achieve their potential in science, and only a minority would study literature, instead of the other way round. This seems to me to make much better sense for most developing states.

A science-oriented language syllabus is entirely feasible. All the basic teaching of a foreign language can be placed just as easily in the framework of learning science as in a framework of everyday discourse (which is in fact what the present syllabuses teach in the early stages). Of course the syllabus must take account of the age and interests of the learner, but there are few existing English or French courses that would not be improved and rendered vastly more interesting to the learners by (for example) replacing stories of King Arthur and the Round Table by extracts from current science fiction, or replacing scenes from the French Revolution by texts about supersonic flight or the potentialities of computers. Much of the effort currently expended in teaching potential engineers in tropical Africa about daffodils or about manners in nineteenth-century England could with profit be rechanneled through syllabuses whose ultimate aims include the preparation of citizens with adequate scientific and technical understanding.

Let me be clear: I envisage the creation of a syllabus and of a full range of teaching materials for particular levels and age-groups, in which English (or French) would be taught from the beginning in the framework of a science course, and science would be taught in English. In such a syllabus the choice of linguistic content would be determined in the first instance by the requirements of the science syllabus; the various categories of concept-formation discussed in this paper would receive deliberate treatment; accompanying materials would all be geared to the aim of exploiting to the maximum the science potential of each learner.

Such a course of action would face considerable difficulties, not only in its preparation but also in the retraining of teachers. Many teachers would find it difficult to adjust their outlook from the artistic imprecision of a "general-cultural" base. The administrative problems would also be great. Nevertheless in the present state of affairs only some such drastic remedy seems likely to provide a massive improvement in the effectiveness of science education in the developing countries.

DISCUSSION

Dr. Strevens told delegates that they should consider a very simple question: how science is taught. It is not taught through telepathy; something happens between the teacher and the taught. What is this?—the exercise of a language between a speaker and a hearer, or a writer and a reader. This has to be a two-way process. Dr. Strevens gave various examples of words that may mean one thing to the teacher and another to the taught—"determined" meaning calculated; "conclusion" meaning ideas formed, not ending; "behave" meaning react; "let" meaning an assumption, not allowing or permitting.

Pupils make mistakes in English in their English classes and their science classes. An English teacher often may not understand science, or the pupil's difficulties in science: sometimes he even disapproves of science and the pupils learning it because he prefers the arts and humanities.

The reforms he is proposing are twofold. The first is the production of new materials of many kinds dealing with the language of scientific concepts, and the familiarization of both English and science teachers with these materials. Such teachers should be brought together to consider jointly the language problems of the children. Secondly, new courses in English should be produced, which will enable students to learn English, through a science course, from the day they began to learn the language.

Dr. Julius Gikonyo Kiano (Kenya) said that the problem of language is not confined to the teaching of science. Language is a means of conveying concepts; these can be scientific or otherwise. Languages change as cultures change. All kinds of new words are entering into Swahili—for instance, "sciansi" meaning "science."

The various functions of language were considered by *Dr. Jerome S. Bruner* (United States). There are expressive functions, as in "Today I feel as if ecstasy has descended upon me"; connotive functions, causing effects at the level of the hearer, as in "Get thee to a nunnery"; poetic functions, as in calling somebody "Horrible Harry"; metalinguistic functions, as in "The man was bitten by the dog" and "The dog bit the man," where words have transformation connotations; a new function recently suggested is to establish or maintain contact, as in "How are you feeling?" Then there is the referential function, referring to things, and the language of science consists basically of finding ways to refer to things by indirect means. Instead of saying, "That's an ashtray," one can refer to it as being made of certain chemical substances, which in turn are governed by certain rules having to do with the conservation of mass, the conservation of energy, and things of that kind. Children who give their address as "Weizmann Institute of Science, Israel, Asia, planet Earth, the Universe" are using this kind of language.

Language teaching should be neither literary nor scientific; it should cover the whole spectrum of language, and has to come from self-consciously organized opportunities to exchange; there has to be talk among people, not talk to people.

Mr. Peter Inocent Mwombela (Tanzania) pointed out that children, particularly those in elementary school, often have great difficulty expressing themselves correctly in a foreign language. They should be encouraged to express themselves in any way they can, in their own vernacular or using incorrect foreign language; mistakes do not matter so much, provided the pupils are able to form concepts, and to express their ideas in some form or another.

The teaching of a foreign language which will be used as a language of instruction must be undertaken as early as possible, maintained Mr. Robert Antoine (Mauritius). Mauritius is a racial mosaic, but everybody understands French. Instruction, at the start, is in English and French; gradually English takes over, and secondary-school education is only in English, although English is not spoken at all in most families. This is unfortunate as the children have to think in a foreign language when they are taught science, so they should learn to speak English as soon as possible.

Dr. Cornelius Olaleye Taiwo (Nigeria) said that the Yoruba langauge is used by many people in Nigeria. The language is growing by itself. They are trying, rather cautiously, to incorporate English words if they seem to express their thoughts more adequately. "Penny," for instance, is "copo," from "copper"; "inch" becomes "insh." Many words have entered the language without difficulty. Teachers should use Yoruba wherever possible, without distorting concepts: when there is no alternative, they should use English.

The whole world is divided, like Gaul, into three parts, M. Moise Lankoande (Upper Volta) observed; these divisions are determined by the great international languages. He pleaded with delegates to be realistic; it is essential to teach the children in one of these languages, whatever the difficulties involved.

Dr. Pinhas Blumenthal (Israel) said that he got the impression that Professor Strevens believes that the humanities should be left for the drop-outs from science; he does not agree with this startling proposition. But clearly there is need for reform. People need two types of language knowledge: passive knowledge and more exact reading knowledge.

Israelis speak a sort of pidgin science, commented Mrs. M. Kaye, (Israel). A graduate student giving a lecture might say "I connected (in Hebrew) the multi-channel analyzer (in English) and I heard (in Hebrew) click-click (in English) and I realized (in Hebrew) that there was a great deal of noise (in English)." Does this kind of language obviate some of the difficulties and complications?

In his reply, Dr. Strevens said that there is no great harm in a mixture of languages during a transitional stage, as long as it is not accepted as a terminal aim. He certainly does not believe that we should lose any humanistic values; his conviction is that the science teacher and the English teacher should work together. He neither deprecates mother tongues nor conceives of any language being superior or inferior to another. Languages only express cultures, and no cultures were superior or inferior.

The important decision is how the children should learn both language and science; the objective they must not lose sight of is that education should be as successful as possible.

26 COLLABORATION BETWEEN CURRICULUM DEVELOPMENT PROJECTS IN DEVELOPED AND DEVELOPING COUNTRIES

By Gerald Holton

Harvard Project Physics,
Harvard University,
United States

Guidelines for Collaboration

The improvement and development of science curriculums is a matter of serious concern in many countries, whether they are developed or not. A great deal has been done or is underway in some countries; in the United States alone, about one hundred million dollars, and hundreds of man-years, have been spent on curriculum development projects in the various sciences during the past decade. Other countries have also had substantial projects of this kind. Developing countries may therefore find it tempting as well as wise to consider how they can best benefit from the application or transfer or adaptation of existing materials and experience.

Moreover, in the developed countries themselves, curriculum development continues, in accord with the fact that from now on such development must be a continuous effort, owing to rapid changes in science, in educational philosophy, and in the social context of education. For it may nowadays be simply postulated that every country is underdeveloped with respect to its own future needs.

Therefore, guidelines and strategies are needed for cooperation between established curriculum development groups and those who are about to begin their work. The temptation for a more or less straightforward adoption of ideas and materials prepared for some one audience in one country to another audience, perhaps in another country, and at another time, must be scrutinized with particular care. Experiments of this sort have already been made, and the successes and failures can now be sorted out. Also, it is becoming clear that great caution and clarity are needed to evaluate the limits of usefulness of non-indigenous materials, for a curriculum development effort can be a device for effecting major changes in the culture of a country.

There seem to me to be nine main propositions that should be discussed before a new curriculum group commits itself to its work. In each case, some existing curriculum groups in developed countries could fruitfully be involved in such discussion and, within the clearly defined limits of their own experience and their local settings, should propose viable models, warn of traps, and offer concrete assistance where asked.

1. It is of course still possible for one person to write a good text that will be widely usable. But all recent experience shows that a national

program needs a larger commitment. If only to take proper advantage of existing educational materials and research—and to use a modern multi-media approach to science teaching, in addition to many other reasons—curriculum groups from the beginning must be large enough and funded over a long enough period of time. Preferably they should involve a variety of experts in addition to scientists and teachers—including, for example, educational psychologists and statisticians, a historian of science, specialists from neighboring fields of science, film and laboratory apparatus makers, etc.

2. Even though the previous point indicates that a nationally used science course will not be cheap to produce, it should be recognized that the real expense has to be two or three times larger still. No national program of curriculum development should be undertaken in any country unless there is at the same time at least a second, preferably quite different effort under way in the same science. In the fast-developing field of education there just is not at present enough certain knowledge about proper directions to put all one's eggs in one basket. Moreover, the monolithic course used in a large part of a nation's schools, even if it should be initially completely successful, in the long run carries with it a number of real dangers. These include the atrophy of competing educational ideas and the demoralization of the most inventive and forward-looking teachers. Experience has shown all too often that any educational innovation is all too likely to become in time a petrified monument. Only a dialogue between differing groups can assure continued updating and creative innovation. It is therefore to be regarded as simply axiomatic that the minimum budget for curriculum development is at least two different and competing efforts in each science per country, perhaps serving different *but overlapping* audiences.

3. In each country, indigenous, representative groups of educators, scientists, administrators, etc. should develop a clear rationale why and how much science education should be introduced, and for what audiences. If left to themselves, the assumption of science curriculum project leaders may be that what the nation needs is primarily a supply of academic chemists or physicists or biologists. The same assumption may be built into a curriculum that was developed abroad and is being blindly imported. But the local realities may demand a much wider spectrum of targets, ranging from prospective academic scientists to technicians to informed parents; the possibility of oversupply of one kind of output may in fact produce sociological distortion as well as manpower problems. Conversely, accentuating the supply of technological manpower without working equally hard to provide the necessary scientific background for nontechnical and nonscientific students may build a cultural split into the educational system which can bring one segment soon out of touch with the rest of society. Educational philosophy has developed quickly during recent years; it is no longer bound to the ideas of the immediate post-Sputnik era. Therefore, the underlying explicit or implicit educational philosophy in existing programs should be brought out into the open and studied before they are considered for adaptation.

4. Before adapting or adopting any component of a program developed inside or outside one's own country, it is necessary to evaluate carefully whether the program is sound and successful even in terms of its own local, stated objectives. The wisest policy is to regard any educational product to be a failure unless proved by actual research to be successful. This means probing for honest figures, and for measures of what, if anything, the intended student groups really got out of the course. Otherwise, in the absence of close educational evaluation, one would rely merely on hope and guesswork—a situation one would never tolerate in scientific work, and that should not be tolerated in education either. Conversely, where educational evaluation efforts have been made by curriculum groups, their techniques of evaluation along with the results should be carefully studied by the importing country prior to any decision, and after suitable tests a local evaluation procedure should be devised and used before any major commitments are made. (Because of the importance and relative novelty of evaluation, some examples obtained for a specific curriculum project will be given below.)

5. Cooperation between a curriculum development group in a developed country and one in a developing country must be based on a spirit of non-paternalistic collaboration instead of unilateral imposition. The two groups must have something concrete to contribute to each other. In this connection, it must be recognized that the words "developed" and "developing" are relativistic words that do not necessarily describe properly the educational situation. For example, in certain economic respects, one country may be said to be underdeveloped compared to another; but in terms of subject-matter competence of science teachers, it may be more developed than the other. The result of cooperation should be the improvement of the work of both groups in their local contexts.
    Feedback to the original group in the developed country should be built in, for example to indicate where the original material might be modified in its parent country to reach hitherto untapped audiences. Thus, certain established science programs in developed countries were tacitly directed to predominantly middle-class students, who had already clearly identified science interests. Collaboration with the developing country can open new classrooms to the original group, too.

6. Straight translation of unmodified use of imported curriculum materials should be the exception rather than the rule. The aim should be to produce locally governed adaptations in collaborative work across the borders. For example, an existing curriculum development group from the developed country can give advice on how to construct a team that would produce adaptation of the materials such as texts or laboratory equipment; it also can furnish advice on the direction and quality of ongoing projects and actually participate in the adaptation work. But the basis and reference of every curriculum must be local needs and opportunities, including the introduction of local history, heroes, and problems into the educational work of a new group.

7.   All work, including collaborative adaptations, should be done under complete administrative control of the local group. The leadership role of the United Nations or UNESCO should also be sought.

8.   No curriculum development should be undertaken without preparing also for in-service and pre-service teacher training. Existing models that invite attention, including some of their successes and failures, should be provided by the group from the developed country for discussion and modification. As in all other respects, unevaluated teacher training models, even if dignified by habit and long use, should be challenged and subjected to test.

9.   In our constantly changing situation, it is axiomatic that any specific science curriculum development cannot be a single, closed, one-time effort. Rather, each country must base its work on a commitment to continuous reevaluation, restructuring, and revision, guided by a serious evaluation study as initiated during the earliest pilot plan stages of the curriculum development and carried on throughout the program.

Some Evaluation Results from Harvard Project Physics

Harvard Project Physics is a national curriculum development effort in secondary school physics, started in the early 1960's by a group of scientists, teachers, historians, and other scholars. Between 1964 and 1969, with the help of about 200 professional colleagues, a great amount of materials (texts, films, laboratory apparatus, etc.) was produced, tested, redesigned, and retested in controlled classroom use. The course is now in production for wide circulation in the United States, and adaptations are being planned with the cooperation of groups in several other countries.

The fundamental philosophy and aims of the project have been presented in detail elsewhere[1] and Professor Watson's paper (pp. 35-39) discusses other features of the course. I am here presenting some of the results of the evaluation effort that was built into the project from the start.

It is a curious phenomenon that scientists, who are so doubly and triply careful about publishing research results in science only after thorough evaluation, are very likely to abandon these scientific methods when it comes

---

[1]   I have summarized the main points in the following (equivalent) articles: "Project Physics: A Report on Its Aims and Current Status," *Physics Teacher*, 5, No. 5 (May, 1967), 198-211.

"Il Harvard Project Physics Suoi Scopi e Suo Stato Attuale di Avanzamento", *Istituto Technico*, Anno VI, N. 1-2, (Gennaio-Guigno 1968), 57-70.

"Harvard Project Physics: A Report on Its Aims and Current Status," *Physics Education*, 4, No. 1 (January, 1969), 19-25.

to educational innovation. Slightly contemptuous perhaps of the large amount of expertise developed in fields outside their own, such as educational research, some scientists are all too likely to publish largely unexamined and untested speculations as if they were fact. Worse still, where research fails, public pronouncements made with authority and great self-confidence takes its place. The danger in all this is of course that sooner or later the initially trusting public finds out, and perhaps even discredits the good along with the bad.

All this does not have to happen at all if care is taken from the beginning to make a curriculum development project responsible with respect to the facts and figures in educational research. There are three principal components in such an enterprise: *feedback* from teachers and students for use by the course improvement project while it is in progress; *evaluation* of changes that have taken place in students, for the information of potential users of the course; and *basic research* in education. All three can be carried on by the same team, if it includes people with competence in statistics, psychology, and educational measurement.

The Use of Feedback

Feedback from teachers and students is the most obvious and in many ways the simplest intellectually, but logistically it is the most difficult. We began to obtain feedback on a large scale in the school year 1964-65, a year after the first trial version had been prepared. A simple example of feedback is the analysis of items on the achievement test designed to test knowledge of specific points made in the text of the course. On a specific question where, for example, only a third of the students chose the correct answer, one carefully inspects to see if the question itself is misleading in some way, but if this is not the case one obviously rewrites that portion of the text, supplements it as needed with teacher guide or activity notes, and tries next year again to see whether the revised portion of the course yields a better result. Since we had the opportunity to revise the course components annually at least four times, we feel fairly confident about the "teachability" of the most important points, at least in the setting of the trial classes. This, incidentally, points up the need to plan and fund any curriculum development group for more than a couple of years, and not to demand quick results.

We also obtained from the students a more informal rating of each chapter—how effective it was in getting ideas across, and also how difficult it was. These two measures are of course closely related in the students' minds. One result that rather surprised us was that the combined student estimate of the difficulty of the chapter correlated remarkably well with the mere number of equations printed in the chapter.

The audience envisaged for the one-year Harvard Project Physics course is a variety of students between the ages of 15 and 17, ranging from those who know that they will never again take a science couse if they can possibly help it to those who may be considering science as a career. But it is in the nature of this population that the latter group will be represented in relatively small numbers, so that the result I mentioned reflects largely the "fear of mathematics" on the part of the large majority of our high-school students. This result, incidentally, does not speak for making the course as free of mathematics as possible, rather it indicates that one should exercise reasonable care about the number of mathematical details one feels has to be included as a minimum for everyone. The idea that different students can get rather different things out of the same printed book or course is precisely one of the chief features of our course, as I have stressed in the articles cited earlier.

Another analysis of usefulness is a measure of the density of new concepts. This can be measured without great difficulty, and plotted to show where page by page the number of new concepts, or the reinforcement of old ones, actually stands. In this manner one sees the text as a steadily rising curve of concepts, with plateaus where ideas are related or expanded without introducing many new ones. One by-product of such a graph is that it forces one to pay attention where concepts are introduced at some point and then mentioned only rarely if at all later. One all too often falls into the old habit of presenting topics with which one has grown up, rather than those that definitely are needed to tell a coherent story. If a concept is mentioned only once or twice, one really must reexamine whether it is needed at all. Under no circumstances should a physical science course become a kind of encyclopedia of unfamiliar terms.

An important part of feedback is, of course, not just what is obtained by questionnaires or text analysis, but what one finds by talking with teachers who are engaged in teaching the course. Therefore regional conferences were arranged periodically in which as many teachers as possible were brought together with the staff that was engaged in preparing the next revision. Also, we hired some of our experienced teachers to spend a year each with us in Cambridge to help revise the course in the light of their recent actual use of a previous edition of the course.

Tests and Measurements

Turning now to the other components of educational research that should be associated with a curriculum development project, I will for reasons of space have to leave aside here the discussion of basic research in science education—research on the factors which may affect learning in a science course: teacher characteristics, the learning environment, student background, and so forth. On the other hand there are a number of evaluation tools which are of interest to scientists concerned with educational improvement, and which I would like to recommend for the guidance of teachers, students, parents, and counselors.

A curriculum development project should be able to describe what happens to different kinds of students in different kinds of classes. We collected some of this information by means of standard published tests; most are fairly well known, and there are data concerning national norms. Examples are the so-called Test on Understanding Science (TOUS), which measures a student's perception of what science is like, what scientists are like, and how science relates to society. There is also, of course, the I.Q. test, one of the most effective predictors of achievement in school. The Study of Values test allows one to get a measure of the student's degree of personal interest in things theoretical, esthetic, social, etc. The Biographical Inventory provides information on the student's home environment, level of education of his parents, etc.

In addition we had to devise several tests of our own: our Physics Achievement Test; a Semantic Differential Test with which one tries to tap underlying attitudes concerning science; and a simple old-fashioned student questionnaire, based on actual statements which we originally gathered from students about their physics courses.

The teachers who participated in the test program during the development period were themselves also subjected to tests, to correlate their characteristics with the successes or failures of their students. I should remark here that we had to decide quite early which teachers to co-opt for collaboration in our development period. We finally decided—and I think correctly—during the early part to work mostly with exceptionally good teachers, although they were spread over a variety of different teaching situations; then during the major test period we added randomly selected teachers who had not previously worked with us. We wanted to know, of course, how the course would work on a general population of physics classes rather than with hand-picked teachers only; so we used the national list of high school physics teachers, and from the nearly 17,000 names picked a random sample of about 70, who agreed to cooperate. About half of these were asked to teach the Harvard Project Physics course; the other half formed a control group, teaching what they were going to teach anyway, but taking part in all our tests, tests both for themselves and for their students.

The purpose of the control group was not to show which course was "best." Rather, we wanted to find out what kinds of students could have obtained what kinds of information and attitudes out of Harvard Project Physics which they would not have received anyway in some other physics course. I should inject here the warning that it is all too easy to prove, by means of one's own tests, that one's own course development is better than anyone else's, or any previously existing course. The temptation should be resisted. Rather, what is interesting is to show specific differences between existing courses and the new development in terms of actual student achievement and attitude changes.

The data we collected included several batteries of tests, questionnaires, and observations obtained at the start of the school year, and again at various points during the year as well as at the very end. The large number of variables requires the use of fairly sophisticated multivariate statistics, and therefore demands the commitment to the lengthy process of planning, setting up, computer runs, analysis, cross-checking, and interpretation. Two documents on our evaluation results are scheduled for publication within the year—one to be the relatively technical book mentioned before, the other a more popularized summary. The results I will discuss here are only samples of a much larger body of data collected.[2] They indicate the type of evaluation items which any national curriculum development project should try to obtain, whether it is an effort in a developed or developing country.

A summary of the cognitive measures (Physics Achievement Test, Test on Understanding Science, Science Progress Inventory) shows that on the average Project Physics students improved their scores significantly more on these three tests than they would have in control group classes taking other physics courses. Also, the final grade that students received from their instructors in their physics courses was on the average higher in the Project Physics group. Physics instructors are traditionally severe graders, so this result represents additional evidence that there was a certain amount of necessary reeducation of the physics teacher, i.e. to get him to use a scale more commensurate with the scales used by teachers of other courses in the same school. In any case, the many different means and media of learning which we provide in our course encourage the teacher to use a broader basis for judging students' success.

We produced four tests for each unit, including multiple-choice, problem, and essay-type questions. Within the test, we included at least a few options for each student to choose among questions that are slanted more toward mathematics, to laboratory experience, or to history and the social consequences of physics. While the majority of each test focuses on the substance content as traditionally defined, on the whole each student has enough choice to make it his individual test and to go beyond rote learning of some absolute, given content. Just as the experience of taking the course should be individual and in principle somewhat different from student to student, so also should be the tests.

The most easily obtained results are average for the whole sample. In order to obtain more meaningful data, one must go on to analyze the results of achievement tests, both with an eye to the mean change in achievement test scores over the year, and also to see how gains depend on previous achievement levels. In our case, the results of the latter type of test indicate that the low- and medium-ability students gain relatively the most from taking this particular course, while the high achievement student in Harvard Project Physics gains in physics achievement about as much as he would in another physics course. One rather interesting result, which also has been noted in some other courses, is that the gain in achievement test scores with respect to their precourse levels is larger for girls than for boys.

Perhaps among the most significant results was the performance of our students on an "external" achievement test, namely the College Entrance Examination Board's achievement test in physics (produced by an independent national organization, the Educational Testing Service, and widely used throughout the country). The mean score of the Project Physics students who, in preparation for college entrance, took the CEEB physics achievement test was essentially the same as the score obtained by all other physics students who took that test at the same time (a mean score of 596 for Harvard Project Physics students, compared with a mean of 593 for all other students). This

[2] The following passages are based on a summary made by Dr. Andrew Ahlgren.

result was gratifying to us because the CEEB tests are expected to be a rather severe hurdle for students coming from a new course which has many aims in addition to those that conventionally get tested by the CEEB physics test. It should be noted that during the early years of the administration of CEEB tests to students of other new curriculum development projects, an average score of about 15 points below the mean was expected and actually obtained by students of other, new curriculum development projects. No such "handicap" was encountered by the students of the Projects Physics course.

There are a number of other variables in the affective realm that can be tested—for example, "interest in physics," for which a semantic differential grading scale is a useful tool. Student questionnaires have been developed into a useful instrument. Finally, there is a group of possible tests which measures some rather elusive but interesting aspects of the learning experience, such as the diversity of the learning environment and the like.

The conclusion I am urging is that course evaluation has been an unjustly neglected tool for the developer of curriculum developments in physical science; that experience and research design now exist that are sharable; and that new groups should avail themselves of these models for their own projects. For our part, for this aspect as for any other, the Harvard Project Physics staff will be glad to consider collaboration with equivalent groups in other countries. The same can be said, I am sure, for other established development projects in our country and throughout the world. We all share the same overall goal: to bring more and better science instruction to more students.

27 AIDS IN SCIENCE TEACHING

By John L. Lewis

Senior Science Master,
Malvern College;
Associate Organizer, Nuffield
Physics Project; and
Editor-in-chief, UNESCO
Source Book on Teaching
Physics in Secondary Schools,
Great Britain

Twenty years ago, a syllabus was considered the basis for a science course in schools. This consisted of a list of topics to be studied, chosen to provide some basic facts about the subject, often as a basis for further education, irrespective of whether or not the child would be studying the subject again. This encouraged the belief that science education amounted to the acquisition of factual knowledge.

In recent years greater attention has been given to our aims in teaching science: *why* science is taught. The reasons are twofold: first, to show pupils what science is about and how a scientist thinks, stressing the limitations as well as the scope of science; secondly, to promote the technological advances which are possible in a scientifically educated country and which lead to increasing well-being in that country.

If a course aims to show how a scientist thinks and something of the nature of science, this inevitably affects both *what* is taught and *how* it is taught. For this reason there has been a movement away from the syllabus and an increasing realization that a complete program is necessary. A syllabus was often a list of topics which might be examined at the end of a course; a program suggests how the course should be developed at each stage, the depth to which it should be taken and how the subject may be presented. Importance must obviously be attached to the subject matter and the way it develops as a logical whole, but even more important is the way in which the teacher handles the subject matter.

The Physical Science Study Committee in the United States was the first to stress the importance of a program rather than a syllabus, though the USSR had seen the need to give guidance to teachers in much greater detail than was contained in a mere syllabus. A further stage in the evolutionary progress has been realized by the Nuffield Foundation's Science Teaching Projects in the United Kingdom, where most of the work is directed at the teacher to help him to achieve a standard.

Whenever a country decides to change its science teaching, it must decide first why it is teaching science at all. The aims of science teaching have already been discussed in another paper and will not therefore be mentioned further here.

Once those aims have been established, a country develops a program to achieve those aims. Inevitably it considers what aids it will need—and what aids it can afford—to achieve the objects of their program.

Talk-and-Chalk or Experimental Science?

Traditional courses in science used to rely on the mere acquisition of factual knowledge—definitions to be learned by heart, formulas to be memorized and a series of mechanical rules to be remembered in order to answer problems. Too often chemistry amounted to learning the properties of gases; too often biology consisted of drawing labeled diagrams and learning names for different parts. A typical question in a physics examination might be:

Define coefficient of linear expansion.
How would you measure it for a metal rod?
A steel tire has a diameter of 99.7 cm. at 15°C. To what temperature must it be raised to enable it to be put on a wheel 100 cm. in diameter? (Coeff. of linear expansion of steel = 0.000012 per °C).

The definition is learned mechanically. The description of the experiment can be memorized irrespective of whether the pupil has ever seen the apparatus. The numerical question merely requires substitution in a formula. The kind of school work done in preparation for such questions is not likely to do much to encourage more pupils to become scientists, nor does it give any understanding of the nature of science.

Science is based on experiment and, if pupils are to get the feel of science, some experimental work must be done. Factual knowledge can be given with the use of talk-and-chalk alone, but real understanding cannot be based on dogmatic assertion by the teacher: the evidence must come from experience. A good science program will encourage pupils to think for themselves, to look for evidence, and to use their judgment; and only if the evidence is produced through experimental work can the judgments be formed.

Accepting that experiments should be part of the course, we must decide what kind of experimental work should be done. Routine measurements or "verification" of a law are of limited use: the number of different ways that were devised for finding the focal length of a lens may be a tribute to the ingenuity of examiners but they do not teach much about the nature of science. Equally "verification of Boyle's Law" teaches little about scientific investigation: the pupil knows that the teacher wants a straight line and he will do his best to give him one whatever his readings!

There can be a place in a course for a precise measurement of some constant, teaching thereby something of the discipline of a scientific investigation, the need for precision, and the elimination of errors, but not all the work should be of this kind. Whenever a child can carry out an investigation and can draw his own conclusions, he will have a far greater understanding and the knowledge he has acquired will be *his own* and not second-hand.

For this reason, whenever time allows, experiments should be done by the pupils themselves rather than as demonstrations by the teacher. There will be occasions when the cost of the apparatus requires that the experiment be a demonstration. A course based on a series of such demonstrations may testify to the skill of the manufacturer in making good equipment and may do much to impress both the teacher himself and his pupils with his skill in carrying out a demonstration, but he will do little for the good name of science and may not encourage pupils to study science themselves. It is personal involvement that is more important than efficiency or precision. These principles inevitably affect the laboratories and the apparatus for use in them.

Laboratories

Even in the more sophisticated countries there has been a tendency in recent years to provide more simple laboratories than was customary ten, twenty, or thirty years ago. The important thing is space. Two major requirements are (1) flexibility in furnishing and layout, and (2) ample accessible storage facilities.

Water supplies, sinks, and gas are necessary, especially for chemistry and biology. These services are most economically provided around the walls of the laboratory. Most modern physics courses will require an electrical supply; it is more economic to provide plenty of mains sockets around the walls and to use portable transformers to provide low voltages than to go to the heavy and unnecessary expense of piping low voltage supplies around the laboratory.

The furnishings should provide a flexible layout: it is far better and cheaper to have robust movable tables than fixed ones with complex supplies. Such tables should not have drawers or cupboards, they should be light enough for two children to carry them, they should be the same height as any fixed benches around the wall. Blackout is invaluable and half-blackout probably essential, particularly in laboratories used for physics.

With the modern tendency to provide large quantities of simple apparatus to enable pupils to do experiments themselves, plenty of storage space is essential. A storeroom must be adjacent to the laboratory so that the apparatus is easily accessible. Expensive, glass-fronted, fixed wooden cupboards are an anachronism. Simple, carefully designed storage units are important and more attention might be given to this than has been customary in many countries in recent years.

Apparatus

"Hear and forget, see and remember, do and understand." If it is accepted that understanding comes through personal involvement, apparatus for pupil experiments must be available in large quantity.

Fortunately in chemistry the same basic apparatus, the same glassware, can be used throughout much of the course. In any program use should be made of local material: it would be absurd in Zambia to import a special chemical from London when a suitable alternative is available locally. Likewise a wise biology course will make the maximum use of local material. Unfortunately such is the nature of physics that apparatus in some quantity is necessary for its proper teaching, but much of the apparatus can be very simple in design.

The Physical Science Study Committee in the United States started the trend toward low-cost apparatus. The Nuffield Physics Project in the United Kindom has developed a large number of kits of apparatus for use in their programs. The electromagnetic kit, for example, consists of a large number of small inexpensive items in sufficient quantity to enable a class of 32 pupils to do the experiments working in pairs. The kit is carefully designed to do between 40 and 50 different experiments—and it can therefore be used for many weeks of a school course. Its versatility, the fact that it can be used over a long period, makes it a good economic proposition.

It will be noted that much of the English apparatus is more robust than the PSSC equivalent apparatus. This is due to the different organization of educational funds in England and the United States. Much PSSC apparatus is deliberately inexpensive and expendable as American schools tend to have a high annual budget for equipment, whereas in England the tradition is to spend less annually but to prefer a larger initial outlay. For this reason, much Nuffield apparatus has been designed to last for five to ten years, but costs more initially. Every country developing its own program has to decide for itself whether to have higher initial costs and lower running expenses or the other way round.

For demonstration apparatus, the important factor is versatility. Few countries will be able to afford an expensive item of demonstration apparatus which is used for only one experiment. On the other hand, a scaler which can be used for a large variety of radioactive experiments and which can also be used extensively as a millisecond clock by incorporating a thousand cycle oscillator is an attractive proposition.

There was a tendency at one time for manufacturers to make an item complete in itself. This is not the most economic way of providing the teacher with the equipment he needs. For example, a general purpose power supply and a general purpose amplifier, both of which can be used in a large variety of different experiments, is better economy than building a power supply and an amplifier into every piece of apparatus requiring such units.

Simplicity is another important factor in teaching apparatus. Equipment designed for industrial use is not always suitable for schools. Simplified versions of industrial apparatus, for example oscilloscopes, may lead to better teaching and be a considerable economy.

In England, the contribution in the last ten years which has probably led to the greatest advance in physics teaching is the acceptance of voltage supplies other than a dry cell or an accumulator. The willingness to use mains-operated power supplies—transformers and d.c. power supplies up to 5000 volts—has transformed secondary science teaching. Safety devices of various kinds make these suitable for school use and they extend greatly the extent of experimental physics that is possible.

Any country developing a new science teaching program must necessarily decide for itself a definite economic policy over apparatus.

Learning Aids

Textbooks

Teachers following traditional courses almost invariably required a textbook for pupil use. The new American programs continued to rely on a textbook. The Nuffield biology course also relies on textbooks, but the Nuffield physics and chemistry courses do not. Much thought has been given to the place of a textbook in a science course, and there is probably a trend away from textbooks in the traditional sense.

No one would question the place that the textbook has for the university student. What is questionable is how necessary a textbook is at the early stages of a secondary-school course.

If the tendency in science teaching is to encourage critical thought and to discourage an authoritarian approach to science, how can we expect a boy or girl to find out something about electric currents in order to make the knowledge his own if the answer is clearly stated three pages further on in his textbook? The role of the textbook is changing. It is becoming much more a background book, pleasantly illustrated and easily readable, relating the experience of the classroom to the outside world.

Another role of a textbook was, in the traditional courses, to provide a collection of questions for the pupils, often for use as homework. There continues to be a need for such questions. Questions were incorporated in the PSSC textbook. In the Nuffield Physics Project, separate question books were written for each year of the course. Thus the material for the pupil consists partly of question books and partly of background books.

Teachers' Guides

Now that new programs lay much emphasis on the method of teaching, a Teachers' Guide must play a most important role. A syllabus alone gives no indication of how deeply a topic should be explored; phrases like "elements and compounds," "radioactive disintegration," "interference effects," all of which have appeared in some syllabuses, could be very differently interpreted by different teachers. They need guidance.

Teachers also need to know *why* certain things have been included in any well-planned program where something studied in one place is an essential basis for something coming later. Such a guide can include experimental details which will enable the teacher to get the most effective use out of the apparatus. He can be advised on the best way to set up an experiment and be given hints and instructions, where it may not be at all advisable to give so much detail to pupils. If laboratory work is to be a true investigation in which the pupils feel the information acquired is their own, precise instructions similar to those in a "cookery book" can do harm, even though at one time it was customary to give them to pupils. The instructions, however, need to be somewhere—and the right place is the Teachers' Guide.

Such guidance does enable an indifferent teacher to achieve a standard. It need not be a restraint on the good teacher who will always want to develop new methods of his own, and should be encouraged to do so, but a guide can make all the difference to a young or inexperienced teacher.

The PSSC scheme was the first to write a detailed guide, but it tended to be mainly subsidiary to the pupils' textbook and outlined solutions to questions. The Nuffield projects have taken the process much further and their main books are in fact the guides written for teachers. The Nuffield Science Teaching Project believed it could exert its greatest influence through the teacher rather than directly to the pupil. It is likely that programs in other countries will all produce detailed guides for teachers.

Films

The powerful contribution that films can make to education is well known, and it is likely that use will be made of them in any new science teaching program.

Elaborate experiments that could never be shown in a classroom can be put on film for pupils to see. Films relating the classroom work to industrial applications are always an asset. Films using special techniques have exciting possibilities: one of the most remarkable teaching films ever made is "Frog Development—Fertilization to Hatching," made by Educational Services Incorporated in the United States. By time-lapse photography, one watches cell division through a microscope—the creation of life for the child to see.

The 8-mm. casette film has already proved itself a powerful aid in science teaching—and there will be much development of this medium in the next ten years.

There are dangers in relying on films too much. Perhaps the worst 8-mm. casette film is one showing an *animated* drawing of a rope being oscillated to show wave motion. Care must always be taken over animation as it is too easy to build incorrect details into it, but, above all, it is absurd to put on film what is more cheaply shown by having real rope in the classroom.

There is a tendency for every new science teaching project to want to set up a film studio and start making films straight away. Film-making is very expensive. There is a danger of overproliferation: there are already too many bad films available, and a substandard surfeit may not be an educational advantage. A country starting a new science teaching project would be wise to examine the films and film-loops of other projects before embarking too quickly on its own expensive film-making process.

Films for Teachers

An interesting development in educational films in recent years has been the series of films made in the United Kingdom by Esso Petroleum in association with the Nuffield project. These films are intended for teachers and are quite unsuitable for showing to pupils.

The problem of teacher training, or teacher retraining, is always important, and it becomes an essential part of any new science teaching program. Films showing new techniques, explaining some of the philosophy of the source, can make a major contribution to this.

Such films, however, can cover in fifteen minutes work which might take the pupils half a term. It would ruin the teaching if the films were seen by such pupils, and much stress is laid on their being suitable only for teachers. They have been extensively used on courses in the United Kingdom and throughout the world. They have been deliberately kept simple in order to keep costs down. They are made by practising teachers, rather than by Nobel prizewinners, in order to give other teachers confidence: "If Bill or Jack can do it, so can I." These films have proved powerful aids and their influence extends far beyond the limited audience that sees them: they can affect many generations of children.

Television and Sound Broadcasting

All countries will wish to bring every resource to the aid of their science teaching: television and sound broadcasting inevitably have a contribution to make. They can educate the general public in an awareness of the new programs; they can have a part to play in teacher training; they can provide enrichment programs and background material to supplement the school course. Television can provide an alternative medium to a film for showing experiments which would be difficult to show in the classroom.

An experiment seen on television is, of course, second-hand and a very poor substitute for an actual experiment in which the pupil is personally involved. It must never be thought that television programs will avoid the need for building laboratories or purchasing apparatus. It can, however, do much to supplement a program, and it will doubtless do so increasingly as video-tape recorders become available, enabling programs to be recorded and played back at times suitable to an individual school.

This is an exciting time to be a teacher of science with so many developments taking place. Fortunately each successive project in each new country becomes cheaper than those that have gone before, because they can build on the experience of others as they produce programs for their particular need. Let us hope that this world-wide activity will produce future generations of young people with a greater understanding of what science is about, as well as encouraging more and more to become scientists and engineers, on whom the future prosperity of mankind will inevitably depend.

DISCUSSION

Illustrating his presentation of his paper by demonstrations on suitable apparatus and by showing appropriate films, Mr. Lewis explained to the audience what is meant by the principle of adaptation, not adoption. The Americans started science reform for the United States; the British took it over, and now 54 percent of the pupils in Great Britain use the Nuffield equipment; then Israel and other countries entered the field. He demonstrated how a timer had been evolved by the American project; the British had taken it and changed it to suit their needs; at the conference he had discovered a third version, the Israeli one, which cost one-eighth of the price of the British timer. The same process has happened with a ripple tank, and other apparatus. He heartily approves of this shameless shoplifting.

Each· country should use material that comes to hand. In America they seem to have a lot of ticker-tape, and use it; other countries do not produce so much ticker-tape. They should take ideas from each other, and materials from what comes to hand.

Dr. Augustus Caine (Liberia) said that he does not agree with Mr. Lewis' approach, because there is too much of a "take it or leave it" attitude involved—either you stick to old curriculums, or you accept the new. But he believes that there are not just two alternatives, there are many possibilities. And he thinks that Mr. Lewis over-stated his case—for example, about dropping textbooks into the abyss of non-relevance. Textbooks will probably still be sources of information, perhaps the only source of information, for a long time to come.

A warning against snap judgments about equipment was given by *Dr. Uri Haber-Schaim* (United States): science educators should not approach the new apparatus as if they are buying hi-fi systems, where it is a fair assumption that the most expensive is the best. Each should be judged entirely on its merits and demerits, all its merits and demerits. The same principle should be applied to textbooks.

Dr. Peter Strevens (Great Britain) thought that some of the delegates came to the conference as to a shop, hoping to see on the shelves neatly packaged parcels of science syllabuses and materials. They may be somewhat perturbed to find that some of the packages are obviously designed for sale to other customers, not to them. There is no cause for alarm—when they think deeply about what they have heard and seen, they will realize that they are learning the need for a change in learning style, and will be able to extract from the packages whatever is good for them.

Replying to the discussion, Mr. Lewis said that the reason he suspects textbooks is that they give all the answers in an authoritative way, they do not encourage the children to go to find out for themselves. Good textbooks that provoke inquiry and do not give all the answers can be used at more advanced levels, but not one book, several books.

28 POPULAR SCIENTIFIC AND TECHNOLOGICAL LITERATURE FOR CHILDREN

By Isaias Raw

Scientific Director, Brazilian Foundation for Science Education Development, Professor of Biochemistry, University of São Paulo, Brazil

The underdeveloped world's adaptation to a continuously changing way of life requires, more than anything else, a proper science education. It is no accident that science is taught in the developing countries only to a small elite. I speak of science education, not science teaching. These are worlds apart. Science education requires that youngsters learn to think scientifically, experiment and rediscover, face new situations, use what they learn, and acquire the critical ability to reason scientifically. Generalizations on scientific method, the history of science, nomenclature, and classifications are no replacement for this.

The developing world in its fight against time in trying to reach the advanced countries is frequently enchanted by the signs of wealth and looks upon industrialization as the solution of its problem without understanding that it is science that characterizes the level of development, not only the economical aspects but the adaptation of the common man in underdeveloped areas to human society.

We have had an opportunity to deal with this problem in Brazil, at a time when most of the developing world had uniform educational programs and curriculums. Biologists know that evolution rests on mutation, and that without variety no selection can be made. Uniform curriculums have prevented the evolution of science education, and reform became an exercise in reshuffling the same titles, sometimes adding a few modern topics, always more than 50 years old, which were never integrated into the rest of the programs or into the thinking process of students.

There has been, of course, an explosion of popular literature in science and technology. Mystery stories have given way to science fiction, but is this type of literature fulfilling the role of science education? Does it help the educational system? Obviously not. At best it can be considered as supplementary reading, describing more interestingly, and with better illustrations, the same things that appear in textbooks, whose authors should read Verne and Asimov to improve their style. A textbook has become something students must buy but do not read, since they take copious notes of their teachers' dissertations.

About 16 years ago in Brazil we began to publish a number of "journals" (chemistry, physics, biology, and general science) for students. These book-kits introduced the idea of experimentation in our schools because youngsters brought them to class and challenged the teachers with "naive" questions. The book-kits look like regular pocketbooks, but they are really boxes containing a booklet and materials for experiments. They have been designed for out-of-school use, but they are being used in schools, nevertheless. In Brazil, as in many developing countries, the shortage of school buildings and teachers limited formal education to a few hours a day. The pocketbook kits provide a new tool; teachers can ask groups of students to obtain them, do experiments with one of the kits, and report on the results in class.

From the preparation of the journals we learned how to write textbooks which would lead students to do their own experiments. We are trying to explore other ways of getting science teaching down to the primary school level. The majority of children in the developing world never get more than perhaps four years of formal education. At this level, one should tackle problems such as health and food production. If one cannot fight the horoscope which, although ancient, is a newcomer in many underdeveloped areas, how can we fight traditional explanations for disease? Why should a boy accept the fact that he may have worms whose eggs he swallowed without seeing them, when at home, which is where he spends most of his time, his father has completely different explanations?

If we cannot convince him about worms, how can we convince him (or even more educated people) about microbes or virus? A kit now in use provides a small one-glass bead microscope that can be used to show worms and their eggs. We hope eventually to have units on erosion, fertilizers, seed selection, etc.

Similarly, we are exploring electricity and electronics. Out kits provide fundamental ideas for the use of electricity at home. In electronics, we try to explore the usual components and their principles.

There are more than fifty of these kits in use and in preparation, with such titles as the following:

Electromagnet	A Computer that Learns
Measuring Electricity	Heat Conduction
Crystal Radio	Osmotic Garden
Playing with Mirrors	Muscle Contraction
Probability	Photography
Making Nylon	Vegetable Tissues

The pocketbook kits are spreading slowly. Several school systems rely on them in Brazil now and we have recently trained 85 Latin Americans, under the sponsorship of UNESCO and UNICEF, in their use. Agreements with several countries for their production have been signed and translations to Spanish, English and French are under way.

DISCUSSION

Professor Raw told the delegates that at one time in Brazil it was impossible to change the curriculum, and, if it had been possible to change the curriculum, it would have been impossible to change the teachers. So the reformers began to prepare materials for outside the classroom that became major factors in changing science education inside the classroom. The idea was to provide students with a sort of open-end experiment that they could do with simple equipment, and with a certain measure of guidance, come to their own conclusions.

So began the saga of the kits. They deal with areas of science that impinge on everybody's daily lives—food, health, electricity, chance in mathematics. The kits are sold for 50 cents to schools, one dollar to out-of-school buyers.

But even 50 cents is too high for the average pupil in Asia, said *Dr. Pradisth Cheosakul* (Thailand). The Science Society of Thailand, a private society, has annual membership dues of $1.50 for a scientist, $1.00 for a student; for this they receive regularly the society's science magazine, which contains useful articles for pupils. The Society also translates textbooks for which they charge only 50 cents. But few people can afford to join. He fears that the Brazilian kits, excellent though they are, cost too much for Asian students.

Dr. Carl Godske (Norway) thought the presentation of the scientific attitude in the form of the kits was ideal. Have they been used for adult education purposes? And what are the reactions of the teachers?

Popular science journals also help to spread scientific and technological knowledge, claimed *Mr. K. Pines* (Israel). Developments in science and technology take place at such startling speed that such a magazine is essential if teacher and pupil are to keep abreast of developments.

In his reply, Dr. Raw said that he also favors popular science journals, provided they remember their objective and remain popular. The *Scientific American*, which began as such a journal, is now so learned that it is suitable for scientists, not for popular reading.

The reaction of teachers to the kits has been very favorable. They have not tried the kits yet for adult education, but it is likely that many fathers use them, just as fathers in America play with their sons' toy trains.

29 THE ROLE OF TELEVISION IN TEACHING SCIENCE TO CHILDREN

By Tadashi Yoshida

*Deputy Director-General of
Broadcasting,
Nippon Hoso Kyokai (NHK),
Japan*

Is it really effective to broadcast television programs on science to schools?

In order to answer the question, the effectiveness of telecasts on science should be compared with the conventional studies that mainly depend on school textbooks occasionally supplemented by laboratory experiments. (The advantage of school telecasts on science will later be confirmed with the aid of some research work conducted in Japan.)

Firstly, it goes without saying that the visual presentation of telecasts has several advantages, particularly in the field of natural science. If the program is well composed, it can stimulate not only inductive and analytic thinking by viewers but also intuitive comprehension.

It seems that both analytic and intuitive thinking are mingled in the process of learning; nevertheless, research on the intuitive approach has been much neglected. Educational telecasts which can make the most of visual communication are expected to be much more useful for encouraging pupils to grasp intuitively the relation of things.

Secondly, school telecasts on science can bring students up to date with academic and technical progress. Scientific knowledge doubles every ten years, which means that the teaching of science (as an independent academic field) needs to be constantly modified.

First, top-class scientists are needed to participate in the reformation of science curriculums for primary and secondary schools. They, only they, have the knowledge of science that is necessary for the important work of deciding what and how to present the latest authentic knowledge to coming generations. Teaching materials, as well as the curriculums, should be constantly improved under the supervision of qualified scientists and the best available teachers. Of all subjects taught in schools, natural science most needs illustration of the contents it covers.

Uses of Science Television Programs

School telecasts, which are full of the latest illustrations and which are produced under the supervision of the best available scholars can answer these two requirements very efficiently. Printed materials, such as textbooks, cannot fully comply with the demand of timeliness, as publishing inevitably takes a longer time and revision cannot be done constantly. Furthermore, the shortage of teachers, particularly in developing countries, is now a vital problem. Though school television never dares to substitute for teachers, it can help them in various ways.

There are two formats of program presentation—one is the direct-teaching type, where school television programs present a self-contained period for instruction; the other is the so-called "curriculum enrichment" type, which confines the function of school programs to providing classroom teachers with teaching materials. The former programs teach by themselves, whereas the "curriculum enrichment" programs do not aim at teaching pupils directly but assist classroom teachers with material to which they can refer in addition to their own teaching. Programs for direct teaching are not going to replace classroom teachers, but the aim is to assist heavy-burdened teachers to cope with challenging tasks by taking a part of their work off their hands. Which to choose depends on the curriculum subjects and conditions of the educational environment. As regards natural science, the direct-teaching type is preferred on the grounds that this type is more practical for the purpose of stimulating the creative thinking of viewers in classrooms (this was confirmed by our researches), and that many teachers feel it difficult to catch up with latest developments in the field of science. Particularly among developing countries, where the shortage of teaching resources always is keenly felt, school programs which are designed to form an independent course for instruction will be most helpful.

A further use of school broadcasts on science is to test the efficiency of laboratory experiments. It is self-evident that direct experiences acquired in laboratories are very important. In this connection, we also know that unlimited examples of scientific experiments are possible. And so television is required to select and demonstrate the most efficient experiments. Some experiments, though they often seem easy to conduct, cannot be carried on in ordinary classrooms, while others can be made either by teachers or by pupils. Even in the latter case, it very often takes much time for preparation, and many pupils cannot understand what the experiments really mean. Television prevents this waste of time and effort.

Besides, not all experiments need to be confirmed by the pupils' own manipulation. Frequently the significance of some laboratory experiments can be far better understood by students when they are presented on television screens. Well-devised television programs can produce very intensive processes of learning by means of a combination of audio-visual aids such as laboratory experiments, filmed scenes, animation films, mock-ups, narration, music, etc., thus stimulating the active thinking of young viewers. In such ways, a TV program itself builds up a process of instruction demanding both analytic and intuitive thinking by viewers.

For instance, instead of plain explanations, continuous posing of questions by the television teacher can be adopted as the basic format of the program. This is one of the reasons why the direct-instruction type of programs, as compared with the curriculum-enrichment type, can be more effective for teaching science. And, as mentioned above, this type of program presentation may be more frequently applied in developing states.

In every case, one program is supposed to pursue a single specific theme (e.g., "light travels straight"). When a program endeavors to follow more than one theme, it cannot be composed effectively enough to elicit children's thinking up to the final point of climax in the program. Unless a program has only one theme it cannot have any climax, and a program without a climax is not a program. Therefore, a program which is skillfully composed on the basis of one specific theme often provides more intensive instruction than easy-going, laboratory experiments carried on by the pupils themselves.

What theme each program should aim at is decided by the structure of the program series. A well-planned composition of the whole series is essential. Teachers' manuals, which are distributed well in advance to schools, clarify the structure of the program series and the aims of the respective programs.

The effectiveness of these well-designed program series and the individual programs have been confirmed by research conducted by an institute of NHK.

Research on a Program Series

One research study showed the favorable results caused by continuous viewing of a television science program series in schools in Japan. Four primary schools, A, B, C, and D, located in a secluded region north of Tokyo were selected for the survey. The choice fell on these four schools because they satisfied the following conditions:
1.   As they were situated in a remote area of the prefecture, the influence of the mass communication media was almost negligible.
2.   No television receiving sets had been installed in the four schools before this survey was conducted.
3.   Once the schools had been equipped with sets, NHK's educational television programs could be received.

In April 1957, a careful survey was made of the respective scholastic achievements, intelligence, interest in study, social attitudes, and home environment of the fifth-grade pupils of the four schools. Upon completion of this survey, television sets were installed in two of the schools (A and B), and these fifth-graders were designated the "television group." They were allowed to view regularly, for 20 minutes each week, the television program entitled "Television Travelogue" and a science program, "Science Class for Fifth-Graders."

The pupils of the corresponding class in the other two schools (C and D) were chosen as the control group and were asked to continue their work without the use of television.

Since then, surveys were carried out at each of the schools four times in the course of one school year. The number of pupils comprising the television group of schools A and B totaled 130, while the control group in schools C and D numbered 72. Testing prior to the study showed no significant difference between the two groups 'in intelligence, social studies achievement, and science achievement.

But what were the achievements of these two groups compared with other children of the same age in the region? As these tests are standardized and given to all school-children in the region, the average for the region is known to be 50. Our two groups proved to be 4 to 5 points below the regional average in intelligence, 6 points below in social studies, and 8 points below in science.

A survey conducted in March 1958, just a year after the preliminary survey indicated that the television group had improved and gained higher scores in intelligence, social studies, and science. The statistical examination showed a significant difference. Of special note is the fact that the television group surpassed the regional average in intelligence (an average of 52.6) and showed a marked improvement in the average achievement in science, (47.9) compared with social studies (45.9).

Comparison of the distribution of scores obtained by the two groups shows that in the television group the number of children making extremely low scores had decreased remarkably. The results of this survey confirm the hypothesis that, in children of lower learning ability, television helps to stimulate an interest in study.

The principal reason why the serial use of our school broadcasts was so effective is thought to be that such programs are closely correlated to each other, so that the whole series can build up a complete course of learning.

Research on Program Structure

Meanwhile, it is needless to say that the construction of each program is no less important than that of the series. In school broadcasting, the period of watching some programs must, by itself, form a process of learning one main theme. How then can this process of learning be built up most effectively in one program? We began preparing a new experiment in 1963, and completed in about two and a half years the following experimental study, made up of two stages—the first stage 1963-1964, in which, by using slides and recording tapes, we made an experiment in a simplified situation; and the second stage 1964-1965, where, on the basis of the results of the first stage, we went on film location and produced three experimental television programs.

The material for experiment was a science program for primary-school sixth-graders, "A Forest." For the first stage, 672 third-, fourth-, and fifth-grade pupils in two primary schools were selected, and, for the second stage, 306 third-, fourth-, and fifth-grade pupils in a primary school.

We decided on three basic ways of using speech connected with the image: three methods of linking them were worked out and the subjects (pupils) were divided into three groups:

a. Orientation type. Simultaneously with the projection of a picture on the screen, we presented words (hints or questions, for instance) to compel the children to catch the import of the picture and direct their minds.

    b. Commentary type. Simultaneously with the projection of a picture on the screen, we presented words describing the picture and explaining its meaning.

    c. *Orientation-commentary type.* Combining *a* with *b* above, we directed the audience to grasp the import of the picture and also to comment on it.

    The results of both stages of this experiment are as follows:

1.   As to the problem of how much of the contents of a program can be understood, the experiment with slides showed that the commentary type was the most effective. But, in the television experiment we found that there was little difference between the commentary and the orientation types.

2.   Considering the points the pupils gained in the test relative to the content of a program, the experiment with slides showed that, while the orientation type scored highly in the test checking the children's application, the commentary type resulted, on the contrary, in poor marks in this test. That is to say, the orientation type of guidance was found to have the merit of bringing into play the children's powers of application. In the television experiment this same advantage of the orientation type of guidance was clearly demonstrated (an average score of 38.8 vs. an average of 30.5 for the commentary program).

3.   Another experiment showed that, while the orientation type resulted in high scores in the test given three weeks later as well as in the one organized immediately after, the reverse was true of the commentary type (a 7.6 percent reduction in score compared to a loss of only 5 percent for the orientation program). In other words, the orientation type seems to have a long-range effect.

4.   The orientation-commentary type, despite its thoroughness, has nearly the same characteristics as the commentary type.

    These results will serve as an answer to the generally held doubt that television teaching materials may be weak in training children's thinking ability.

    The above research suggests that the orientation type of program, which provides a constant stimulus to the students, can easily become a very effective teaching process. Educational programs, especially those aimed at an assembled class, must always allow the pupils to grasp something significant; that is, they must teach something.

    Teaching one theme by means of a program is our goal. Not merely by explaining the materials, but by letting the students guess and think positively for themselves by means of hints, questions, and pauses with the skillful use of pictures, narration, and sound, we must always try to draw the children's minds towards the final comprehension of the central theme at the climax of one program.

    I must again emphasize the importance of a systematic build-up of the whole series. One program series is expected to form a self-contained teaching course. Unless each theme of every program is fully incorporated into the central aim of the series as a whole, the impact of each theme, namely of each program, will be weakened and thus the effect will be lost.

It seems to me that these principles can be applied to school broadcasts not only in developing countries but also in industrialized countries, considering the fact that reform of the school curriculum is now in progress everywhere.

And so, to the question posed at the outset of this article "Is it really effective to broadcast TV programs on science to schools?," I can answer "Yes!"

DISCUSSION

Mr. Yoshida reported that his corporation transmits 69 different types of programs every week. Programs are prepared for kindergartens, elementary schools, junior high and senior high schools. The carefully selected television teachers encourage students to think for themselves, posing questions and stimulating the viewers' thinking. Science programs never aim at mere communication, but at the development of the child's interest and ability to acquire knowledge.

In an era in which there has been an explosion of knowledge, no school teacher or textbook can keep up to date with new developments. This is where a program like this can help. The NHK corporation recently started a film library, which, though new, already has 70 or 80 programs and are published in international editions.

M. Meshler (Israel) said that he found two great drawbacks in educational television, when he was consulted about preparing programs. One is the aspect of time—it takes three times as long as teaching in class. The other is the one-way communication—not knowing how the children are reacting.

The problem of disadvantaged children at the receiving end of television lessons worried *Dr. Herbert D. Thier* (United States). Television teachers have to rely on verbal language; they do not know the language patterns of the children of the slums in the United States, for example, nor how to convey mathematics to them. Furthermore, can television help such children to begin to think naturally, to analyze, to evaluate, to make judgments, to change their thinking patterns?

In the United States, where there are so many television sets, it is easy to use television to train teachers, thought *Dr. Gerald Holton* (United States). Another use of television is to promote interest in scientific developments and technological know-how. Unfortunately, Harvard Project Physics finds that children get bored very quickly, and the maximum time for such films is four minutes.

Mr. Gilbert Ratsitohara (Malagasy Republic) said that his country began with educational films, went on to educational radio, and introduced instructional television two years ago. But only one of the six provinces in the country has any television sets at all, so what can be the role of television in education?

Television is simply a delivery system, said *Dr. Seth Spaulding* (UNESCO). There are alternative delivery systems, such as cartridge film projectors and a large supply of 8-mm. cartridges. The question is what one has to deliver, and what is the best way to deliver it. There is no other principle involved.

Replying to the discussion, Mr. Yoshida said that Japan has special programs for mentally handicapped and mute children. The point about time is true to some extent: one school, under pressure to prepare for entrance examinations, suspended its use of the television programs. But he does not approve of education for entrance examinations under pressure. Time is not so important a factor. As for American children getting bored in four minutes, in Japan they could take 15. But he agrees, in respect to younger children, that the principle should be the shorter, the better.

30

MUSEUMS, WORKSHOPS, AND EXHIBITIONS

By Jean Adolphe Rose

Director, Palais de la Découverte,
University of Paris,
France

First of all, it is essential to define what we mean by "museum" nowadays, if we want to consider to what extent such institutions can contribute to efforts designed to improve the condition of developing countries. Until recent years, a museum was merely regarded as designed to show collections of objects, often of great value and historical nature, in the field of the arts as well as in that of the sciences. Nowadays, this conception has expanded considerably, and the museum has become an active cultural center with an educational function in which it employs all the resources of audio-visual teaching and cooperates closely with universities and major scientific research institutions.

Developing this trend even further, the museum becomes a complex equipped with laboratories, lecture halls, and similar facilities offering courses and demonstrations for the teaching profession enabling it to keep pace with scientific progress and new teaching methods. Equipment and materials are made available to teachers wishing to construct and try out new teaching aids. Pupils may use the workshops to build models and show them at great competitions organized in connection with national or regional scientific exhibitions. Many examples of centers of this kind could be mentioned.

The principal aims to be achieved in the activities of cultural centers are in the first place providing information to the population, and subsequently educating and training it; information in the scientific and technical field, permanent education and training in a specific area are the main targets presently pursued by most scientific cultural centers.

To achieve these aims they use a variety of methods; they resort to all forms of presentation capable of arousing the senses, captivating the attention, holding the interest of anyone who wants to be informed, whatever his cultural level. By means of human contact they must "tame" the visitor, interest him and make him feel the need to ask questions; in short, create the need to understand and the climate which favors the development of intelligence.

The Palace of Discovery in Paris was one of the first cultural centers conceived on these lines, and it conducts a wide range of activities designed to involve the visitor. Special efforts are made for the young. Introducing the young to scientific thought is, in fact, to be regarded as one of the most important tasks of the cultural centers. Workshops for physics, chemistry, biology, and other disciplines are organized. They take place in the laboratories

265

of the center, and are sometimes preceded by visits to industrial or university laboratories or trips with a geological, mineralogical or biological interest, organized by professors who volunteer their services. The program of these workshops is not designed to repeat work performed at school, but to provide an idea of the roads specialization in certain subjects may open up, so that the participants have an opportunity of testing their preferences and discovering their vocation.

This experimentation-based activity of the Palace of Discovery also takes the form of temporary scientific exhibitions with topical themes. Exhibitions of more general scope are also arranged for educational purposes.

In addition to these experimentation-based activities, the work of the Palace also includes the arranging of series of lectures; general lectures given by researchers, professors or engineers, cycles of special lectures by members of great research organizations, cycles of introductory lectures by staff members of the Cultural Service, and informative lectures with demonstrations of experiments on topical subjects. Arranging film shows of a scientific nature also ranks high on the program of general activities. The science film is in fact a highly valuable—in some cases an indispensable—educational instrument.

Obviously, wide opportunity is also provided for individual work and documentation: the library offers facilities for consulting scientific and advanced popular scientific works and periodicals, while the photographic library makes a wide range of documents available for inspection.

Thus the cultural centers use a wide range of means to carry out their function. One may query whether, if these means are effective in developed countries, they may not be ill suited to the problems that present themselves in developing countries; but that is not likely. It is a mistake to believe that the cultural poverty of adults is due to lack of schooling. One of the latest examples, that of the science exhibition organized in Costa Rica by the Deutsche Museum, shows to what degree a presentation designed to prove that science is exciting can hold the attention of visitors of any age, occupation, and social level. It is a mistake to believe that it is impossible to explain to these people, by means of simple experiments, the natural phenomena with which everyone is familiar, and thus to disperse the cloak of mystery in which they are wrapped for lack of explanation. Superstition is merely an aspect of the fear and distrust caused by lack of knowledge.

Thus the wide range of their activities enables the cultural centers to make an effective contribution to the discovery and the scientific and technical training of an elite and can be used directly to assure the operation of pilot centers as nuclei of an industrial development based on the exploitation of natural resources and consequently of the progressive improvement of the living standard of the peoples concerned.

But in order to reach that stage, it is essential—and the point can hardly be overstressed—to make first all efforts necessary to obtain an objective picture of the mentality and philosophy of life of the people which is to be aided, in order to know at which points the efforts should be aimed, in which fields our own ways of thinking can be adapted to those countries, on what occasions it is of advantage to suggest an activity.

Fruitful collaboration can only flourish in an atmosphere of mutual understanding.

The purpose of aiding underdeveloped countries should not be merely to offer knowledge of an intellectual and economic nature. The population must be brought to a point where they are capable of using the methods necessary to acquire that knowledge. Only thus can they be helped to find their place, step by step, in the intellectual, political and economic world of today and—even more important—of tomorrow. Only when they have reached this point can they be full-fledged, autonomous partners and do without outside aid. That is the conclusion from attempts undertaken so far in this direction by several existing cultural centers, attempts that permit us to state that they can play a basic part on the effort to solve one of the crucial problems on which the future of humanity depends.

DISCUSSION

Professor Joseph Gillis (Israel) was doubtful about the value of adding sporadic and nonintegrated facts to a child's knowledge. It is only in the classroom that the child gets integrated education; in the museum or the club he may pick up some odd and interesting items, but these are no substitute for real lessons in the classrooms. Poor students will not make up what they have missed, good students may be encouraged and stimulated. But extracurricular activities cannot replace the curriculum.

A plea for science films was made by *Dr. Eric Huppert* (Israel). His is a voluntary body, which shows the latest science films wherever it can and whenever it gets a chance. Often the science museum in Tel Aviv gives them a room. They made a survey which showed that there were 5,000 to 6,000 scientific films available through the embassies. Despite language difficulties, the films are a great success.

Mr. Rose replied to Professor Gillis simply by quoting figures. Annually 400,000 visitors come to his museum, of whom one-quarter are teachers who come to watch experiments they cannot carry out in their schools. Two hundred thousand are school youngsters who come to watch these experiments, and 5,000 visiting children belong to various science clubs.

PART VII

SUMMARY AND CONCLUSIONS

31
WORKSHOP REPORTS AND COMMENTS OF DELEGATES

Dr. Gerald Holton (United States) said that three types of problems have been discussed: intellectual, managerial, and economic-political. Among the intellectual problems is the question of the approach to science—should the schools teach pure science or an ecological view or a humanistic view? A further problem is how to use the discoveries of psychology that there are multiple channels for cognition. Further, shall educators try to concentrate their efforts on a talented minority?

The conference has not produced solutions to all problems. But what has emerged clearly is a technique for finding solutions. There are two stages: the experts should work out alternatives, the political decision-makers should then examine them and decide.

Among managerial problems are teacher-training, planning of projects, formation of teams, planning of time schedules. Here the solutions proposed stress regional projects, regional centers, with UNESCO acting as broker.

In the field of political and economic problems, much emphasis is placed on the need for collaboration between ministers, scientists, administrators, and teachers.

Three reporters summarized the discussions that took place in the workshops.

Mr. D. G. Chisman (Great Britain) reporting on Workshop A, expressed the general enthusiasm for the novel programs with new apparatus and curriculums available in several countries. These can be adapted for use in developing countries, but only after they have been suitably modified and tested.

One great difficulty that keeps arising is that of children who have to learn science in a language other than their mother tongue. Often the pupil has trouble, not with the science, but with the language. The science teacher does not understand the language problems, the language teacher does not comprehend the science.

It is generally agreed that vocational, agricultural, and technical education are of great importance to increase production; it is suggested that the humanistic sciences are needed to improve our knowledge of motivation.

As it is clear that it is impossible for developing countries to provide a full 12-year educational system, or all the laboratories and facilities one would like, priorities have to be determined. The first of these, perhaps, is teacher-training.

Everybody agrees that one of the main aims of science teaching must be to inculcate the scientific method of assessing the available evidence and estimating consequences in making decisions.

Dr. Robert H. Maybury (UNESCO) summed up the discussions in workshop B on "Methodology and Organization." He said that it might well have been subtitled "The Care and Feeding of Manpower in Developing Countries." The workshop directed its attention to ways of increasing the amount of manpower available and improving its quality.

They faced such critical questions as where to find manpower, what type of training is best, what can be done to plug the brain drain.

There is "an awareness of technological needs in science teaching and a dimension of science in technological teaching": this awareness became sharply defined in the discussions. For every scientist, five technologists and twenty technicians are needed. Stopping the brain drain requires a more sympathetic attitude on the part of the developed countries, but developing nations must have jobs for people when they train them.

Considerable attention has been given to the problem of money and where to find it. One method is to try indirect taxes—everyone agrees, whatever the method, that the ministry of finance has to be involved in units planning education.

There is unanimous accord about the value of regional projects. Science centers in various countries have been described and discussed. Their strength lies in the pooling of resources. The weaknesses may be that the centers may lie outside the normal educational framework. Delegates are studying the existing regional centers as potential models.

Dr. Wilton S. Dillon (United States) reported on Workshop C. This was essentially a very practical workshop. They discussed specific aids to education, such as television, the preparation of cheap pocket-sized science kits like those prepared so imaginatively in Brazil, the use of science clubs, fairs, and museums.

The workshop saw many excellent films, and they have come to appreciate that the learning process involves collaboration between statesmen, administrators, professors, teachers, parents, television producers, museum curators—and children.

Various speakers outlined the ideas that they are taking home from the conference.

Mr. Stanislas Spéro Adotevi (Dahomey) has no doubt that science will be introduced into Africa. But he has become convinced by the discussions that the educator-planners must gain deep and real understanding of the regions into which scientific techniques are to be introduced. Side by side with the teaching of science, they have to see to it that psychologists, psychiatrists, and historians are trained, and that they operate at the level of the planning services. Africa today is not only underdeveloped, but is also gripped by an immense neurosis.

The phiosophy of science education that has emerged at the conference has been to train children to be self-reliant, to think for themselves, to analyze, to pose, and to solve problems. This is really a revolutionary idea in education, going away from the established systems of world learning—from books, from definitions. Until now children have always been given answers but not problems. They have regurgitated these answers in examinations, but have never been taught to ask questions or to have the confidence to provide their own answers. They have been given memory, but the thinking has been reserved for the adults.

It is very good to change all this, but changes must be seen from the point of view of the children. What is relevant to children may seem irrelevant to adults. If they want to follow a crawling insect, they should be allowed to do so. The new programs must be introduced with courage and care.

Following up the remarks of Mr. Adotevi *Mr. Godfrey Eugene Lardner* (UNECA) said that one of the things that has emerged at the conference is that the social sciences cannot be neglected, although they are not as predictive as the physical sciences. They have an important part to play in planning science education, and, indeed, in activating the processes of economic change and development which everybody so ardently desires in order to make the world that paradise which men have always sought.

Mr. Peter Inocent Mwombela (Tanzania) first wanted to stress how inspired is the basic approach of the Rehovot Conference—bringing together politicians, administrators, teachers, and scientists. But he objects to a concept that the developing countries have come to Rehovot on a shopping expedition. The idea of "shopping," of buying, has been applied for 50 or 60 years, and has resulted only in confusion. The process that is needed is one of cooperation: both developed and developing countries have something to give, and they are pooling their ideas.

Mr. Théo J. M. Lefèvre (Belgium) thought that the idea of regional projects is perhaps the most valuable to come out of the conference. Neighboring countries should work out what they have in common—language for teaching, human resources, and so on—and should work out their problems together, so as to get the maximum use of whatever funds are placed at their disposal.

The teaching of science and technology has to be thought of in the context of the culture into which it is being introduced, said *Dr. Jerome S. Bruner* (United States). There is a well-known maxim in physical anthropology that "every innovation, be it a digging stick or a written language, takes a very long time to be absorbed into a culture because each such technical innovation requires a social innovation in order for its adoption to be assured."

Dr. David Samuel (Israel) recalled his earlier discussion of "Elegance or Relevance." It seems to him that the conference has shown a preference for relevance, for science teaching to be applied to the environment. He hopes that the pendulum has not swung too far: they should not neglect "science for its own sake" entirely.

The many discussions about teaching science in a foreign language led him to suggest that a pilot project should be set up to study which language is best, and at what age, and in what manner it should be taught.

Dr. Augustus Caine (Liberia) said that the delegates have come to Rehovot to consider the content of science education. What should be taught? What methods should be used to train teachers, to develop teaching aids and other materials, what political issues or social issues are involved in introducing changes? It seems that the conference has been so successful, not because it has come up with ready-made answers to the problems, but because it has suggested a wide range of alternatives. It is now up to the delegates to go home and to try out these alternatives, on an experimental basis.

They have come to realize the importance of the social sciences. If a country wishes to be developed, it can only do so with the aid of people who identified with it, who had a psychological commitment to it. Physical science can help a country to develop economically, social sciences will help to make people appreciate their own moral values and culture. This understanding may even help to close the brain drain to a certain extent.

One of the lasting impressions that he will take home is that science teaching means *doing* science, said *Dr. Onofre Corpuz* (Philippines). Development itself is nothing but *doing*. The conference has confirmed the wisdom of some of the things they are doing, while others they will have to change.

Chief Stephen O. Awokoya (UNESCO) said that, speaking both as a representative of UNESCO and as a man coming from a developing country, it seems to him that the conference has touched on four overriding problems:

The first is that of leadership—a dynamic leadership with vision, a sense of history, a leadership with knowledge and above all with managerial ability. Leadership cannot come from outside, cannot be given by a foreign expert, although a foreign expert can help the local leader.

The second problem is planning, comprehensive planning, to include pure, applied, humanistic, and social sciences. Third is the problem of experts in a country that has no experts. The first step should be to appoint somebody to take charge, however meager his knowledge, and to give him a chance to grow with the job, perhaps to go overseas to increase his competence, perhaps to learn from foreign experts. Then a cadre of people already on the spot should be built up.

Fourth comes the getting of resources. First of all, they have to include in their team somebody who speaks the sort of language ministers of finance understand. Then they have to have somebody to approach foreign governments and international governments in a language *they* understand. Scientists, technologists, and teachers are generally not ideal for these purposes, because there are political implications involved—so this is where the political people come in. That is why he is so pleased with the Rehovot Conference—the politicians have been drawn in as well as the teachers and scientists.

Mr. John L. Lewis (Great Britain) said that the need for accurate information is one thing that has emerged from their discussions. He would like to see UNESCO publish a volume giving information on how to make appartus cheaply and easily in different countries, for both primary and secondary education. There should also be information providing critical appraisals of all the science films available, which should show clearly the purpose for which these films are intended.

UNESCO generally can be of great help, said *Dr. Seth Spaulding* (UNESCO). The agency can provide planners, experts, money, information, materials. Delegates should pass on their requests, either through the local U.N. Resident Representative or direct. For him it has been a tremendous conference because it has taken an integrated look at science education from the policy level, the operational level, and the planning level.

Dr. Marcelo Alonso (OAS) said that the conference has emphasized the need for regional collaboration: perhaps they can take it a stage further, and promote a more intense dialogue between regions. The

Latin Americans have much to learn from the West Africans, and vice versa.

The conference has only begun to scratch the surface in educational reform, stressed *Dr. Uri Haber-Schaim* (United States) and he thought it would be more economical for the developing countries to implement programs that are available rather than rediscover what has been discovered, at the same time applying their creative energies to problems other countries have not yet tackled.

Dr. Julius Gikonyo Kiano (Kenya) was pleased that the conference has discovered that politicans also have a contribution to make; scientists and scholars often disparage his profession. The politicans are needed to provide the social environment in which the scientists and scholars can operate. Politics is not necessarily a dirty game, it can be a vital and constructive profession.

Despite all their difficulties, the developing countries are developing. Man is a learning animal, and does not need to repeat a lengthy routine of discovery; the developing countries can achieve in decades things that have taken other countries centuries. There is no need for despair. The Rehovot Conferences provide a vision of what can be accomplished by human societies.

At the closing ceremony, *Mr. Zalman Aranne* (Israel) pointed out that "underdevelopment" does not apply only to countries, it applies inside countries, however wealthy, to large portions of the population. Israel has absorbed a large number of immigrants, coming from countries with different cultures. The country's educational policy is based on the profound conviction that appropriate education can go far toward compensating for a deprived social and cultural environment. Nor is Israel guided by I.Q. tests or other such categories: it assumes that these are only evidence of the environment, and can be changed. All children are endowed with abilities and aptitudes.

Israel is applying a precept from the Book of Psalms: "The Wisdom of Hands." This has been interpreted to mean a synthesis between the wisdom that guides and the hands that labor. This concept is being converted into the reality of vocational and agricultural schools.

Closing the Fifth Rehovot Conference, *Mr. Abba Eban*, Israel's Foreign Minister, said that it has proved the value of science in our day, not only as a means of producing more abundance, but also because it stands for the forces of reason against those of irrationality, which are now challenging the minds of men.

APPENDIXES

APPENDIX A

COUNTRY REPORTS

Reports on the following countries, prepared for the Rehovot Conference, are not included in the above record, but can be obtained from the office of the Rehovot Conferences, Weizmann Institute of Science, Israel:

BOTSWANA
CHAD*
CONGO (KINSHASA)*
COSTA RICA**
CYPRUS
DAHOMEY
GABON
THE GAMBIA
GHANA
GUATEMALA**
IVORY COAST
LAOS*
LESOTHO

LIBERIA
MALAWI
NEPAL
PHILIPPINES
SIERRA LEONE
SINGAPORE
SWAZILAND
THAILAND
TOGO
TURKEY
URUGUAY**
UPPER VOLTA*
ZAMBIA

*French only
**Spanish only.

APPENDIX B

ORGANIZATION OF THE CONFERENCE

The fifth Rehovot Conference was organized by the Continuation Committee of the International Conference on Science in the Advancement of New States. It was sponsored jointly by the Hebrew University of Jerusalem and the Weizmann Institute of Science.

HONORARY PRESIDENTS

Mr. ZALMAN ARANNE
Minister for Education and Culture

Mr. ABBA EBAN
Minister for Foreign Affairs

Mr. ABRAHAM HARMAN
*President of the Hebrew University
of Jerusalem*

Mr. MEYER W. WEISGAL
*President of the Weizmann
Institute of Science*

CHAIRMAN OF THE
REHOVOT CONFERENCES

Mr. ABBA EBAN
Minister for Foreign Affairs

SECRETARY-GENERAL: DR. AMOS MANOR

ACKNOWLEDGMENTS

The assistance rendered by government and public institutions abroad as well as in Israel is gratefully acknowledged. These organizations include:

ABROAD: *The Asia Foundation, San Francisco*
           The Axel Springer Foundation, Berlin
           *UNESCO — United Nations Educational, Scientific and
           Cultural Organization, Paris*
IN ISRAEL: *The Israel Science Teaching Center*
           The Israel Academy of Sciences and Humanities
           Ministry for Education and Culture
           Ministry for Foreign Affairs
           The Rothschild Trust

SCIENTIFIC PREPARATORY COMMITTEE

Dr. Amos DE SHALIT, Chairman
Weizmann Institute of Science

Dr. David SAMUEL, Deputy Chairman
Weizmann Institute of Science

Dr. Moshe AVIDOR
Israel representative at UNESCO

Dr. Joseph GILLIS
Weizmann Institute of Science

Dr. Michael FELDMAN
Weizmann Institute of Science

Dr. Alexandra POLJAKOFF-MAYBER
Hebrew University of Jerusalem

Dr. Nathan SHARON
Weizmann Institute of Science

SCIENTIFIC SECRETARIES

Dr. Nathan SHARON, Coordinator
Weizmann Institute of Science

Mr. Maurice ALGRANATI
Weizmann Institute of Science

Dr. Michael CHEN
University of Tel Aviv

Mr. Zvi GELLER
Science Teaching Department
Weizmann Institute of Science

Mr. Michael CAHN
Ministry of Education and Culture

Dr. Nathan TRAININ
Weizmann Institute of Science

Mr. Raphael COHEN
Science Teaching Department
Weizmann Institute of Science

Dr. Paul VARDIN
Science Teaching Department
Weizmann Institute of Science

APPENDIX C

LIST OF PARTICIPANTS

AFRICA

BOTSWANA
The Hon. Benjamin Cojo THEMA, M.B.E., Minister of Education, Health and Labour

CENTRAL AFRICAN REPUBLIC
H. E. Albert SATO
Ambassador of Central African Republic in Israel

CHAD
H. E. Pierre DESSANDE
Minister of Information and Tourism

CONGO (KINSHASA)
Msgr. Tharcisse TSHIBANGU
Rector, Lovanium University

DAHOMEY
H. E. Mama CHABI
Minister of National Education

Mr. Stanislas Spéro ADOTEVI
General Commissioner for Youth and Culture

ETHIOPIA
Dr. Wadajo MULUGETTA
Vice-President, Haile Selassie University

GABON
H. E. Jean Baptiste OBIANG-EKOMIE
Minister of Youth, Sports and Culture

THE GAMBIA
Alhaji The Hon. Ibrahim M. GARBAJAHUMPA, M. P., J. P., Minister of Education, Labour and Social Welfare

Mr. Samuel Horton Maurice JONES
Director of Education, Ministry of Education

GHANA
Mr. Samuel Maxwell ADU-AMPOMA
Principal Education Officer (Science and Agriculture)
Ministry of Education

IVORY COAST
H. E. Lambert AMON TANOH
Minister of National Education

Mr. Yao Paul AKOTO
Director-General of Education, Ministry of National Education

KENYA
The Hon. Dr. Julius Gikonyo KIANO
Minister of Education

Mr. Kyale MWENDWA
Chief Education Officer, Ministry of Education

LESOTHO
Mr. Evelly Selai MOHAPI
Science Education Officer, Ministry of Education and Culture

LIBERIA
The Hon. Dr. Augustus CAINE
Secretary of Education

MALAGASY REPUBLIC
Mr. Gilbert RATSITOHARA
Secretary of State for Cultural Affairs in charge of Youth and Sports

Mr. Eugène RAZAFY
Director, Institut National Supérieur de Recherche et de Formation Pédagogique

MALAWI
Dr. N. Peter MWANZA
Lecturer in Biology, University of Malawi

MALI
H. E. Yaya BAGAYOGO
Minister of National Education, Youth and Sports

MAURITIUS
Mr. Robert ANTOINE, M.B.E.,
Director, Sugar Research Institute

NIGERIA
The Hon. Dr. V. O. S. OLUNLOYO
Commissioner of Education, Western State

Dr. Cornelius Olaleye TAIWO
Provost, College of Education, University of Lagos

SIERRA LEONE
The Hon. J. Barthes WILSON
Minister of Education

Mr. William Farquhar CONTON
Chief Education Officer, Ministry of Education

Dr. Kosonike THOMAS
Dean, Faculty of Pure and Applied Sciences, Fourah Bay College, Sierra Leone University

SWAZILAND
Senator The Hon. Dr. A. B. GAMEDE
Minister of Education

TANZANIA
Rev. Joseph ELSTGEEST
Head, Department of Science Education, Morogoro Teachers' College

Mr. Peter Inocent MWOMBELA
Assistant Director of National Education, Directorate of Curriculum Development and Examinations, Ministry of National Education

TOGO
Mr. Michel K. AGBETIAFA
Director of Education, Ministry of National Education

UGANDA
Mr. Michael K. SOZI
Secretary to Council; Director, Center for Continuing Education, Makerere University College

UPPER VOLTA
H. E. Moise D. LANKOANDE
Minister of National Education, Youth and Sports

Lic. Charles Youami TAMINI
Principal, Lycee Philippe Zinda Kabore

ZAMBIA
Mr. J. B. HUXLEY
Inspector of Education, Ministry of Education

Dr. Sitali Mundia SILANGWA
Senior Lecturer in Zoology, University of Lusaka; Chairman, Agricultural Research Council

ASIA AND MEDITERRANEAN

CYPRUS
Mr. Frixos VRAHAS
Head of Higher and Secondary Education, Ministry of Education

ISRAEL
Mr. Meir AVIGAD
Director, Department of Vocational and Technical Training, Ministry of Education and Culture

Dr. Michael FELDMAN
Dean, Feinberg Graduate School, Weizmann Institute of Science

Mr. Peretz F. HARBURGER
Head, Department for Youth and Vocational Education,
Ministry of Labour

Dr. David SAMUEL
Isotope Department
Weizmann Institute of Science

JAPAN
Mr. Tadashi YOSHIDA
Deputy Director-General of Broadcasting, Nippon Hoso Kyokai (Japan National Broadcasting Corp.)

LAOS
Dr. SOMPHOU OUDOMVILAY
Inspector-General of Education, Ministry of Education.

NEPAL
Dr. Harka B. GURUNG
Member, National Planning Commission; Secretary, Nepal Geographical Society

PHILIPPINES
The Hon. Dr. Onofre CORPUZ
Secretary of Education

Dr. Dolores F. HERNANDEZ
Director, Science Education Center, University of The Philippines

SINGAPORE
Dr. LEE KUM TATT
Chairman, Science Council of Singapore and Singapore Institute of Standards and Industrial Research

THAILAND
Dr. Bhunthin ATTAGARA
Director-General, Teacher Training Department, Ministry of Education

Dr. Pradisth CHEOSAKUL
Deputy Secretary-General, National Research Council

TURKEY
Dr. Fatma VARIS
Chairman, Department of Instruction, Faculty of Education, University of Ankara

CENTRAL AND SOUTH AMERICA

ARGENTINA
Dr. Emilio Fermin MIGNONE
Vice-Minister of Education
Mr. Jorge Alberto SABATO
Head, Technology Branch, Department of Metallurgy, National Commission for Atomic Energy

BARBADOS
Mr. Alvin F. E. BARNETT
Senior Tutor, Barbados Community College

BRAZIL
Dr. Isaias RAW
Scientific Director, Brazilian Foundation for the Development of Science Teaching
Dr. Edison Dias TEIXEIRA
Secretary of Science and Technology in The State of Guanabara

COSTA RICA
H. E. José Guillermo MALAVASSI
Minister of Public Education

DOMINICAN REPUBLIC
H. E. Adolfo Rafael CAMERENA
Ambassador of Dominican Republic in Israel

ECUADOR
H. E. Dr. Luis E. JARAMILLO
Charge d'Affaires, Embassy of Ecuador in Israel

GUATEMALA
H. E. Miss Francisca FERNANDEZ HALL
Ambassador of Guatemala in Israel

H. E. Dr. Carlos MARTINEZ DURAN
Minister of Education

MEXICO
Dr. Salvador ZUBIRAN
Director, National Institute of Nutrition
Dr. Arquimedes CABALLERO
Chief, Department of Mathematics Teaching in Secondary School System, Ministry of Public Education
Dr. Carlos DIAZ ROMAN
Rector, Universidad Veracruzana
Dr. Hector FERNANDEZ GONZALEZ
Rector, Universidad de Nueva Leon
Dr. Miguel HUERTA MALDONADO
Consejo Nacional de Ciencias y Humanidades de Mexico
Dr. Enrique Leon LOPEZ
Technical Assistant; Director-General of National Polytechnic Institute
Ing. Manuel PEREZ ROCHA
Comision Tecnica de Planeacion Universitaria de la Universidad Nacional Autonoma de Mexico
Dr. Augusto Vives ZAMUDIO
Coordinator de Ciencias de la Universidad Veracruzana

PANAMA
Miss Berta ARANGO U.
Vice-Minister of Education

PERU
Dr. Fernando Raul ROMERO
Member, National Board of Research; President, Universidad del Pacifico

URUGUAY
H. E. Dr. Federico GARCIA CAPURRO
Minister of Culture

VENEZUELA

Dr. Hugo Ramon MANZANILLA
Executive Secretary, Dividendo Voluntario para la Comunidad; Member of Board, Instituto de Estudios Superiores de Administracion Universidad Central de Venezuela

Dr. Jose Rafael REVENGA
Assistant Professor, School of Philosophy, Universidad Central de Venezuela and School of Social Sciences, Universidad Catolica Andrés Bello

NORTH AMERICA

CANADA

Dr. Leon KATZ
Head, Department of Physics, Director Accelerator Laboratory, University of Saskatchewan

UNITED STATES OF AMERICA

Dr. Jerome S. BRUNER
Center for Cognitive Studies, Harvard University
Mr. Daniel V. DE SIMONE Director, Office of Invention and Innovation, National Bureau of Standards, U.S. Department of Commerce
Dr. Wilton S. DILLON
Director of Seminars, Smithsonian Institution
Dr. Jack S. GOLDSTEIN
Chairman, Astrophysics Institute and Physics Department, Brandeis University; Director, African Primary Science Program, EDC
Dr. Uri HABER-SCHAIM
Project Director, Physical Science Group, Education Development Center
Dr. Werner Z. HIRSCH
Director, Institute of Government and Public Affairs, University of California, Los Angeles

Mr. Donald G. HOFFMAN
General Manager, International Division of Encyclopedia Britannica Educational Corporation
Dr. Gerald HOLTON
Co-Director, Harvard Project Physics, Harvard University
Dr. Arthur H. LIVERMORE
Deputy Director of Education, American Association for the Advancement of Science
Mr. Frederick STEINER
Department of Social Services, New York
Mrs. Pearl STEINER
Guidance Counselor, Elementary School, New York
Mr. Harold TAUBIN
Senior Analyst, Office of Planning and Design, University of Pennsylvania
Dr. Sara TAUBIN
Assistant Professor, Human Behavior and Development, Drexel Institute of Technology
Dr. Herbert D. THIER
Assistant Director, Science Curriculum Improvement Study, University of California, Berkeley
Dr. Fletcher G. WATSON
Henry Lee Shattuck Professor of Education, Harvard University

EUROPE

BELGIUM
H. E. Théo J. M. LEFÈVRE
Minister of Science Policies and Programming

FRANCE
Mr. Jean Adolphe ROSE
Director, Palais de la Découverte, University of Paris

WEST GERMANY
Dr. Franz Karl MUTSCHELLER
President, German Association for the Advancement of Mathematics and Science Teaching
Dr. Eberhard STAHN
Head, Department for German and International Meetings, German Foundation for Developing Countries

GREAT BRITAIN
Mr. B. T. CHADWICK
Science Education Officer, The British Council, Ibadan, Nigeria
Mr. D. G. CHISMAN
Assistant Director, Center for Curriculum Renewal and Educational Development Overseas

Dr. Isaac D. DOUEK
Research Fellow, Imperial College
Dr. Josephine A. DOUEK
Lecturer In Inorganic Chemistry, Borough Polytechnic, London
Mr. John L. LEWIS
Senior Science Master, Malvern College; and Associate Organizer, Nuffield Physics Project
Miss Janet Mary LLOYD
Assistant Representative, The British Council in Israel
Dr. Peter STREVENS
Director, Language Centre, University of Essex
Dr. John Murray WILSON
Acting Representative, Science Officer, The British Council in New Delhi, India

NORWAY
Dr. Carl L. GODSKE
Geophysics Institute, Bergen University

SWEDEN
Mr. Emanual WARIL
National Board of Education

INTERNATIONAL ORGANIZATIONS

ORGANIZATION OF AMERICAN STATES (OAS)
Dr. Marcelo ALONSO
Deputy Director, Department of Scientific Affairs, Washington, D.C.

UNITED NATIONS

UNITED NATIONS DEVELOPMENT PROGRAM (UNDP)
Mr. Paul Marc HENRY
Assistant Administrator and Associate Director, Bureau of Operations and Programming, New York

UNITED NATIONS ECONOMIC COMMISSION FOR AFRICA (ECA)
Dr. Ademola BANJO
Head, Science and Technology Section, Natural Resources and Transport Division, Addis Ababa
Mr. Godfrey Eugene LARDNER
Director, Division of Natural Resources and Transport, Addis Ababa

UNITED NATIONS EDUCATIONAL, SCIENTIFIC AND CULTURAL ORGANIZATION (UNESCO)
Mr. René MAHEU
Director-General, Paris
Chief Stephen O. AWOKOYA
Director, Department of Science Teaching, Technological Education and Research, Paris

Mrs. Sheila M. HAGGIS
Coordinator, UNESCO Seminar on Science Teaching at Primary School Level, Paris
Mr. M. JIMENEZ
Director, Executive Office, Paris
Dr. Robert H. MAYBURY
Senior Scientific Officer, Division of Science Teaching, AVS, Paris, and Liaison Officer for Rehovot Conference
Dr. Seth SPAULDING
Director, Department of School and Higher Eduction, Paris

UNITED NATIONS OFFICE FOR SCIENCE AND TECHNOLOGY (ECOSOC)
Dr. Albert V. BAEZ
Consultant to Office for Science and Technology
Dr. Benjamin BARG
Chief, Advisory Services and Development Section

WORLD ORT UNION

Mr. Max A. BRAUDE
Director-General, Geneva

SOCIAL SCIENCE LIBRARY

Oxford University Library Services
Manor Road
Oxford OX1 3UQ
Tel: (2)71093 (enquiries and renewals)
http://www.ssl.ox.ac.uk

This is a NORMAL LOAN item.

We will email you a reminder before this item is due.

Please see http://www.ssl.ox.ac.uk/lending.html
for details on:

- loan policies; these are also displayed on the notice boards and in our library guide.

- how to check when your books are due back.

- how to renew your books, including information on the maximum number of renewals. Items may be renewed if not reserved by another reader. Items must be renewed before the library closes on the due date.

- level of fines; fines are charged on overdue books.

Please note that this item may be recalled during Term.